The New World of the OCEANS

Men and Oceanography

The New World

Men and Oceanography

Boston · Toronto

of the OCEANS

by DANIEL BEHRMAN

with photographs

 Little, Brown and Company

To Lidik

Acknowledgments

Without the patience and kind cooperation of a large number of persons, this book never could have been written. Their number is so large that a complete list of acknowledgments no doubt would resemble an index. Suffice to say, all those interviewed and quoted in these pages deserve a citation for helpfulness far beyond the line of duty.

Several persons, however, must be mentioned because of their invaluable counsel and guidance. Dr. Warren Wooster and Dr. Arthur Maxwell piloted the author respectively through the Scripps Institution of Oceanography and the Woods Hole Oceanographic Institution during his legwork. Dr. G. E. R. Deacon opened the doors of the National Institute of Oceanography in Great Britain to him so that he could plan the book at a time when it was only a gleam in the publisher's eye. And Dr. Victor A. Kovda, leading soil scientist in the U.S.S.R. and former head of UNESCO's science department, taught him that science can speak an international language.

Help came from all quarters. It was thanks to Mrs. Sally Shelley of UNESCO that publisher and writer became aware of each other's existence. It was thanks to a study grant from UNESCO that the writer was able to assure his own existence while producing this book on his own responsibility. Dr. Charles B. Officer, chairman of Alpine Geophysical Associates, served as scientific adviser and went over the manuscript. It was also read by Jacques Richardson of *Science and Technology*, whose advice and pertinent comments have been precious. Mrs. Viviane Miller provided the typing and encouragement. Mr. Roger Picard donated for a few weeks to the cause of oceanography a spare room as a study in his Country Club Hotel at Samois-sur-Seine. Mrs. Lea Chagot, an old friend of the family, often kept the boat from rocking.

But credit must go, above all, to the person who read and edited the manuscript in its rawest form and who suffered life with a man living, sleeping and dreaming in the ocean for nearly two years. She is my wife, Lida, to whom this book is lovingly dedicated.

Contents

Illustrations

The New World of the OCEANS

Men and Oceanography

1. The Unearthly Ocean

Not so long ago, I had the same outlook on the ocean as most of my landloving contemporaries. It was fun to swim in, slow to travel on, wondrous to look at, irresistible to read about and easy to ignore except on Sundays, holidays and vacations. As a source of food, it had represented to me at an early age a possibility of choking to death, and at a later one, an opportunity for costly self-indulgence that could be equally deadly if taken too seriously. (I have lived for many years in France, where Vatel, the Prince of Condé's chef, ran himself through with his sword because the fish for Louis XIV wasn't fresh.) As a mode of transportation for anything not measured by the kiloton, its future seemed mainly as a wide open space where there was no one to complain about sonic booms.

Like my fellow terrestrians, I found the ocean unearthly. It did not fit into any scheme of things. In no time at all, it could turn a lazy barefoot stroll along a beach into a damp scramble among rocks encrusted with old razor blades. At the edge of its boundary, it would heave up all sorts of extraneous objects: empty shells that other people always were able to identify, driftwood, decapitated fish, seaweed put there to sustain conventions of flies, jellyfish in quivering repulsive blobs. Marine life was familiar to me principally in aquariums and freezer counters. I knew the difference between port and starboard, but I had never navigated anything bigger than a pedal boat. I could take the sea or I could leave it alone.

The trouble was, it would not leave me alone. Things kept happening in the ocean. It sloshed up against the walls of my life. Nuclear submarines flitted eternally beneath the waters like Flying Dutchmen, ready to have the last word in a dialogue where they probably would be the only remaining interlocutors. The ocean seeped into cocktail party global thinking. Too many people being born? Too many people to be fed? Solve it with two words: the pill and the sea. Anything that big must have something to eat in it. Next problem . . .

The ocean became entertainment. Jacques-Yves Cousteau made a movie about his work, called it *The Silent World*, and brought more human beings back under the sea, albeit vicariously, than since the day their ancestors had laboriously hauled themselves out of it. As I remember the picture in its French version, its star was a fish called Jojo le Mérou, whose name reminded me of a Marseilles underworld character until I looked up *mérou* in a dictionary and it turned out to be a grouper. But Cousteau could not be blamed for such miscasting. He had made oceanography a household word, even though among many oceanographers, Cousteau is almost a swearword (sedentary family men with research grants, tenure and a tendency to seasickness, oceanographers are weary of explaining why they do not go to work in aqualungs and flippers).

It was about this time that I began to get slightly wet myself professionally. (Here, parentheses are needed. This is a sample of the seaspeak often used by American research institutions, industries and scientific policy shapers with a stake in the ocean. An aerospace firm gets wet when it decides to build a research submersible. A company that has been making only trawling nets for years is all wet but never knew it before. Etymologists of seaspeak hold that the brewery supplying standard beer bottles for a drift study of surface currents is only slightly moist, almost a dry brewery. A widespread use of the term is "wet NASA" to indicate a possible one big ocean agency for all in Washington. It has the advantage of including an acronym and, by association, a hopeful price tag.) My own wetness, only a few drops at first, came from my job of reporting on global scientific enterprises encouraged by the United Nations Educational, Scientific and Cultural Organization. As one of its manifold functions, UNESCO has traditionally served as a foster home in Paris for sciences in need of a place to hang their international hats, offering a maximum of independence as long as they were willing to accept a minimum of money. (This is true of science everywhere — the amounts of independence and money are inversely related.) It is something like those little French country cafés that post signs announcing they will take customers who bring their own provisions.

About ten years ago, the oceanographers brought their ideas and their own budgets for research cruises, while UNESCO gave them a place to sit down. Nations are all the readier to bury their hatchets and cooperate in science when the real estate involved does not stir any covetous urgings — the middle of the ocean is one good example, Antarctica is now another — and when efforts to achieve airtight top secrecy are more trouble than they are worth. *You* may need accurate bottom charts so you can run your nuclear submarines without crashing into seamounts, but there is no way to stop *me* from compiling them, too. You may carefully overlook my existence in all your political pronouncements, but I am very interested in learning when the sardines start running off your coast because they do not listen to your speeches and always swim my way. Oceanographers in international politics were not converts to brotherly love, they were just realists.

They knew the ocean was big enough to hold all of them because, in fact, it was bigger than any of them. It was this very size of the ocean that first struck me when I began to look at it with their eyes. It is a truism to state that it covers 70.8 percent of the earth's surface, but that is only a number. From the viewpoint of the oceanographers, as displayed on the charts with which they papered the walls of their meeting rooms, the Pacific Ocean was a water hemisphere, bigger than all the earth's land masses put together. To some, the Pacific was the world's only true ocean since it extended from pole to pole. They tended to look down on the Atlantic because of the shallow sills that separated it from the Arctic on their charts. As for the Arctic, penned up behind those sills, it was only a mediterranean sea like the Caspian, the Black or the Mediterranean. With bikinis on the walruses . . .

All the comfortable surroundings of my earth — the well-worn chairs, the old shoes, the familiar cracks in the plaster — were disappearing. Currents, storing and transporting future weather changes, crept over the reassuring empty blue of my mind's map. Of course, I had known about the Gulf Stream that explains why Europe sneezes when America sweats, but I had to fit a Gulf Stream undercurrent around it. Little arrows ran off in whorls and broad swaths around my map: Kuroshio and Oyashio, Benguela and Agulhas, Somali and Labrador, Humboldt and Cromwell. Some moved like rivers in flood, others drifted almost imperceptibly. New ones were being constantly found, as if another Nile or Mississippi were added every few years to the list of the world's rivers. To discover them, oceanographers sailed off for nowhere and ran a web of cruise tracks over it once they got there.

What was good dry land to me was only a few outcroppings of overcrowded islands to them. Not only did they have 97 percent of the water of the planet, but below it, they had that 70.8 percent of its land perfectly shielded from the weathering that is the despair of the terrestrial geologist when he seeks the earth's origins. They had ocean trenches deep enough to bury Mount Everest, with a small Alp to spare. They had their own mountain range, the winding mid-ocean ridge system, 40,000 miles long, 800 miles wide on an average, and dwarfing any other feature of the earth's crust. Most disturbing of all to the cherished conceptions of a terrestrian, they had the opportunity to look over the Creator's shoulder and explain how it all came about. The bottom of the deep sea that, so I thought, told no tales was becoming very talkative indeed. It spoke to the geophysical oceanographer as he bombed it with TNT to wreak his own private earthquakes, or towed instruments over it to record the variations in its magnetism. Since the geological oceanographer could not get down there with his pick and hammer to take samples, he played a planetary game of darts, dropping spears into the bottom, odd devices with shafts ten or twenty yards long and with half a ton of ballast to drive them home. Then he would haul them up, extract what had been rammed into their hollow shafts, and announce the age of the ocean floor or how the world might end. These oceanographers spoke in meetings as if they held the whole world in their hands. They slid slabs hundreds of miles square over the floor of the Pacific like bathroom tiles. Some shifted continents — thus indicating movements that required millions of years — with such aplomb that I wondered how they could ever return to a man-sized time scale and remember to get to the airport on time when the meeting was over.

At first, when I knew no better or at least no more than a terrestrian is expected to know, I waited for them to talk about getting fish out of the sea and into the frying pan. Just as the United States Congress opens its sessions with a prayer, they would begin their meetings with ringing pronouncements about the biological resources of the ocean and how research could lead to their better exploitation if it were properly financed. But they did not take the biological oceanographer seriously. After all, he was unable to say how fast the shores of the Red Sea were spreading or show in equations how a warm spell in the equatorial Pacific might mean a cold winter for Europe. He could only lower his net into the water, hope that it opened at the right depth, and bring it up with thousands of minute critters and the problem of finding someone to count and sort them, for they could not be cranked into a computer. This has been compared to taking a census of the United States by lowering a grab every few hundred miles from a high-flying plane and then trying to guess how many people live there and how they behave toward each other. The biological oceanographers tended to feel left out of the big money. All their minute marine organisms could be relied upon to die and eventually become petroleum, but that meant waiting for biology to become geology. Yet I found them a cheerful lot, willing to talk to me for hours about their little peepholes into the sea. Some looked only at benthos, the life of the bottom, others concentrated on the upper two inches of the surface. Depending on where they opened their nets and the size of the mesh they used, they obtained a completely different picture. Each of them had his own ocean.

As I watched and listened to the oceanographers in the environment of conference halls in Paris — where some seemed to survive like the big tunas that researchers bring up on deck at sea and keep alive by hosing seawater through their gills — I became aware of a disturbing fact. These men did not think like anyone else I knew. Their world was upside down, almost a mirror image of mine. They went down to mountaintops, they looked up at waves. Light, that fleetest messenger of all, was quickly hobbled in the sea and radio was equally useless. For most purposes, they could communicate only with sound, they could see only with sound, but under the right conditions, they could hear a shot around the world. They moved at a different pace than ours — the crawl of their ships, the ponderous motion of their currents. If they explored their environment as divers, they knew that an inadvertent move up to light and life might be death. Millions of miles away in outer space, unmanned laboratories telemeter observations for months on end, but oceanographers were trying to get a signal for a few weeks from an instrument only 20,000 feet away — but 20,000 feet down. They could stand on a beach in California and identify storm waves from Australia, yet when at sea, they considered it a triumph when they could come within a few city blocks of where they wanted to go. They listened with quizzical amusement to proponents of sophisticated shortcuts in gadgetry because they knew that, in the sea, the sharks bite free everything that the currents have worked loose and the water has corroded, after the barnacles have fouled it beyond recognition.

They were called oceanographers, but the name confused more than it explained. It was like placing the same tag on botanists, zoologists, chemists, physicists, meteorologists, geologists, geophysicists or physiologists because they go to work on land. Oceanography, I have been told, is so interdisciplinary that it is hard to call it a discipline. It is also hard to call this a definition.

It began to dawn on me that the oceanographers belonged to another world or, perhaps, another dimension. Even the ones who never went to sea, who did their oceanography on the Potomac or on the boards of corporative conglomerates, were living on what I decided could be best summed up as Planet Ocean. I was fortunate enough to be able to visit some of them there in three of their major capitals and elsewhere. This was quite a change from observing them in Paris, where sea gulls during an infrequent hard winter are the only signs one ever has of the existence of an ocean.

Not all Oceanians are oceanographers nor are all those associated with oceanography Oceanians (since the inhabitants of the Pacific islands known as Oceania have never staked a claim to the nationality, I must assume that it is up for grabs). The world's two biggest research institutions in the science, Scripps Institution of Oceanography at La Jolla, California, and Woods Hole Oceanographic Institution on Cape Cod, are headed by nonoceanographers who were plainly selected for their ability to bring the Oceanians up to earth whenever necessary. And there are men who have spent their entire lives at sea, first out of necessity and then out of inertia, who regard a voyage as the shortest distance between two ports, and who probably are not as Oceanian as the woman who works with a roomful of file cases containing depth and temperature readings.

I do not claim Oceanian citizenship myself. To make my trip to Planet Ocean, I spent two weeks on one of the world's most comfortable ships, the *France*, and a day on one of the world's most uncomfortable, a cluttered, tinny converted army workboat — about the proper ratio for civilized seagoing. I wedged into mini-submarines on dry land, I banged my head and barked my shins prowling through unpadded steel cells euphemistically known as shipboard laboratories, I reached for and invariably missed ladders that were supposed to take me from a moving deck to a stable platform, barely escaping the ignominy of being hoisted up with a block and tackle. Mainly, though, I listened to the Oceanians and I trust they will forgive me for now attempting to act as their self-appointed spokesman.

The story I want to tell may seem at times to be only incidentally concerned with the ocean itself. In all its infinitely varied features, it has been described in a number of books written at first hand by oceanographers themselves, so enrapt by their universe that they feel a missionary urge to explain it to the profane. One tends to forget, for example, that the late Rachel Carson, who poetized the sea even more than she popularized it, was a marine biologist at the start of her career. There are a large number of oceanographers who write more like humanists than scientific specialists. Their works have been invaluable to me and I have quoted from them liberally. In an appended list, I have suggested some for the reader who has been tempted by this adventure.

For the study, the exploitation and the colonization (in the Greek sense of the word) of the sea are an adventure, perhaps the last remaining for man before he becomes a completely passive spectator. Even the very ownership of the deep sea and its resources poses problems whose solution can offer us a God-given chance, again perhaps our last one, to look beyond the petty horizons of our islands. This adventure brings us to a scene as remote as the moon and as challenging as outer space, though it lies before our eyes and at our feet. It is here, as I have learned from stays at three American research centers and from my visits to other men and institutions sharing this experience, that a new age of discovery is in the making.

As I was told time and again, the major resource to be gotten from the ocean is neither fish nor fresh water, neither ores nor oil. It is the opportunity to grasp this new dimension, Planet Ocean.

2. *The Fairest Corner of*
Heaven-on-Earth

At one point in my journey to the ocean people, I found myself driving through La Jolla, California, in a rented German Volkswagen and listening to *mariachis* from a nearby Mexican radio station. I was headed for dinner at the home of an English chemist of Canadian nationality whom I had first heard lecture at a scientific congress in Moscow. This, I presume, is what the official parents of the Scripps Institution of Oceanography, the University of California at San Diego, have in mind when they explain in a pamphlet for prospective students that "La Jolla has long attracted exceptional residents from all over the world."

La Jolla is a remote part of San Diego whose fissioned nucleus lies fourteen miles to the south. The home of both Scripps and the university, it claims unabashedly that it is the richest community in the United States, making it the richest town in the richest state of the richest country in the world. On Girard Avenue, its main shopping street, there is not a trace of a Woolworth's, but shoppers have their choice between

Saks or I. Magnin and can work up from there. Some residents have to park a Lincoln Continental in their driveway because there is only room for two in their garage. If they want to sell their homes, they make the fact known by word-of-whisper, for no For Sale signs or any others are permitted in the community. When one asks the leading local garage owner, a charming fellow who spends three months a year roaming the Greek islands, for modest transportation, he will obligingly scour his lot until he comes up with a red Camaro flaunting a pro-jai alai sticker on its back bumper. The La Jolla *Sentinel*, which shares local readership with another weekly, the La Jolla *Light*, flies from its masthead the proclamation that it is Guardian and Champion of the Best Interests of the Fairest Corner of Heaven-on-Earth.

In all honesty, this is barely an overstatement. La Jolla, now a town of 25,000, originally cuddled around a wooded cove and then began to march inland, conquering dry barren soil, fit only for growing people, with a year-round gentle artificial rain from sprinklers that never know a water shortage. It marched first as neo-Spanish and pseudo-Provençal settlements under faded round tiles and towering eucalyptus trees, then it began to scale the foothills of Mount Soledad (elevation 822 feet, now sharing its *soledad* with a TV relay tower) with cantilevered aeries hanging by an equation from the lips of private canyons. It spread its green lawns and purple gardens over a coastal semidesert which is still religiously preserved and worshiped at a distance, five miles to the north at Torrey Pines State Reserve, where the wilderness can run to the sea. It's a nice place to visit, but I would live there gladly.

Shortly after dawn on a Sunday morning, the parking lot behind the beach at La Jolla Shores begins to sprout campers, station wagons, and tangerine-flake babies, some looking like four-wheeled sharks with inverted fins of surfboards on their roof racks. Brawny blond kids pile out and metamorphose into black amphibious beetles as they put on rubber suits. They hand-paddle industriously out to sea, loll on the waves like jellyfish, then race in with the breakers, only to start all over again in an endless cycle like a production line or ants bearing provisions. The same pamphlet issued by UCSD informs readers that "dormitories are equipped with lockers for surfboards and the championship Windansea surfing beach is close by."

This is the setting of Scripps, the world's largest institution of oceanography. Superlatives can be misleading, though, for it is easy to be a relative giant among midgets. In 1967, Scripps had a staff of slightly under 800, including the night watchmen: 39 in faculty, 130 considered as "other academic staff," 619 nonacademics; and there were 161 students. Its overall expenditures were $15 million, and the value of its plant, including land, ships and buildings, was $50 million. There are not many branches of scientific activity these days where such numbers are biggest, but this is the scale of oceanography.

Its physical plant is functional, unprepossessing, and magnificent thanks to the scenery. It is dominated by an arrangement of crouching new buildings in a happy sea-blue tiling, but a close look shows the usual traces of rapid growth. The prewar (pre–World War I, that is) director's house, a homey two-story shake siding affair, serves as offices, and so do cottages built for the original staff during more austere days. Temporary structures, too, have a way of becoming permanent. But all this lies at the end of La Jolla beach, butting against the coast under the wild cliffs that run north past Torrey Pines State Reserve. Scripps, like the state of California, is by the sea but not of it. At first sight, it ends at the beach. Its pier pointing a thousand-foot finger across the Pacific serves as a haven only for small boats lowered on davits. The institution's ships use its Chester W. Nimitz Marine Facility ten miles away on Point Loma, the spit that protects the entrance to San Diego harbor and is occupied mainly by a United States Naval Reservation. Deep water begins almost within swimming distance off Scripps, one of the reasons for its original choice as a site for ocean research, and makes it as inhospitable to shipping as the rest of the California coast, which does not possess a single natural harbor between San Diego and San Francisco. Still, there are plenty of big ships going by, particularly naval vessels that wallow at a standstill offshore, catching their breath after running the measured mile staked out on the cliffs next to Scripps to check their logs. The Navy also makes its presence felt with teeth-rattling sonic booms produced by planes at its Miramar Air Station five miles inland. The involuntary experiment does not seem to affect the progress of science. Geophysicists may swear when they are boomed while trying to calibrate a magnetometer, but life otherwise goes on imperturbably, though one would think Joshua had blown his horn.

Scripps's lease on its isolation is running out, and this is a good thing if the ocean is to be brought into the realm of normal human pursuits. Above the cliffs, the University of California at San Diego started to spread its wings in 1964. Recently, there were 2,300 students in Revelle College, named after Dr. Roger Revelle, who ran Scripps from 1951 to 1964 when he became director of the Harvard Center of Population Studies, leaving a legend behind him. His name will be constantly mentioned in this book, as it must in anything written about the prime movers in modern oceanic research. By 1995, there will be 27,500 students in twelve colleges on the upper campus, a prospect for most La Jolla homeowners that is fortunately as remote as it is unpleasant.

For the next few years, the Scripps Institution of Oceanography will probably remain as it was when I saw it, an unfenced range where minds roam freely under a year-round sun. The beach, the blue sky, the green Pacific, the white surf create the feeling of a paradise from which all toil is banned, but one should not be fooled. Just as there are places where the imitation of work is an art, the Scripps oceanographer is a master at shamming leisure. He goes to his office in a T-shirt and sandals, or shoeless in Bermudas if he has a big enough name, but he goes from eight to five. He brings his lunch in a brown paper bag and eats it in the sole lunchroom of the institution, a stretch of lawn in front of the library equipped with tables, chairs, parasols, and sunning secretaries or lab assistants who are responsible for its unofficial name of Bikini Plaza. Coats and ties are worn mainly by those who must interface with people using this word as a verb. But on the weekends, when the interfacers are in their gardens as coolie labor for their wives, the oceanographer is at his desk in his office or at home, producing.

He had better be. Scripps's editorial board noted in its report for 1966–67 that it had examined 5.1 manuscripts per week in 1966 to be approved for inclusion in *Scripps Contributions*, containing scientific papers first published elsewhere by its staff. In 1965, 4.9 a week had been submitted to it, but they were coming in at the rate of 5.3 a week in 1967. This is a hive without drones.

Volume 35 of the *Contributions* opens with No. 1783, "Reestablishment of the Northern Elephant Seal (*Mirounga angustirostris*) off Central California," and ends with No. 1925, "The Existence of a Secondary Sound Channel along the Northern Edge of the Subtropical Region in the North Pacific." Leafing through its table of contents, one can see from the titles of papers picked at random that oceanography is a blanket science: How tuna see a net; Diving saucer descents into submarine canyons; On heat transfer through the ocean floor (with a triple signature

Scripps Pier points a thousand-foot finger across the Pacific.

including two Soviets); Concentrations of common lead in Greenland snows; The quiet gray whale (*Eschrichtus glaucus*); Color of "pure" water; On the possibility of a helium flux through the ocean floor; The concentration of atmospheric carbon dioxide in Hawaii; El marco geofísico del Golfo de California; The origin of manganese nodules on the ocean floor; Data on speed and underwater exhalation of a humpback whale accompanying ship; The worldwide oceanic rise-ridge system; On the calculation of vertical motion in eastern boundary currents from determinations of horizontal motion; Magnetic prospecting in Southern California; Exceptional carotenoid metabolism in the Andean flamingo; T phases from 80 Alaskan earthquakes . . .

High productivity does not lead to low spirits. On the contrary, there is a sophomoric air about Scripps that I found in other oceanographic institutions, even or particularly among men old enough to be my father. I attended several of the weekly staff luncheons (brown bag, no tie) in Room 202, Scripps Building . . . and once I witnessed a visiting guest speaker being mercilessly hazed because he had not done his homework.

"Now exactly how do you put the gold plating on this calorimeter?"

"We, er-r, we send it to a commercial firm in San Francisco."

The chairman saved the speaker *in extremis* by wondering aloud if anyone had noticed the unusual concentration on the beach of *Velella*, gelatinous-looking little creatures that are also known as the by-the-wind sailor because they sport a low diagonal sail running along a flat elliptical "hull." After some remarks from the floor about *Velella*'s ability to tack and whether or not the sail might point the opposite way in the southern hemisphere, the meeting adjourned to the beach for an *in situ* study and the speaker, an engineer, fled unnoticed.

Certain quarters of Scripps like to post signs on doors. Two of my favorites were:

"Don't nominate yourself for the Nobel Prize. If you do, you won't get it." — Harold Urey (who won it for chemistry in 1934 after isolating heavy hydrogen and is one of the most prized members of the UCSD faculty on the upper campus).

"It may be an accident. It may not." — C. Goles.

The most effective was: "Do not enter this laboratory unless you are properly equipped to withstand extremely poisonous BrF_5 vapor."

All this is part of the mores of many a small research or university community, but there is also a sea breeze blowing gently through Scripps. Outside the director's office hangs a quotation from Byron:

Icing the pole or in the torrid clime,
Dark — heaving — boundless — endless and sublime.

Next to the coffeepots, as ubiquitous in the labs as electronic micro-circuitry, stand Navy mugs inscribed with the name of their owner or a ship. The weekly *Scripps Information Exchange Bulletin* carries the usual listing of special events in academic and leisure activities, but it always ends with ship news, messages received by the institution's radio station. Nothing can catch the flavor of the place as much as the few samples in this composite bulletin:

Monday	1530, Oceanography Seminar, Sumner Auditorium, Richard W. Sternberg: Friction factors in tidal channels of differing bed roughness.
Tuesday	1205, Marine Biology Seminar, 307 Vaughan Hall, Theodore Enns: Urea excretion by shark kidneys.
Wednesday	1300, Institute of Geophysics and Planetary Physics Seminar, IGPP Conference Room, M. S. Longuet-Higgins: The spectrum of fluid oscillations on a rotating globe. To be preceded by a sack lunch.
Friday	2000, Scripps Peoples Cultural Association, Movie, Sumner Auditorium, *Cry the Beloved Country*, Canada Lee, Sidney Poitier, and *The Fatal Glass of Beer*, W. C. Fields.

ANNOUNCEMENTS

Muir Outing Club	The Monterey cypress that died near T–6 has been replaced with two small acadias ($6.24) and a larger Monterey pine ($67.60) out of monies ($57.84) collected from the Scripps community. Contributions toward the $16 still needed will be accepted.

SHIP NEWS

ALPHA HELIX: AMAZON expedition; presently anchored at Gaviao Island. Message: "First six-man stormproof living quarters almost ready. Bunking three native workers. Labs humming. All in high spirits. Five projects completed and reports written. Suga has audiograms from four species of bats, three species of edentates and an insect. Norris got first recording of freshwater dolphin echo locating sounds in field thanks to new type Lockheed portable ultrasonic tape recorder. Livingston and Lindsley have data on Pavlovian conditioning and maze learning in good-sized series of sloths."

ARGO: NOVA expedition; en route to Pago Pago. Message: "Running routine airgun operation continuously at eleven knots. Crossed extensive area pseudo abyssal plain west of Midway showing hills under thick sediments. Completed successfully second hydrographic station. All atmospheric collection systems working. Picked up Jones and observed mating dance of gooney birds on Midway."

ARGO, another message: "Rendezvoused 0323 PST with brand-new cargo liner M/V Oriental Queen of Orient Overseas Line bound for New York. Chinese owned Liberian registry. Boarded at 0400. Dr. McMillan of ARGO operated successfully 2 hours on crew member with acute appendicitis. Operation performed in kneeling position not necessarily an attitude of prayer. Captain Phinney of ARGO assisted. Patient out of danger. Captain William W. Hsuan of Oriental Queen most grateful. All aboard ARGO happy to have been of help."

This composite bulletin, it should be emphasized, offers only a slight sketch of a week at Scripps and the facilities it has at its disposal. When I visited the institution, it was running a scientific ship line with eight vessels, the smallest 99 tons and the largest, the *Argo*, 2,079. They had steamed a million miles since the Mid-Pacific Expedition of 1950 when Scripps really started deepwater exploration. On land, the 158-acre campus is starting to fill up with the affiliated institutions that always flock to such a fountainhead of research: the Institute of Geophysics and Planetary Physics and the Institute of Marine Resources, both under the University of California, and a fishery oceanography center run by the U.S. Bureau of Commercial Fisheries. The state of California sponsors a marine life research group, the federal government supports a marine physical laboratory, a physiological research laboratory and a visibility laboratory. While all these bodies can be fiercely independent at times, they have learned to lean on each other and Scripps offers them the opportunity to do so.

Scripps was not always this big. Even as recently as the eve of the

Second World War, the *total* oceanographic fleet of the United States amounted to no more than 700 tons. Scripps's beginnings were even more humble: a rented bathhouse for a lab, a gasoline launch named *Elsie* for a ship. That was back in 1892, before the embryo of the present institution came into existence.

The story of Scripps was given to me by Mrs. Helen Raitt, a lively white-haired lady who has just coauthored a book on its first fifty years. "It's been so sad," she confessed. "Many of those who knew the story have now died, and much of it is lost in people's memories." This is Mrs. Raitt's second book, her first having been an account of her experiences with Scripps's Capricorn Expedition to the central Pacific in early 1953 on which she accompanied her husband, a marine geologist, as the only woman aboard on one long stretch. She kindly lent me the results of her digging through archives and memories.

The prologue to the history of Scripps is rather romantic. In 1891, a zoology professor from the University of California at Berkeley, William Ritter, came to San Diego on a honeymoon with his bride, a physician. I don't know what present-day oceanographers do on their wedding trips, but the Ritters looked up some physician friends of theirs in San Diego, Dr. Fred and Dr. Charlotte Baker, and they all went hunting in the bay for a blind fish.

Ritter wanted to do marine biology and he was looking for a proper site. The next year, he rented the bathhouse and the launch in San Pedro near Long Beach, but he could not have assurances of either local support or clean water free of harbor pollution. Baker, very much the intelligent local booster, heard of his problems and asked him to come to San Diego. In 1903, Ritter agreed to make a try if his price could be met: $500 for a laboratory, $500 for a boat.

Enter *deus ex machina*. Baker and the secretary of the local chamber of commerce had the idea of tapping E. W. Scripps, the newspaper publisher, who lived at Miramar. Scripps gave $500, and his half sister, Miss Ellen B. Scripps, also donated. So Ritter was able to move his books and apparatus into the boathouse of the Coronado Hotel for a summer of fieldwork on San Diego Bay. His marine facility consisted of the schooner *Lura*, captained by a fisherman with a crew of one.

E. W. Scripps was now bitten by oceanography, or possibly vice versa. Things began to move at a nonacademic rate. In September 1903, a Marine Biological Association was set up in San Diego with his encouragement, and this is generally taken as the semiofficial starting date of the present institution. The association was incorporated in 1904 with a grain merchant as its president, for Scripps had a very low opinion of scientists as businessmen. Ritter was the scientific director.

The governor of the state, pleading poverty, vetoed the idea of participation by the University of California, but E.W. was less broke than the governor. He lent the association his yacht, the *Loma*, equipping it out of his own pocket. This was quite typical of the heroic days of oceanography, when the only people who could afford it were the ones who did not have to worry about how much it cost. Even today, the yacht club approach still survives here and there. It's very pleasant, and time and again it has proven that wealth is no barrier to good science.

Poor Ritter, however, was becoming weary of trying to look into a microscope in a shaky boathouse and he had his eye on La Jolla, rich in marine life, with deep clean water right offshore. In 1905, a local minister passed the hat and collected $878 to put up a wooden building on La Jolla Cove at a final total cost of $992.50. Ritter, two assistants and sixteen students moved into the building for the summer.

But very quickly expenses were driven up over the three-figure mark. La Jolla real estate was already a big item and citizens eyed the cove as an outlet for raw sewage. Miss Ellen stepped in with the first kilobucks in our story, offering the biological station an endowment of $50,000 if the sewer problem could be solved.

It was a dramatic moment. Come-hither looks were being cast from elsewhere at the marine biological station, particularly by the town of Del Mar six miles to the north, which offered forty acres of land and a sewage system. Three scientists came out from the East to survey the situation and, Mrs. Raitt noted with amusement, turned down Del Mar in a statement saying that "the living expenses of visiting professors would be less in a place like La Jolla than in a place such as you intend to make Del Mar — a rather aristocratic and high-toned resort." Old E.W. may have been right about scientists as businessmen.

As if there had not been enough excitement, the *Loma* ran on a reef in 1906 and had to be written off as a total loss. E.W. took it in his stride. When he heard of the wreck, he simply commented: "Well, it will kill those damn fleas." Just another yacht. She was replaced the next year by the *Alexander Agassiz,* which was run with a five-man crew for $22 a day. (A ship in the class of *Argo* today costs an American oceanographic institution $3,000 a day to operate unless, as has been done elsewhere, it is put under a Panamanian flag.)

E.W. had other things on his mind. From his seat on Mount Olympus, he coolly watched while the sewer issue was being fought out on the La Jolla Cove site. When it was on the verge of being settled, he loosed his thunderbolt: he had his eye on a new site of 158 acres on public land to the north of La Jolla's beach, where there was a "certainty for all time of ocean water uncontaminated by human habitations." With Miss Ellen, who apparently served as E.W.'s foundation in those blissful taxless days, promising to build a new road and E.W. offering trees from his Miramar ranch, the common mortals did not stand a chance. La Jolla ceded the site for $1,000, Ritter was appointed as full-time director, and knowing a good thing when it saw it, the University of California accepted the station in 1912 as the Scripps Institution for Biological Research. Twelve houses were built for the staff at a cost of $1,000 each that year, the pier was put out into the sea in 1915 (with Miss Ellen footing the $39,000 bill), and scientists were hired for $100 a month. One of them, Dr. Francis Sumner, later wrote in his *History of an American Naturalist* of the visits of E.W., who apparently did not know the difference between a biological laboratory and a city room:

"E.W. was a familiar figure at the Institution with his high boots, his still somewhat reddish beard, his rather querulous voice and his half-buttoned vest, liberally sprinkled with cigar ashes. He would drive over in his limousine from his home at Miramar, ascend the stairway of the laboratory building and call for Ritter. In Ritter's absence, I was frequently second choice. In such cases, we sat down for an hour or two or three and talked. Or at least he talked."

Sumner, who was working on deer mice at the time, also notes that Scripps was thinking of establishing a colony of anthropoid apes. He apparently settled for scientists, because in 1916 we find him acquiring forty acres north of the institution for a real estate development which he called "an odd place, where high thinking and modest living is to be the rule" (he was obviously convinced that the opposite had to be true for everyone except newspaper publishers). He offered an acre lot free to any member of the institution as long as a house not costing more than

$2,500 was put on it. Only two took the offer and the site has long since passed into other hands. Mostly people from the institution still live there, but no more modestly than anywhere else.

In 1926, when E.W. died, the name of the biological station was changed to Scripps Institution of Oceanography. It continued to operate, however, on the same humble scale: the new title was almost as long as the research ships used in those days.

One of them, a 64-foot ex-fishing boat renamed the *Scripps*, ran from 1926 to 1936, when she blew up in San Diego Bay. Her hull was raised and sold to a garbage hauler on the condition that he change the name. She was replaced by the *E. W. Scripps*, a schooner originally built for ocean racing and owned by Lewis Stone, the actor, as the *Serena* before she became oceanographic. She did her job dutifully until 1955, when she was sold, used in movies, and finally slipped out of history as a copra boat in the Society Islands, a fit ending.

It was in 1936 that Dr. Harald U. Sverdrup from Norway, one of the founders of modern oceanography, took over as the institution's director. Sverdrup had been scientific leader of Amundsen's arctic expeditions on the *Maud* and he had gone along on the *Nautilus* in 1931 when Sir Hubert Wilkins made his abortive attempt to reach the North Pole in a decrepit submarine. He was a deep-sea man — and Scripps was a deep-sea institution by the time he left in 1948 to direct the Norwegian Polar Institute in Oslo. He set the stage for the role that Scripps is now playing.

I was fortunate enough to be able to see some of Scripps's activities and leading figures at first hand (not all of them: at these places, there is always someone you want to see who is on a research cruise or who has just come back from one and should be avoided while in labor). I have not tried to compile a complete survey of its work — which would be far beyond my depth — but simply to show what goes on inside the world's biggest and oldest oceanographic institution.

Despite its size, it has not played false to William Ritter, its director until 1923, who once remarked: "How big is this station likely to be? My ambition for it is that it should be great rather than big."

3. *A Wild, Uncontrolled Curiosity*

During my stay at Scripps, I found myself subconsciously looking forward to the appearance of its weekly information exchange bulletin the way, as a boy, I used to await *Argosy* or *Flying Aces* at my neighborhood pulp dealer's. I was hooked on the ship news from the *Alpha Helix*. Reports from this vessel with its unusual name were sent by the skipper, James Faughan, a combination of seaman, scientist and keen observer that goes back to the early days of exploration. Since he was at sea, I never met him, but I considered him as a friend.

Instead of using the usual scientific shorthand like "high equatorial carbon dioxide values again confirmed with sudden increase near 4° north and 0°30' north," Captain Faughan let himself go. He would note one week from his ship, rolling south to the Amazon: "Many turtles and one large manta ray off Cape San Lucas yesterday; first flying fish this morning. Shifting to tropical uniforms today. Hope to outfumble weather forming in Gulf of Tehuanepec. All well." Somewhat later, his position was: "About ten miles southeast of Aruba, heading towards Curaçao. Aruba all lighted up like neon heaven and heavy ship traffic in passage. Flying fish increasing in size and abundance but other life limited to one lonely eight-foot shark . . . Departing the southern end of Curaçao in the setting sun last evening, we are now well on our way in the general direction of Tortuga, which we should raise some time around midnight tonight. All well and hungry." I was eager to see his comments on the Amazon, and when he reached it, he did not disappoint me: "Our position about one hour's run up the fork of the big river following a thrilling daylight transit of the narrows west of the big island Marajo. We are now on the Rio Amazonas and having stopped long enough to obtain a sample of its waters we feel the expedition officially launched. Al Pelz made first confirmed sight of pink porpoise this morning." A few weeks later came messages like: "Increasing daily rains slowed down some maintenance and construction items but progress otherwise satisfactory. Should have second sleeping hut finished early next week. Night fishing still good and increasing number of anglers enter catfish derby. All well."

It sounded like high adventure, but was it oceanography? Roger Revelle once suggested that oceanographers should study Mars because it did not have an ocean. Such an outlook has enabled Scripps to stretch the definition of its subject far enough to take in a mind like the one belonging to Dr. Per Scholander, the man behind the *Alpha Helix* and its expeditions. Later, he would tell me: "When people talk about research in the ocean, they tend to forget something very basic: the ocean will yield not only fish and protein but knowledge as well. And this knowledge is not restricted to the ocean. To me, there is no difference between plants and animals anywhere if you are interested in systems. They all operate on the same basic parameters, but emphases are different and comparisons rewarding."

I had already caught a few glimpses of Scholander in the alfresco dining room on Bikini Plaza. He always turned up not with an academic brown bag, but an elaborate plastic lunchbox, like a workman. He was a burly, forceful man in his sixties, tanned to a reddish-brown, and wearing one of those Western ties that looks to me like a shoelace. He was always surrounded by cronies of respectable age and importance, and he definitely seemed to enjoy life.

His kingdom began at the entrance to the Physiological Research

Laboratory, where a plaque next to the door informs the visitor that "this building, its pools and the research vessel *Alpha Helix* were donated to Scripps Institution of Oceanography by the American people through the National Science Foundation and are dedicated to the quest for biological and medical knowledge through the study of life in the sea." I knew that NSF was helping the Amazon expedition with a $600,-000 grant. With such backing, the Physiological Research Laboratory had to be one of the strongest powers in the Scripps confederation.

The building is one of the few at Scripps that can lay any claim to intrinsic beauty. Through doors of tinted glass, one enters a hushed atmosphere where the sun has been strained to a soft glow. The walls are punctuated every few feet by excellent photographs: a ship in polar ice, an Australian aborigine diver, or Scholander himself, sitting under a topee on a folding chair in some kind of swamp, stripped to the waist, in utter concentration, his feet awash.

When I requested an appointment with Scholander, I made it a point to ask his very competent and devoted secretary for some copies of his writings that I could consult in the meanwhile. This was a shortcut that I had quickly learned in interviewing scientists. From the bibliography of a man's publications, one can quickly see where his interests lie. They also show at once if his career has been focused on a single subject or if on the contrary it has been one of many quests. Many men of the latter type have tended to gravitate towards oceanographic institutions. Scholander, though, was no example — he was unique. He was born in Sweden in 1905, moved to Norway as a child, took an M.D. degree at the University of Oslo and then, to judge from his writings, proceeded to forsake medicine (he practiced it only one day) to fall hopelessly and eternally in love with research. He first published in 1932 on Greenland lichens, those hardy plants that thrive where few others can.

He did not become the world's foremost authority on the Greenland lichen. Instead, it led him to examine other situations where life hangs by a thread. Eight years later, after he had emigrated to the United States in 1939, he was reporting on his experimental studies of breathing in diving mammals and birds. These studies led him to look closely at the seal and the Florida manatee (the sea cow that is said to have been taken for a mermaid by sailors, who had no doubt forgotten what a woman looked like) and to devise instruments to measure their respiration. In 1942, he joined some United States Air Force experiments dealing with the carbon monoxide poisoning of human beings in tents and snowhouses. He examined breathing processes in animals as varied as the armadillo, the sloth and man; he roamed from the tropics to the arctic. He has always sought to study life at its geographical and physiological extremes.

Endeavoring to see how organisms defend themselves at the moment of truth, he watched mammals in water, or fish in air. In both cases, he and other researchers noted a sharp drop in heart rates and a cutting-off of circulation to the outer parts of the body, the blood flowing principally from the heart to the brain, which would otherwise be destroyed in a few seconds. Scholander has called this process the "master switch of life" and he has found it almost everywhere. In one article he even mused that "it would be interesting to obtain an electrocardiogram of a flying fish taking off on a natural flight," but admitted that "this would call for a rather tricky technique." The flying fish is about the only form of life that has been too tricky for Scholander and his associates. As I learned later, they have been able to painlessly instrument seals, porpoises, hippopotamuses and human beings to find out what happens to their heart and circulation when they dive.

He has also been interested in situations where life must defend itself against extremes of heat and cold rather than lack of oxygen. In one series of experiments, he and some co-workers ran tests on naked men sleeping in arctic huts, concluding that man is a tropical animal. My own interest was whetted by a paper he had produced on supercooling and freezing in poikilotherms, once my dictionary had told me that these are simply cold-blooded creatures like fish, unable to regulate their body temperature. (The reader probably would fight if anybody ever told it to him in a bar but he's a homeotherm, a warm-blooded animal whose temperature remains steady though his environment may become hotter or colder.) Scholander observed that fish at the bottom of deep fjords in Labrador live all year round in water at temperatures between -1.7 degrees C. and -1.9 degrees C., close to the freezing point of seawater, even though they freeze solid between -0.8 and -1 degrees C. Like water that can be chilled below freezing and turns to ice only when it is disturbed, the fish are supercooled. When they are brought to the surface, they immediately congeal and die if touched with a piece of ice to "seed" the freezing process. They survive in deep water because no such seeding occurs there. In a remark that sheds light on the ultimate purpose of his work, Scholander concluded: "Evolution pushes on blindly,

In utter concentration, his feet awash, Per Scholander studies sap tension in mangroves in a Miami swamp.

as it were, to any niche where survival is possible, and it matters not whether the risk stems from supercooling and crystallization in the arctic or from overheating and desiccation in the desert."

I was entranced by one double-headed case of Scholander inquisitiveness. In 1959, he and some colleagues were aboard a chartered Norwegian sealer bound for Greenland to take samples of ice so they could analyze air frozen into it centuries ago as bubbles. They would approach an iceberg, wait until it "calved," herd the baby to the ship's side and cut it up in the water with a homemade steam knife. That summer, they hoisted 400 tons aboard their little ship for cooking in a vacuum boiler, for they had to melt sixteen tons of ice at a time to get a sample big enough for radiocarbon dating of the air bubbles it contained. Unfortunately, they discovered that the air had been disturbed during its imprisonment, and concluded that Antarctica would be a better source for deep-frozen samples.

Scholander must have been looking over the bow of the sealer as she plowed through a chilly fjord on her way to the ice pack. To anyone else, this would have been an idle moment. To Scholander, it was an opportunity to test an idea he had about how dolphins ride the bow wave of a ship. The sealer's machine shop constructed for him a small streamlined vane which could be set at any angle to simulate the position of a dolphin's tail fluke. When he measured the thrust produced by the vane in the water at a downward slant of 28 degrees, he learned it was enough to drive a dolphin. His report on his work in *Science* shot some holes in previous theories holding that the dolphin did the trick by letting enough air out of his lungs to lose buoyancy, then literally sliding downhill through the water. Scholander, however, thought that the tail fluke was a more efficient method for the dolphin and remarked: "Moreover, as this mode of propulsion does not require that his lungs be empty, he need not take his ride in silence but may whistle to his fellow freeloaders as much as he deems fit. This, I believe, is the way dolphins ride the bow wave, and if it is not, they should try."

As one might expect, this little article generated one of those raging scientific controversies for which *Science*, published by the American Association for the Advancement of Science, is famous. A proponent of the old theory had pointed out that the dolphin would topple over with his fluke in such a position. Scholander replied drily in *Science* that "we ourselves can beautifully handle unstable conditions, like standing upright, and no doubt the dolphin is equally proficient in similar control functions." Instead of pressing in for the coup de grace, he gracefully bowed out with a typical conclusion: "When playing around in the ocean, dolphins are pleasing to the eye no end, but let it only add to your thrill that these rascals are a graveyard to our wits. For is not finding out infinitely more exciting than knowing the answer?"

When I saw Scholander, he was preparing to run to Washington to make arrangements for the next *Alpha Helix* expedition. The ship's maiden voyage had taken her to the Great Barrier Reef off Australia, she was then on the Amazon and now he was planning a further voyage to British Columbia and the Arctic, where, among other things, he wanted to look at the formation of cholesterol and atherosclerosis in salmon.

"I'm interested in systems, whether plants, animals or men," he told me. "We don't give a damn about salmon, we want to learn about atherosclerosis. All salmon get it, but some of them get rid of it. We are looking for species that have something to give of a general nature. It's an integral approach. We're not special marine biologists or marine physiologists. We don't believe in marine genetics any more than we would in marine mathematics."

I had looked at the cruise program of the *Alpha Helix* as it had been presented to the national advisory board of scientists that helps plan its operations. From the Amazon, Scholander wanted to take her the following year to the Bering Sea, which he had already visited by air in a DC-3 to make sure that she would have enough ice-free water in which to work. In fact, he was leaving for Washington to make arrangements for an icebreaker escort. Then, he foresaw the possibility of moving her to the Galápagos and the Humboldt Current off Peru to work on the nerve fibers of the squid (which is unfortunate enough to possess a giant axon 50 to 1,000 times greater in diameter than that of other animals, making it an ideal subject for laboratory study of how nerve impulses are transmitted). Afterwards, she might move south to the Straits of Magellan for a study of "cold-water forms including the bloodless fish" and over to Antarctica for a look at birds, mammals and perhaps ancient atmosphere trapped in the ice. Or else she could return to Australia, the scene of her maiden expedition in 1966, to go deeper into the problem of how mangroves get fresh water from the sea.

What could such places have in common? Scholander leaned back in his chair: "The weakest link in all scientific operations is the human mind. By looking at extremes, you get big figures and it is easier to see how things work. Those fish in the fjords of Labrador were living at an extreme. Their supercooled environment is a sort of precarious condition. It is a metastable state, like walking the streets of New York [my dictionary defines metastable as marked by only a slight margin of stability].

"The desert and seawater may appear as opposite extremes, but they pose an identical problem: they are both hellishly hard to get fresh water out of. Yet the mangroves on the Great Barrier Reef do it by reverse osmosis. They can maintain negative pressures as high as minus 900 pounds per square inch and never less than minus 350 pounds per square inch. Such natural systems could be useful in agriculture. Plants are so much more efficient than machines."

(In reverse osmosis, the ordinary flow that one would expect to take place if pure and salt water are separated by a semipermeable membrane goes the other way when sufficient negative pressure is applied to the "pure" side. Instead of salt molecules flowing into the pure water, it is the water molecules that move out of the seawater, leaving the salt behind the membrane. This is how mangroves can dip their roots in salt water and bring fresh water up into their woody tissue. Industry is imitating them by experimenting with reverse osmosis as a way of desalting water in places where big nuclear plants are not feasible.)

Then why have an oceanographic research ship to look at mangroves in Australia? That question was like waving a red cape in a bullring. Scholander charged joyously: "*Alpha Helix* is not an oceanographic research ship, she's an experimental biological laboratory. I'd be perfectly happy to jack her up on land."

On the greenboard in his office, there was a photo of the *Alpha Helix*, which he referred to as "just a tuna clipper." She did have the lines of the small ships in the fishing fleet that ties up on the Embarcadero in San Diego: a high bow, a great deal of superstructure, an almost yacht-like appearance. The *Alpha Helix*, as I learned from a document that Scholander gave me before he left to catch his plane, was no bigger: 512 tons, 133 feet long. Her name, so the document finally told me, "honors the discovery of the helical configuration of proteins and genetic material." She carries a six-page list of equipment that begins with 1 Air Conditioner, Fedders, Model FA11F2, and ends with 1 Harpoon Gun, serial x5710 (Kongsberg Fangstgevaer, M 52) and accessories. On board she has not only the whole instrumental array of a biological laboratory, but also a jeep and two large auxiliary boats for use at her destinations, either to chase specimens or to act as water buses for scientists commuting between the ship and the shore camp that is always set up. She can accommodate only ten scientists on board, but scientific teams are rotated about every three months and there are more living facilities on shore. Sixty to seventy scientists a year participate in her expeditions. Of her crew of twelve, four are usually students who are expected to serve as part-time scientific assistants — another boost in productivity. It should be noted here that men going out on the *Alpha Helix* or on the long expeditions of oceanographic vessels never kiss their wives good-bye for a year anymore. Instead, the scientists are flown out to the ship once she has reached the phase of her voyage in which they are interested. In this respect, the jet airliner has wrought a tremendous change in work at sea, eliminating long unproductive periods in transit for scientists. Crews too are often rotated by air.

To Scholander, the *Alpha Helix* is an opportunity for seeking out the brightest available minds, telling them in effect: "Have lab, will travel," and inviting them along. "The ship is available for any good program with imagination, anything which needs a laboratory and a high intellectual content," he went on. "We've all been on suitcase expeditions before, but here we can't say: 'Sorry, we were limited,' when we get back. The ship is a floating seminar that runs all day and all night. It's an institute for advanced research, a constellation. We might have a senior scientist aboard as a sparring partner, just to fertilize the milieu. We don't care who the hell comes up with ideas as long as something happens.

"It's like music. We give people a chance to play together."

They take this literally and bring instruments aboard. Scholander himself plays the violin and he recalled that on the expedition to Australia, there was a good flutist and a first-rate viola on the ship. They held chamber music recitals in the library of the *Alpha Helix*.

Scholander was particularly proud of the library: "We always stock it up with books about the places we are going. In Brazil, we had the finest works about the Amazon on the shelves and Villa-Lobos on our hi-fi. This is just a faint shade of the way the old explorers did things, but it's important. A scientist likes to have a tidy laboratory, he wants to sit down in a library with artistically pleasant surroundings instead of ropes, rust, nuts and bolts. I insisted on flat floors in the lab instead of a curved deck. This too is important. Otherwise, nothing fits.

"The lab is the point, the ship is built around it. She is always anchored in quiet water, you can't have a lab that goes like this and that. Why stack the cards against you? And we've kept economy in mind all along. The ship is busy all year round, nothing costs more than an idle ship. She is so crammed that we carry two little plywood labs, about half the size of this office, that we set up on shore. Six to eight people can work in them and this is a very inexpensive way of increasing the size of the ship."

Scholander smiled mischievously as he admitted that shipboard science had some advantages: "It's good to have a captive group of people, it makes for a concentration of wits. They like it, too. Oh, I know that a hell of a lot of people would give their right arms to see the Great Barrier Reef and I know the Amazon has a lure, but we proposed to go to the Bering Sea in February and we were mobbed with offers."

Scholander told me proudly that less than one-fifth of the members of the first expedition to the Great Barrier Reef were from Scripps. In keeping with his conception of the *Alpha Helix* as "a symposium with all the advantages and none of the disadvantages," he had filled her with scientists from a number of American and European universities. He had done even better on the Amazon expedition: in addition to several men from Scripps, there were scientists from universities and research centers in the United States, Germany, France, Great Britain, Norway and Brazil, including Scripps's East Coast pendant and friendly archrival, the Woods Hole Oceanographic Institution.

Scholander's work always has a practical slant. In the Amazon, Dr. Jacob Biale of the University of California at Los Angeles was aboard the *Alpha Helix*. A plant physiologist who specializes in problems of ripening fruits, he worked with a team of Brazilian scientists looking for ways to put the Amazon more prominently on their country's economic map. It was easy, too, to grasp the implications of Scholander's interest in the salmon's hardened arteries. His classical experiments with diving mammals, as I was to see shortly afterwards, could be applied to situations not involving any water at all.

Scholander is now in his sixties, laden with honors and administrative responsibilities. I couldn't help wondering where he would turn next or if he was finally ready to stop turning. "It's true, I'm now on the bottom of the cake," he said. "I have to sit here, I have to keep running to Washington for some sort of hocus-pocus. But I am interested in calcification, I want to apply knowledge of plants to animal systems, I want to look at osmotic mechanisms. I want to know how fish keep such a low salt concentration in the sea, I want to know how freshwater fish keep from bloating.

"If you mention some of these things to any school kid, he will tell you to go look them up in a book. The trouble is, I don't understand what everybody else understands."

Among the honors heaped on Scholander had been a 240-page volume presented to him in 1965 on his sixtieth birthday. It was composed of papers by sixty scientists working along the trails he had blazed. From it, I had gained a headspinning glimpse of where this was all leading. One writer had captured and anesthetized elephant seals off Baja California in Mexico, then equipped them with telemetering devices which showed that their heart rate dropped to four beats a minute in a dive. Decompression sickness in Okinawan divers had been studied; so had the ability of the amphibious mudskipper fish to adapt to very salty water. I learned why the sloth is slothful: his body temperature is so low, the diameter of his nerve fibers is so small and the contraction time of his muscles is so slow (a quarter of the cat's) that he could not move fast even if he wanted to.

Scholander's colleagues are not resting on their laurels — as if he would let them. The document he had given me about the *Alpha Helix* contained, not unexpectedly, the snake that one always finds in these scientific Edens. "Each member of the expedition," it stated, "is requested to write an abstract of his scientific accomplishments before leaving the ship." Publish or walk the plank, one is tempted to think, but participants are of such a high level that the ship has never known a sluggard racking his brains over an abstract, his plane ticket home just out of reach.

The expedition to the Great Barrier Reef, so Scholander told me, had produced thirty-five abstracts in six months. They gave me the impression that there was never a dull moment aboard. My vote for the abstract with the most enticing title went to "On the Rapid Running of the Ghost Crab." Two researchers found that it loped along at 2.5 meters per second or "up to 4 meters a second on the ship's deck"; that is, about nine miles an hour at top speed. They learned that it kept its fifth leg raised while running, and when they put an electrode through its shell, its heart rate went up to 720 beats per minute (it was "much disturbed" at the time).

In another experiment, tests were made on a giant clam to see how hard it clammed. One specimen weighing 220 pounds produced 1,100 pounds of tension when the scientists tried to open it. It was able to snap shut with a force of 375 pounds, as compared to a mere 165 pounds registered by a "male volunteer." There was a report, too, on "Regulation of Internal Body Temperature in the Blue-tongued Skink" . . . oh, the devil take the blue-tongued skink (a lizard, not a typographical error).

One member of the expedition, Dr. Theodore H. Bullock, had been interested in the nerve net of corals, just about as low down as one can get on life's ladder and still find a nervous system. He had shot a thousand feet of color film on his experiments with three species of coral, for which he used an electric generator and a "stimulator" in a small boat. It took three divers to film a twitching coral: one to go down and hold electrodes on it, a second to run the underwater camera and a third to signal by hand up to the "stimulator" operator on the boat.

Bullock had been to the Amazon as well, but he had to be flown home after developing a fever whose causes could not be diagnosed. A few days after I saw Scholander, I had a chance to talk to Bullock when he invited me to sit down over a few sandwiches on Bikini Plaza. He had quickly recovered from whatever had afflicted him in Brazil, where the *Alpha Helix* had established a base camp 200 miles up the Rio Negro from Manaus on the Amazon. Bullock, a professor of neuro-sciences at the UCSD medical school on the upper campus, was a jovial man with a weakness for academic humor. At one point in our conversation, he remarked that the next expedition to the Arctic would enable scientists on the *Alpha Helix* to test a new method of seal catching.

"What is it?" I asked, holding my pencil in one hand, my notebook in the other and a salami sandwich in my mouth.

"Well, you bore a hole in the ice, you put a ring of green peas around it, then you wait."

"For what?"

"For the seal to come up and take a pea."

His distinguished friends at the table all chuckled heartily. Obviously, they were delighted that Bullock had a chance to tell that story again without waiting for the fall semester and a new class.

This atmosphere was no accident but another of the ingredients that Scholander has used in his scientific cuisine. One of our tablemates was Dr. A. Baird Hastings, a warm, urbane old gentleman who was emeritus from more universities than he cared to remember. He had been the first chairman of the national advisory board set up for the *Alpha Helix*, and Bullock was the present one. Scholander's stroke of genius consisted of having on his advisory board scientists whose first concern has remained experimental basic research rather than administration — in other words, men who never age but simply mellow.

Bullock had been chief scientist on the Amazon expedition and he was half-apologetic about his illness: "I think it must have been psychosomatic, I was trying to get out of responsibility." Still, he had been there long enough to get some work done, and shortly afterwards I heard him lecture on the upper campus, sharing his rostrum with a pair of wriggling electric fish from the Amazon that sent out signals over an amplifier.

One of the multifarious problems that were being investigated on the Amazon was the behavior of the piranha, usually written as "ferocious piranha" in all accounts of expeditions to the heart of Brazil. I asked Bullock about them and he begged to differ.

"The piranhas? They're cowards. Most species are not aggressive and it's hard to get them to attack. There are two that are aggressive, but they're frightened by anything bigger than themselves. They won't attack an ordinary fish if it is moving normally. But if it flaps or flops, if it looks weak, then they go for it, first the tail, then the fins."

Feeling ferocious, I took a bite out of the tail of my weakening salami sandwich.

"They don't attack each other and they defend their territories, using visual recognition. To tell the truth, when we went swimming in the Rio Negro, we were much more worried about catfish. They'll eat anything. In their stomachs, we found plastic bags, T-bones from the ship's garbage."

Bullock saw me writing and interrupted: "There's one important thing about the *Alpha Helix* that you don't want to forget. We have room for graduate students on board and it's an inspiration to them. Otherwise, they never watch us work. Here, graduate students see me sitting at my desk, answering the telephone most of the time."

At this point, carrying his big plastic lunchbox, Scholander had sat down at the table: "And don't forget the living quarters. It's like doing fieldwork with a beautiful air-conditioned motel a few feet away."

"That's true," Bullock agreed. "You never know what's going on outside. In Australia, we had squalls all the time but I never knew except when I came up on deck or I went ashore for lunch."

Scholander was in La Jolla, but his mind was on the Rio Negro.

"What about that damn airplane?" he asked. "Is it still a bottleneck?"

"Yes, and the small boats are a problem," Bullock replied.

"I thought the captain had rented a few canoes. What we need is a bunch of nesting boats with outboard motors on the ship . . . By the way, did you get any rays?"

"We caught two on a hook on the Rio Branco," said Bullock. "They were big ones, the size of this table. We had plenty of animals for our tanks. But you know, about those boa constrictors . . . we lost one for several weeks. It turned up wrapped around the relay rack of the electrophysiological apparatus. It had just shed its skin and it was beautiful. Pete Hartline liked it so much that he couldn't kill it. He wore it around his middle and he never let go of it. One day, though, he lost it over the fantail."

At the table, Scholander introduced me to a tall, scholarly-looking man in his forties, wearing glasses under a rising forehead: "I'd like to show you around the lab, but I've just got back from Washington and I'm leaving for Oslo. Bob Elsner knows as much about the place as I do. He's doing some interesting work on asphyxial defense. And don't forget to have him take you to the animal colony up on the hill."

After we had finished munching our apples, Dr. Robert W. Elsner invited me to drop in at his lab on the ground floor of the Physiological Research Laboratory building. While he had not come so far as Scholander to join Scripps, Elsner was no native Californian. His accent betrayed his Boston origins and he had started his studies at New York University, getting his Ph.D. only in 1959 from the University of Washington when he was thirty-nine. "I was a dropout. Otherwise, I probably would not have met Scholander. In 1942, I was working at the meteorological station on top of Mount Washington in New Hampshire. He

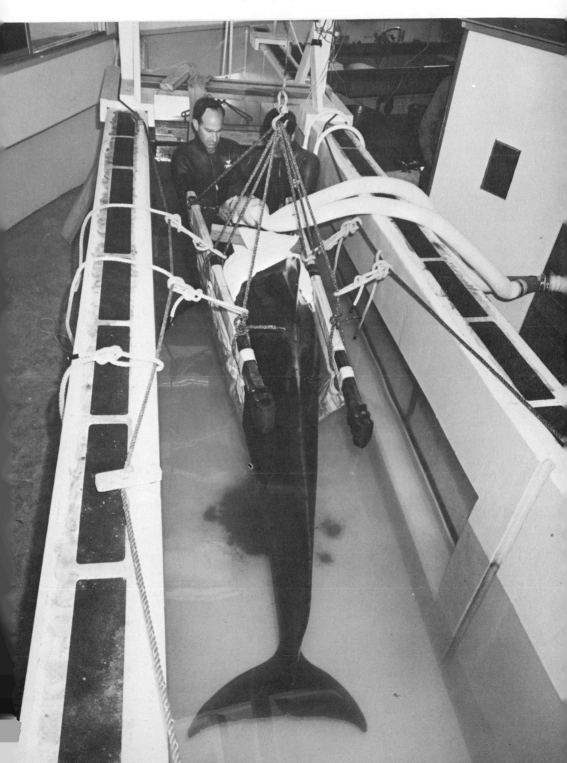

Robert Elsner (left) and his assistant, William Castro, work on Baby Jean, their cooperative pilot whale.

came up there testing equipment for the Air Force. I was fascinated by him, by his wild, uncontrolled curiosity. In the middle of the winter, he wanted to build a snowhouse and sleep in it overnight. He was making tests to determine the accumulation of carbon monoxide in tents. He asked for volunteers. No one joined him, except me.

"After that, our paths crossed occasionally. Then I went out on his expedition to southern Chile in 1959. We were studying the adaptability to cold of the Tierra del Fuegans, the Alakaluf Indians that Darwin had observed. There were only fifty-five of their descendants left. On that trip, Scholander invited me here to spend a year. I came in 1961 just to do a few projects, but I've been here ever since."

Basically, Elsner is using modern electronic instruments to update and expand Scholander's pioneering research on diving animals. There is a century of history behind such experiments, which began in 1870 when a French physiologist, Paul Bert, observed that blood volume was greater in ducks than in hens — thereby giving them more oxygen capacity — and that a duck's heart slowed from 100 to 14 beats per minute during a seven-minute dive. Early experimenters quickly concluded that a difference in oxygen storage capacity was not enough to explain why some animals dived better than others. The answer lay in their ability to slow their hearts and limit circulation only to vital organs, converting themselves into what have been called "heart-brain machines."

"A seal's blood is high in hemoglobin, the stuff that binds oxygen into the blood," Elsner continued. "It has a high myoglobin content in its muscles and that's another oxygen binder. But all this does not show why a seal can dive more than ten times longer than a man, for it can store only twice as much oxygen."

Seals have been observed to dive for periods of 15 to 40 minutes. The record, Elsner told me, seems to have been set with the help of an ingenious scientist named Dr. Gerald Kooyman from the University of Arizona who went down to the Antarctic and captured some Weddell seals at a breathing hole in the ice. He then moved them to another stretch of ice free of holes and cut one of his own. "It was built-in retrieval," Elsner commented with a note of admiration. "The seals had to come back. Kooyman strapped a depth-time instrument on his seals and sent them down. The maximum diving time was 43 minutes and the greatest depth 1,800 feet."

At Scripps, Elsner conducts experiments on a different scale. His ocean there consists of a row of three pools next to the main building of the Physiological Research Laboratory. The first is a square tank, then there is a small circular tank, and finally a big 55,000-gallon pool that forms a round moat with a laboratory inside it. The moat is bridged by an electric cart that runs around it on rails at a top speed of six miles an hour, fast enough to follow a human swimmer or test current meters but not to keep up with a dolphin.

These pools are linked by channels that can be dammed to drain them individually or to herd animals wherever needed. When I was there, their swimming population consisted of three dolphins, Alice, Felipe and José, and a pilot whale, Baby Jean ("I didn't name them," Elsner emphasized). Poor Alice, who had been used for experiments on underwater sound transmission by another researcher, was suffering from pneumonia, listing to port with fluid in her left lung and eating only two and a half instead of twenty pounds of fish a day. She later died, despite massive doses of penicillin.

Baby Jean, though, was in rollicking good health, all 900 pounds of her. When Elsner slapped the side of the circular pool around the lab, she came up to him with a slight squeaking noise, politely exhaling through the blowhole on her back. She then opened her jaws, displaying two rows of triangular teeth, and Elsner scratched the roof of her mouth. Scratching the roof of Baby Jean's mouth is a favorite pastime at Scripps both for herself and anyone who happens to be passing by, so much so that Elsner tries unsuccessfully to maintain her in some kind of seclusion.

She is a very docile animal, Elsner told me, and she readily swims from the moat to a side channel leading inside the central lab, where she can be hoisted up in a sling for various tests. Inside that lab, I found a model of the *Alpha Helix* and a cast of her figurehead, a mermaid with her tail entwined around a double spiral. There was also a magnificent wax model of a frieze depicting the wanderings of Ulysses. It had been executed by the same artist responsible for the ship's figurehead and someday it would hopefully bloom to full size around the circular lab.

Elsner was a latecomer to research on animals. Reversing the usual progression, he had started with human beings, including himself, as we saw, on Mount Washington. Later work led him not only to Tierra del Fuego but also to Australia, the Canadian Arctic, Peru and Lapland to see how peoples untouched by civilization adapt to harsh climates. This may explain what he termed his "dedication to the principle of nonde-structive techniques" and his efforts to study animals in a state as near as possible to normal.

"If you have to anesthetize an animal, you're changing its state," he said. "If you strap it to a board and force it to dive, you cannot expect its reactions to be normal. It's an unnatural experience. We try to measure the performance of an animal in an unrestrained, unanesthetized state." Elsner knew only one way to do this, and he took it: he became an amateur animal trainer. For months, he drove in every morning to the oceanarium of the San Diego Zoo and served his apprenticeship to the animal trainer working with California sea lions. He wanted to be able to convince animals to dive voluntarily, either in a pool or by putting their heads into a basin of water.

"Animal training is great fun, but it's an art," Elsner explained. "The key is to observe the animal until he performs one thing that you want him to do. Then you give him a piece of fish and, immediately, a signal to serve as a bridging stimulus. For example, you must get him to eat food out of your hand. So you put your hand under water, you give him food and then you blow a whistle."

This technique enabled Elsner to show that a trained seal's heart slowed from 140 to 40 beats a minute during a voluntary dive as compared to 5 to 10 beats a minute in a forced dive. "We don't know exactly why, but it would seem that the restrained animal knows it can't get up. So it turns on a full-blown defense mechanism."

Training dolphins is higher education. Elsner set out to convince one to keep his nose on a target underwater, again with leads from his body connected to an electrocardiograph apparatus. "The trouble is, the dolphin is very bright and alert. You have to be precise and crisp in your commands or else you will train him to do the wrong thing. If you nod your head inadvertently when you blow your whistle, he may take the nod as a signal instead of the whistle."

Results of this research have added another little proof to growing evidence of the dolphin's superiority over other animals. His heart beats about 90 times a minute when he is swimming, then slows to 40 or 50 when he dives normally. "But if you train him to hold his nose on a target, his heart rate falls from 90 to 12 beats, then goes up to 20. At first sight, he resembles a seal in a forced dive, but this isn't the case. The dolphin has a conscious or semiconscious capability of turning on full capacity in a voluntary dive. There is no way of testing him in a forced dive and I don't intend to try. If you strap him onto a board, he'll probably die. That was what happened in some earlier experiments twenty years or so ago. He becomes so frightened that he either stops breathing or he takes in water and drowns."

Elsner has conducted his experiments on human beings, too. In most cases, his subjects "dive" by placing their faces in a pan of water, like his trained seals. The water is important: a human being's heart slows much more if his face is immersed than if he just holds his breath. Most human beings experience a one-third drop in their heart rates during such dives, although one subject tested by Elsner showed a fall from 90 to 13 beats per minute.

He has been slightly disappointed by his studies of people who spend time underwater professionally. "We've examined lots of human divers and they are no better than we are. With training, it is possible to stay under for a couple of minutes, but the Australian aborigine divers or the Japanese Ama girls stay below only a minute or less. The difference is one of skill: they make better use of their time underwater. There were six Japanese Ama girls at the Sea World show in San Diego and we persuaded them to come here to submit to this experimentation. Their circulatory responses to the face immersion experiments were not essentially different from those of graduate students."

In his research on diving mammals, he decided that he could not omit the hippopotamus. Elsner and a keeper at the San Diego Zoo picked out a baby 200-pound hippo for tests. "We hand-fed him, we patted him on the head, we scratched him under the chin for ten days until he became accustomed to us. Then one day, before he knew what happened, we slapped two big pieces of rubber on his back with contact cement to keep our surface electrodes in place. He walked down into the water, trailing the wires to our electrocardiograph machine behind him. His heart rate was 90 beats a minute, but it slowed to 30 when he went in, and after a minute and a half it was down to 10. That was the longest he ever dived in the zoo, though I've known a frightened hippo in Uganda to stay under for six minutes."

None of these animals can approach the diving prowess of the whales, Elsner reminded me. A harpooned bottle-nosed whale has been known to sound for two hours, and a dead sperm whale was once recovered from a depth of 3,718 feet where he had fought an undersea cable, wrecking it but suffocating in the process.

In 1965, Elsner himself decided to film the capture of a whale at Scammon Lagoon off the Mexican coast of Baja California south of San Diego. This lagoon is about the last secluded place that California gray whales have to mate, and one Scripps scientist has plans to study them from a hot-air balloon floating unobserved over the waters of the lagoon. Elsner had a catamaran sailboat and what I thought was a pathological oblivion to his own well-being: "I guess we did get pretty close to him. You see, I have a Japanese friend who works in a filling station in Los Angeles. He used to be the skipper of a Japanese whaling boat. First we tried to net our whale, but then we harpooned him. He wasn't too big, only 3,500 pounds, and we put him in an improvised tank on a ship until we could get him to Sea World in San Diego, where we did some breathing measurements on him."

Such work seemed to be closer to oceanography, which after all is what Scripps is supposed to be doing, but Elsner is not tied to sea life. He feels that he is studying a "continuum" which ignores the boundaries of marine biology: he is carrying out research on fetal lambs. "As a fetus, the lamb or any mammal is an aquatic animal of sorts," Elsner began. "It is enclosed in a sack, and at the moment of birth, it is exposed to asphyxia. The fetus needs special equipment to bridge the gap between an aquatic and an air existence. Asphyxia is universally experienced by mammals at birth and it can lead to cerebral palsy in human beings. If the human fetus could do as well as aquatic mammals, then risks of cerebral palsy would be lessened. We don't know much about this and I'm not making a dogmatic statement. In any case, cerebral palsy can occur in a perfectly normal fetus. But some births lead to extreme asphyxia, as for example in a complicated delivery or when the umbilical cord is looped around the fetus's neck."

It is here that electronics comes in. Elsner wanted to get accurate measurements of blood flow within vital arteries during moments of oxygen stress. To do this, his lab has devised a blood-flow transducer. (A transducer is a device that converts one form of energy into another.) It consists of a piezoelectric (meaning that it converts pressure into electricity) crystal inside a small plastic cylinder. One end is linked to a clamp on the artery to be measured, the other to a power pack outside the animal, which does not appear to be bothered by it any more than a human being with a heart pacer.

In a harbor seal, whose heart rate dropped from between 80 and 100 beats a minute down to 5 or 6 beats in a dive, this instrument showed that blood flow fell to zero in the main kidney and abdominal arteries while blood pressure remained the same: the heart was working less, and in addition was irrigating a much smaller area. A result much closer to home, if home is eventual applications in medical science, was found with a pregnant ewe. When her face was ducked under water, blood flow to her extremities dropped as it did with other animals tested, but she maintained a normal supply to the uterine artery, the staff of life for her lamb.

One line of research he was following had led to Elsner's being written up in a publication that would be the last place where anyone would expect to see the activities of an institution of oceanography, *The Horseman and Fair World*. Preceding a story headlined "Record-Breaking Entry in Breeders' Filly Stakes," a correspondent responsible for training news at the Del Mar trotting track north of La Jolla had described how Elsner and two of his assistants turned up to learn how much oxygen a horse consumes.

"I like to call this applied oceanography," Elsner said as he showed me the article illustrated with a picture of his subject, an eight-year-old named Royal Jerry. I could see a horse stepping out with a long cylindrical bag over his nose and a heavy sulky, known to the trade as a jog cart, behind him. From the hood, a tube ran along the shafts like an exhaust pipe to a balloon swelling behind the cart. Beneath the wheels, there was a battery-powered vacuum cleaner to suck up his expired air. The cart also carried a driver and a researcher.

"These experiments on racehorses originated from the questions that we were asking about oxygen transport in marine mammals," Elsner remarked. "No science, including marine biology, has a fixed boundary line. We must not have inhibitions about crossing the interface between ocean and land at the tidal zone."

At Del Mar, Elsner and his assistants learned that their horse could take in more oxygen, in terms of body weight, and accelerate its heart much faster than a top human athlete. In the stall, a racehorse's heart idles at 25 to 30 beats a minute, then starts pounding at 250 to 320 beats per minute when he is flying down a track. An untrained human's heart can go from 70 to 180 beats per minute, an athlete's from 60 to 200. When I saw him, Elsner was still working on the equipment for this experiment because Royal Jerry was producing far more carbon dioxide than had been expected by the designers of the apparatus. He had not drawn any conclusions, nor had the correspondent of *The Horseman and Fair World*, who commented regretfully: "There's no basis to the thought that there are any hot tips to be had from the oxygen consumption of various steeds. All of this research is purely scientific." Elsner suspects that a horse's performance could be estimated on the basis of physiological tests, but he has no desire to pursue the matter.

He has other horses for experimentation at the Scripps animal colony, an ex-garbage dump half a mile up in the hills next to the institution's radio station and amidst the sparse wild vegetation that still reigns in Southern California beyond the sprinkler's reach. There he showed me two mares, a couple of fifteen-year-old rodeo veterans, that had been instrumented to measure blood flow in the iliac artery — which supplies their hind limbs — while they exercise. (The measurements either go into a tape recorder on the saddle or can be telemetered through an antenna to an observer.) Besides the mares, the population of the animal colony consisted of one lamb, whose blood flow had been recorded at birth, five dogs, a rhesus macaque monkey, and assorted uncounted squirrels and rabbits wandering in and out. The colony was being run jointly by Elsner and Dean Franklin, an electronics engineer from the University of California at San Diego. Its most auspicious piece of oceanographic gear was a corral and a short track where the mares could work out. But Elsner did not find this incongruous:

"Remember, we must be able to compare one form of life with another at any time. If you took only marine forms, you would get a warped side of the picture. You'd be almost sure to go way wrong at first. Land animals, including man, are benchmarks for our work with other species."

After we had returned to his office in Room 118 of the physiological research laboratory building, Elsner hesitated before he showed me his latest idea. "It's pretty wild," he apologized. "You see, I've fixed up an incubator, an investment of eight dollars. We're drilling holes through the shells of eggs, then taking blood from the membrane of the embryo. This gives us a chance to look at the development of the embryo's blood supply and also the exchange of oxygen and carbon dioxide that goes on in the shell.

"I don't know where this will take us, but it should give you a good tag line for your story. You can always say that we've got everything here from whales to chick embryos."

4. *Any Boy's Mind Works the Same Way*

I hardly had time to settle down at Scripps with a temporary office in Room 3244, Ritter Hall, and to admire a predecessor's arcane equations on my greenboard (a sample of indigenous pop art that I preserved to impress visitors) when people began to wonder why I had not already seen John Isaacs. Scripps's public relations office always trotted him out for reporters. Isaacs had photographed a marine monster with an underwater camera, he had suggested tying a satellite to the earth with a long wire, he wanted to tow an iceberg up from the Antarctic to bring fresh water to Los Angeles, he had a possible solution to the planet's power requirements, he knew what had happened to the vanishing California sardine, he was trying to record weather over and under the Pacific, he had written about fish-farming, he had talked about the year 2000 on television. He sounded like a wet Paul Bunyan.

Seeing Isaacs was not all that easy. His dual role at Scripps as professor of oceanography and director of marine life research brought so many people to his door that he preferred to work much of the time twenty-five miles to the north at exurban Rancho Santa Fe, where he had built a handsome home on a spot locally known as Rattlesnake Hill. (The Isaacses learned of the name only after they had started to build and the rattlesnakes were a long time forgetting it.) He readily made several appointments with me and had to break each of them at the last minute because of the unexpected advent of a committee from Washington or a delegation from Sacramento.

Then I was unexpectedly informed that Professor Isaacs had some free time. I broke an appointment of my own and went downstairs to see him in his office on the ground floor of Ritter Hall. When I arrived, I caught a scant glimpse of a big man, well over six feet, with a trim white beard and a full head of rumpled white hair. As if this was not enough to make him stand out, he was wearing a suit and smoking a cigarette. (Hardly anyone else smoked cigarettes at Scripps except the director, Dr. William Nierenberg, who lives under a cloud of Gauloise fumes, but he's neither a Californian nor an oceanographer.) Isaacs said he would be right back and told me to sit down and make myself at home in his office.

As soon as he left, I got up and began to note the titles on the bookshelf closest to his desk. From right to left, I could see *The Compleat Angler* by Izaak Walton, *The Outline of History* by H. G. Wells, *The Devil's Dictionary* by Ambrose Bierce, *Roget's Thesaurus, Textbook of Toxicology, Applied Fluid Mechanics, Paleontology of the Marine Tertiary Formations of Oregon and Washington, Marine Boring and Fouling Organisms, The Voice of the Dolphins* by Leo Szilard, and *Eight Great Tragedies*. If I had hoped to find a shortcut to the man, I was worse off than when I started. A dartboard on the wall facing his desk was no great help, either.

When Isaacs came back, I asked him what was the purpose of the dartboard.

"Decision-making," he answered.

Seeking some kind of a lead, I then asked him how he had been able to maintain so great an interest in so many different things.

"There's nothing unusual about that," he said. "That's the way any boy's mind works — as children, we are interested in everything. I don't see any need to do a thing in a certain way because that is the way it has always been done. The more I look at traditional measurements, the more suspect they are. Take the heating of the sea's surface water by the sun as an example. One always assumes a flat surface. At high latitudes, this means that most of the sunlight is reflected. But what if the surface is ripped by waves? What if the sun gets through from many angles and the heating of surface water is far greater than the assumption would predict?

"A boy looks at nature and asks questions. For a long time, scientists did the same. They were men of the world, interested in many things. They looked at people and nature, they tried to put them together. Then, in the last 150 years, they became impressed by the so-called scientific method. They strove for certainty by analysis — maybe people fixed on certainty when they grew dubious about their gods. They became highly skilled specialists in taking things apart. After nearly two centuries of analysis, we are now baffled by the task of putting even moderately complex things together. Planetary physics, of which oceanography is only one branch, is trying. I regard oceanography as a challenger and an integrator for the sciences."

There would be nothing unusual, it is true, if Isaacs were a small boy and not well into his fifties. He was born in 1913 in Spokane, Washington, but he spent his childhood on the family's ranch in central Oregon. "It was a 250,000-acre ranch. You could take off in any direction for days."

He was born with some strong genes. His grandfather, John D. Isaacs (the grandson is John D. III), had been chief engineer of the Central Pacific. When Leland Stanford, the owner of the railroad, became interested in how a racehorse runs, he turned the problem over to Isaacs in 1872. Grandfather Isaacs devised a battery of electrically tripped cameras that enabled pictures to be made for the first time of fast-moving objects. Eadweard Muybridge took the photographs on Stanford's stock farm at Palo Alto.

"The family always told me I would be an engineer-inventor and I always fought hard against it," Isaacs said. "I wanted to be a fisherman. When an aunt finally urged me to settle down and be a fisherman, I went to school to study engineering."

His aunt's application of adolescent psychology soon backfired. Isaacs was bored with college, quit, "bummed around," became a logger, a fire lookout, a merchant seaman, then a commercial fisherman. "I ran a deep-sea boat for a few years starting in 1935. It's a good introduction to oceanography. At night, I used to sit on the side of my fishing boat, stare down into the deep water and ask questions. I sent some to Scripps. They were good questions. I still can't answer many of them.

"It has taught me to respect lay opinions. That's why I spend so goddam much time talking at women's clubs and sportsmen's meetings. Lay people don't get enough credit. Look at the history of scientific discoveries. Everyone knows Jenner discovered that cowpox could provide immunity to smallpox, but what were the names of the cowmaids he talked to? They had made all the observations and told him the answer!"

Among Isaacs's favorite laymen are the Polynesians who navigated the Pacific without chart, compass or sextant. Isaacs is among those who believe that they read the sea, the patterns of its swells, the changing light of its horizons. He too has looked at the color of reflected light in the sky from a small boat. He could see some of the clues, but not all. He concluded that the Polynesians had been able to find other clues to which "our modern senses are blunted."

Isaacs might have gone on as a fisherman sending in questions to Scripps if the sea had not stepped in on the side of his aunt. Coming into the mouth of the Columbia River in Oregon one day, he broke down in rough water over the Jetty Sands and broke up on the jetty, losing his boat and spending several hours swimming to safety. He has since described the sea as an "ambuscade" and he admitted to me: "The sea scares the hell out of me. I get awful cold feet when I'm on it. That's one reason why I go." He never forgets that experience on the Columbia River, not even when he listens to music. Discussing the destruction of the ship in *Scheherazade*, Isaacs remarked in an article he wrote for *Portal*, a brave little Southern California quarterly: "I have always been a bit resentful of Rimsky-Korsakov, for though his rhythm may be impeccable for the seas of the Persian Gulf, the respite between blows is entirely too brief a period for the long breakers of the Pacific from which I once cringed."

Whether it was the hand of destiny or the breakers over the Jetty Sands that wrecked his boat, Isaacs was pitched into his grandfather's footsteps. During World War II, he worked on the construction of seaplane bases and that led him into such matters as the effect of waves on shore installations. In 1944, he went back to the University of California at Berkeley, earning his B.S. degree in engineering at the none-too-precocious age of thirty-two. Though he is a full professor, this is the only degree he holds. Scripps runs only graduate courses in oceanography, and more often than not, Isaacs's students are higher up the diploma scale than he is. A large number of leading oceanographers either have no doctorates or were too busy working at sea to get them until relatively late in life. Such a disregard of the academic pecking order is another refreshing aspect of oceanographic research institutions, although not likely to last.

Isaacs worked on amphibious landing problems, beaches and surf. He was led into deep water when he went along on the Bikini atomic bomb tests in 1946, photographing the explosions with a time-lapse camera. This is a camera set to take still pictures of an event at regular intervals, whether split seconds or minutes. When the film is run through a movie projector, the original duration of the event is greatly compressed, giving an effect opposite to that of slow-motion photography.) Grandfather had sighted his cameras on a running horse, Isaacs focused his on splitting atoms.

Isaacs still sits figuratively on the side of his boat and wonders. His principal interests, he told me, lie in the process of things as well as in things themselves. "I look at a thing and then I can't help asking myself: 'How much did God have to know to invent it?' I want to see how it was invented."

One is tempted to think that two highly personal experiences, his shipwreck in the Columbia River and his eyewitnessing of the Bikini and later tests, led to some of his ideas about reinventing the world. He certainly does not think much of natural harbors like the one where he met his match. Isaacs once pointed out that we have put nearly all our harbors in the wrong places. They are at the mouths of rivers where they must inevitably catch all the sediment the streams bring down. Consequently, he remarked, a sum amounting to about half the income of all shipping using American harbors must be spent every year to maintain them, mainly by dredging. Rivers not only pour silt into the bottom of a harbor but fresh water over its surface, making it more vulnerable to winter freezing.

Or else we choose sites without paying attention to the inexorable movement of sand along a coast that builds up shoals at harbor entrances. It was such a mistake that almost cost Isaacs his life at the entrance to the Columbia River. The error was repeated at Santa Barbara on the California coast. To create an artificial harbor, a breakwater was built right in

John Isaacs (left) and Willard Bascom at sea on a "marine monster hunt" with Isaacs's underwater camera.

the path of this flow of sand along the shore. Not only does the harbor clog but beaches down the coast are starved of the sand they used to get before the breakwater was put up.

To Isaacs, the answer is man-made harbors created with atomic explosions on rocky coasts free of sand and rivers bearing silt. Casting his eye around the globe for an example, he found that nature had already done the job at Pago Pago on Samoa with a volcanic explosion. A breach in the drowned crater gives ships over 200 feet of water at the harbor entrance and they have 100 feet inside. Pago Pago has already been inadvertently duplicated at Bikini, where, as Isaacs once remarked with his weakness for rhetoric, "the deep blue man-made harbors seem to be harbingers of the new muscular power that man now possesses to better the world in which he lives." He used these words in a paper he presented to a symposium on Operation Plowshare devoted to peaceful uses of atomic energy and he typically prefaced it with a clinching quotation, this one from Leonardo da Vinci: "This is the way to dredge a harbor, and the plough . . . will have in front of it spikes shaped like ploughshares."

Atomic harbors can come in all sizes. Small ones, Isaacs thinks, could make a big difference for most of the world's underdeveloped and underfed peoples who live on coasts where there may not be a natural port within fifty or a hundred miles. To fish for food, they must use canoes and other primitive craft small enough to be carried up on land and too small to go a few miles offshore where the fish are running. An "atomic hole in the wall" might change this.

As for big man-made harbors, they could herald a revolution in shipping and shipbuilding, the most lagging of American industries and technologies. Silt-ridden ports and channels limit the draft of ships to about fifty feet and this limits their length. Isaacs reminds us that a ship is like a beam: if you do not want it to bend and buckle when you lengthen it, then you must increase its thickness and height. And a ship must not break when her bow or stern pitches out of the water with no visible support. Isaacs has calculated that a ship half a mile long would span more than twice the distance of the longest ocean swells and would never be in such a predicament. She would draw 150 feet of water, and with atomically blasted harbors ready to receive her, she could be built: 3,000 feet long, 3 million tons. She could carry oil or ore at a third the cost of present-day freighters and the ailing American merchant marine would regain a place it has not held since the days of clipper ships.

When I asked Isaacs if he really thought a million-ton ship feasible, he answered: "Why not a billion tons?" He could doubtless prove with one of the fifty pencils he keeps sharpened on his desk that there is no limit to what the ocean can transport. Every year, it nonchalantly hefts the 7,650 *trillion* metric tons of icebergs that start their journeys from the polar ice caps, 93 percent of them from Antarctica. That is a lot of frozen fresh water.

The sea's unchallenged weight-lifting supremacy led Isaacs into what is probably the most popularized of his oneiric engineering schemes. He has estimated that a "small" Antarctic berg can be worth $200 million at the current wholesale price of fresh water in Southern California. Delivering it would simply be a matter of towing it into the great currents sweeping north to the equator and once more letting the ocean do the work. The job might take a year, Isaacs thinks, and wind power could be enlisted as well, with sail-driven tugs exerting small but steady guidance at two or three knots.

Nature performs the feat time and again. Bergs are occasionally sighted in tropical waters and some were once helped into Callao in Peru, providing an unexpected bonanza of ice. Isaacs has pointed out that the world's coastal deserts, like that of Peru, lie along these cold currents bound for the equator: "In the southern hemisphere, at least, the great Antarctic bergs are poised at the entries to natural highways that lead to the deserts."

Isaacs never arrives at a terminus in his reasoning. What should be the end of the line is only a transfer point. From the iceberg and coastal deserts, it was quite logical by his lights that he should go on to the water shortage everywhere. He had no trouble putting it into the proper perspective.

Not enough water to drink? The world ocean loses a meter (about 3 feet, 3 inches) of water every year to the atmosphere by evaporation, and all the water the human race has ever drunk represents no more than three-tenths of one percent of what the ocean provides so bountifully in a single year.

Desalinized water is too expensive for drinking? Even under present methods, it would cost only an additional thirty cents a year per capita to provide all of America's drinking and cooking water by ordinary distillation. Here, Isaacs has indulged as he often does in his love of numerical hyperbole. Desalinized water for drinking costs $300 an acre-foot and voices in some quarters cry this is too high. But the price per acre-foot of coffee or beer is $800,000; of bar whiskey, $20 million; of Chanel No. 5, $40 million. Isaacs impaled upon his slide rule a suggestion that water could be saved by placing a brick in the tank of each flush toilet. He found it an excellent investment: the cost of an eight-cent brick would be amortized in two or three years.

Then where is the problem of man's use of water? Isaacs has turned the question inside out: water is using man. Western civilization is a prisoner of its early history that began in the dry climates of the Near East. Water was precious to tribes wandering in the desert. It brought life to the river valleys where cities arose with irrigation canals as their first great public works. But is the worship of water appropriate in a temperate climate? Isaacs quotes a friend who remarked that "our great religious progenitors struck the rock and made the water flow and the desert bloom . . . none of them cleared rain forests or drained a swamp!"

In the United States, Isaacs thinks, the prophets have been replaced by the politicians and the miracles by irrigation projects subsidized to the point where the water to grow a crop costs almost as much as the price of the harvest. Even if the ocean were fresh water, it still could not be pumped up to water the highlands of the continental interior under normal economics. What Isaacs wants us to do is to stop putting expensive irrigation water over soil and start putting soil under cheap rainwater. On the east coast of the United States, "worn-out" land is going back to the deer and the wilderness.

Wouldn't it be more reasonable, if less religious, to restore soil there than to bring water to the desert?

Couldn't a fraction of the money spent on desalinization research be devoted to developing fertilizers capable of putting the thin soil of rain forests — fifteen percent of the earth's land area — to productive use?

Would it not be more sensible to use the genetic resources of salt-resistant marsh plants to breed crops capable of thriving on salty soil instead of waterlogging and salting more soil with "monumental and hence politically appealing irrigation works"?

Isaacs does not expect an answer to such questions. I like to think that he poses them as a sort of marine gadfly trying to drive us out of the ruts of our earthbound thinking. As long as we remain in these ruts, his suggestions will not be applicable. Americans will go on playing golf on greens watered amidst scorched rocks; Arabs and Israelis will go on reclaiming more and more desert to grow crops until some planetary system of distributing resources comes along.

Mention resources to Isaacs and he immediately returns to the rationality of the sea, which has not been carved up according to the whims of political geography. Instead of a gaggle of national entities squabbling like Norman peasants over a heritage, he finds a cornucopia free of flags. Desert-born civilizations have trouble imposing their values in the ocean, where Isaacs is a prophet.

Anyone on such friendly terms with big numbers as he is cannot be frightened by the forecast of a world population of ten billion. From the sea, Isaacs sees not a crowded earth, but mainly thick scabs of people along the coasts and vast stretches of room behind them. "The human race is barely becoming successful," he has said, "and we, from a reaction of apprehension and perhaps nostalgia, wish already to suppress it." The demands of ten billion people would be only a drop in the oceanic bucket. The sea could still offer *each one* of them 200 million tons of water, 6 million tons of salt, 200,000 tons of magnesium, 50,000 tons of potassium, a ton of iron and two pounds of gold. On the bottom lie 200 billion tons of manganese nodules waiting for the right economic moment (which some think is now) to be picked up with the appropriate technology.

Isaacs does not believe that a planet of ten billion need go protein-hungry. It will require 50 million tons of animal protein a year, and the sea annually produces at least seven times as much, though only some 50 million tons of fish (representing about 10 million tons of animal protein) are now being caught yearly. Isaacs is one of a growing chorus of oceanographers who try to remind us of the inane way we get food from the ocean. The tuna, the salmon, the halibut and our other delicacies are actually fearsome predators, the tigers of the sea. It is like raising cows, throwing them to tigers and then marketing tiger steaks. The classical, and far from accurate, picture of the food pyramid of the sea might begin with 1,000 pounds of phytoplankton, the microscopic marine plants that drift and thrive in the sunlit layer of the ocean. This produces 100 pounds of zooplankton, small feebly swimming animals that are also moved by the currents. They support ten pounds of herring or anchovies, which could yield a pound of bonito and a tenth of a pound of tuna. After I had learned this picture, I was particularly amused by New York subway advertisements extolling the virtues of tuna as a cat food. The cat, preying on the tuna, is thereby elevated to the same rank as the killer whale. Since I am not Isaacs, I was unable to figure how many tons of phytoplankton are needed to grow a pound of cat.

Isaacs and some others who have looked into this problem see a yearly production of 350 million tons of animal protein at the level of the herring, the sardine, the anchovy, the menhaden, the squid and other organisms feeding low down on the pyramid at the zooplankton level. It would make sense, though not gastronomically, to hunt down the tuna and the salmon that prey on these grazing cattle just as Western cowmen put a bounty on wolves and coyotes.

The worst coyote of all is man, particularly in America and western Europe. To please their customers, fishermen take selected varieties of fish, with only a dozen of 20,000 known species comprising 75 percent of the world catch. At a certain stage in selective fishing, a species dwindles to the point where its competitors in the sea move into its territory. Isaacs will tell you that the Japanese and the Russians, so often accused of overfishing, actually do less damage than more discriminating fishermen. They take far more species on the same floor of the pyramid, and leave untouched the relative strength of each group competing for what there is to eat.

At Scripps, Isaacs's marine life research group turned its attention to a notorious instance of human tinkering with such biological equilibriums, the futile effort of the Pacific sardine to keep up with the northern anchovy off California. Hundreds of thousands of tons of sardines used to be landed before World War II on the West Coast, but the catch has since shrunk almost to the vanishing point. Studies by Isaacs's group showed that the combined population of hunted sardines and scorned anchovies remained more or less constant, the anchovies multiplying to fill the empty niche left by the sardines.

Those studies led the Scripps researchers on to a much more interesting path. Off Santa Barbara, they found that sediments deposited so rapidly on the bottom in undisturbed water that they were shut off from the destructive action of oxygen and burrowing organisms. Like tree rings, they offer what Isaacs has called "an annual memory of events." Variations in the kinds and amounts of marine life at different layers can indicate changes of climate or short variations in the positions of the great currents teeming with this life.

The sediments told the full story of the sardine. A sample three feet deep and going back 1,500 years contained fish scales indicating that the hake and the anchovy had been the dominant inhabitants of the area over this period. As for the sardine, it was just passing through, having been plentiful only during two periods, one 700 years ago and the other in recent years. Heavy fishing had hastened the exit it probably would have made anyway. Isaacs believes that such detailed histories exist elsewhere on the sea floor, though they are not widespread, and could make valuable reading for nations before they develop large fisheries to feed their peoples.

The ocean is useful not only for what we can get out of it but for its capacity to receive the things, generally unwanted, that we put into it. This capacity is not unlimited, as was once conveniently believed, but Isaacs sees several ways that the ocean can put a lid on garbage. One of the handiest is its ability to take in radioactive wastes from nuclear power plants. He and Dr. Harmon Craig of Scripps have estimated that the ocean can safely absorb radioactive products from the fission of eighty tons of uranium a year. This represents the equivalent of twice the world's present output of electricity if it were generated solely by nuclear reactors.

Again, the ocean is an upside-down image of the land. It is not its water but its chemical elements that dilute radioactivity. Now, the proportions of these elements on land and sea are almost exactly reversed. The land is commonly short of such elements as iodine, calcium or strontium because they have been eternally washed into the sea by rains and rivers. The sea is therefore rich in them. When we introduce their radioisotopes into the ocean, they are quickly diluted by vast quantities of their natural forms.

With such an abundance of riches, marine organisms need not concentrate either these elements or their isotopes. Not so on land. We and the animals we eat do concentrate them. Their isotopes should be kept away from us and put into the sea.

Isaacs and others trace this biological lid back to "evolutionary design" that began when life emerged from the ocean. Since they no longer needed it, land plants and animals alike lost their ability to take up rare sea elements. Consequently, as Isaacs has stated, "the elements that are the most worrisome on the land are among the least worrisome in the ocean. The concentration of radioactive strontium in the bones of the fish at Bikini, where many millions of curies of radioactive waste have been 'disposed' in the last decades is not as high as that in the bones of the sheep of Wales, a highly leached country [heavily washed-out land]."

The biological lid is bound to lift, however, if too much atomic garbage is put under it. Isaacs regards it as nothing more than a way of buying time until the atomic waste problem can be solved in safer ways. With nuclear fission taking over more and more from conventional sources of power, he estimates that the upper limit of eighty tons of uranium wastes would be reached by 1980. A world of ten billion people would have to get rid of the waste products of 1,000 tons of uranium a year. This would double the radioactivity of the sea and burst all lids.

Some radioactive materials are sealed in drums or concrete, then sent to the bottom at selected deepwater sites. Like any other oceanographer who has tried to make something work on the sea floor, Isaacs hesitates to believe that anything can stay sealed there forever. Not only that, but fish and other marine organisms flock to any new object on the bottom. He thinks that scientists would do well to listen to lay opinions here. "When someone once proposed to put atomic waste into drums and dump them in the Gulf of Mexico, the issue was treated as an erudite problem. But I talked to conservationists, to rod and gun clubs, to sportsmen and commercial fishermen. They know that if you put something on the bottom in such water, fish will come and sit on it." Drum-dumping is defended on the grounds that radioactivity from a leaking container in the deep would be diffused at the slow pace in which the oceans "turn over" — measured in hundreds of years. Anti-dumpers argue that fish and other organisms might absorb it, carry it into the food pyramid and possibly provide a biological shortcut to the human consumer.

I was not surprised to learn that Isaacs had a surprising answer to this. Not content with putting the depth of the ocean — a piddling average of 12,000 feet — between humanity and hot radioactive waste, he has suggested drilling another 1,000 feet down into the sediments on the sea floor and burying it there. In this instance, at least, reality has almost caught up with him. As I learned later, such deep-sea drilling may be going on right now, though for far loftier scientific purposes than atomic waste disposal.

Even as a garbageman, Isaacs cannot help being creative. When he shifted his attention from high-level radioisotopes to the low level of common sewage, he again found a barrier to separate us from our refuse (especially when we are swimming). Among other things, sewage is fresh water and naturally rises to the surface of the salt sea. It wouldn't, Isaacs reasoned, if it were mixed with silt from, perhaps, the dredging we will be forced to do until we move our harbors to where he thinks they belong.

Then there is waste in the form of heat from power plants and industry, with much more on the way from nuclear reactors desalinizing seawater necessarily on the shore. Some engineers are still astonished when they are told that clean hot water is heat pollution. Released on the surface, it can change local conditions for marine life, not always for the better. Instead, Isaacs would use it to drive up cold water to a barren surface, bringing phosphates and nitrates to the marine plants living in the layer, anywhere from 30 to 300 feet deep, where sunlight penetrates and photosynthesis can go on.

Such a prospect is another of those transfer points in Isaacs's thinking which inevitably leads to Texas-sized numbers. He never adds two and two; instead, he keeps multiplying numbers over and over until he reaches the kind of figure with which he feels at ease. It is usually something on the order of 10^{14} (that is, one followed by fourteen zeroes), with calories or kilowatts or tons after it. He was confronted by two problems: how to fertilize the upper levels of the sea with nutrients from the deep, and how to generate power for ten billion people without dumping the wastes from 1,000 tons of uranium into the ocean. So he combined the two.

Ten billion people will need ten million megawatts (a megawatt is a million watts) of energy, which Isaacs also expresses as the equivalent of exploding 2,800 hundred-megaton bombs. Even a blue-sky scheme like a proposal to dam the Red Sea, let it evaporate until it drops hundreds of feet and then produce hydroelectric power with an oceanic Niagara cascading down from the Gulf of Aden would have to be repeated 350 times to meet such a demand. All the energy represented by the tides is only a tenth of it.

Peering into the ocean, Isaacs found another lid. The difference in temperature between the top and the bottom of the sea could represent 200 times those 10 million megawatts. He told me that what he had in mind was the application of modern technology to Claude's machine.

I fought off the urge to ask a silly question and waited until I could get to a library with Larousse's *La Science: ses Progrès, ses Applications*. There, I learned that Georges Claude (1870–1960) had not only done practical things in France like synthesizing ammonia during World War I and putting neon gas into light bulbs in 1910, but had also been quite an engineer-visionary himself.

On the fifteenth of November 1926, Claude read a paper to the French Academy of Science where he pointed out that in the tropics, the temperature of water 3,000 feet down is about 40 degrees F. as compared to 80 or 85 degrees on the surface. Put a pipe 3,000 feet down and the deep water would find its own level and rise to the surface.

Once it got there, Claude wanted to pump it into a condenser to create a slight vacuum that would enable the surface water, at 85 degrees F., to produce low-pressure steam. Experimenting with five gallons of water at 82 degrees on one end of his machine and a cake of ice on the other, he had driven a small turbine. Claude foresaw "immense stations, whose size would enable them to ride out deep-sea storms, transmitting torrents of power to land." In deep water near shore, they could also air-condition a tropical city.

Claude got to work in a hurry because, as he told the academy in 1926, "The Federal Oil Conservation Board of the United States estimates that the United States has only enough oil to last for six years." In 1930, he went to Matanzas Bay in Cuba and put a pipe 1,800 feet down. He obtained 22 kilowatts from this plant — but the word got around that he had to put in more than 22 kilowatts to pump water into his condenser and eject gases. He was never able to try again.

Isaacs thinks Claude was a victim of bad public relations. "He built a model plant on a one-tenth scale. But since he could not 'model' heat loss through his intake pipe, he built a full-sized intake and pumped the full-scale water flow through it! Naturally, this took more power than he generated, but it showed that the full-scale plant would be valuable. No matter how often he explained this, no one would look beyond the fact that he got less power than he put in. Besides, Claude had only the crudest sort of intake pipe to work with — a cooper's product of barrel staves and tar. We could do this so much better today and we also know far better locations, places where differences of 20 degrees F. occur almost on the surface."

Isaacs likes to play with the idea of improving Claude's process. While it may not be a very efficient way to generate power, it is unbeatable when it comes to lifting all that richly fertilized deep water to a point where ocean plant life can get at it. It would be silly, of course, to pour the nutrients back into the open ocean. Taking one of his needle-pointed pencils, Isaacs has calculated that if a plant hoisted deep water into a shallow lagoon on an atoll like Kwajalein in the central Pacific, a fish yield of almost a ton an acre could result. Such an atoll could turn out animal protein for 16 million people a year and generate 10 million horsepower as a by-product.

Isaacs does not insist on using the Claude machine, which after all, poses the question of what to do with 10 million horsepower in the central Pacific. A nuclear reactor could be used to bring water up from the deep. Or there is the private joke of the oceanographer, the salt fountain.

Over much of the ocean, surface water is potentially denser than the deep water over which it floats because the sun's evaporation has made it saltier. It stays on top only because of its higher temperature. If one puts a copper tube down into the sea (one has never tried) and starts an upward flow of cold water, that flow will never stop. As the cold water rises, it warms up and becomes lighter than the saltier surface water. It will just keep coming up.

One reason why Claude's machine has remained a dream and the salt fountain a freak to enliven oceanography textbooks is that the heaving ocean is no place to try to keep a pipe hanging vertically from a ship. Isaacs proposes to get around this difficulty by using a stable platform, a greatly enlarged version of the FLIP vessel used by Scripps, which I was able to visit later. Weight a telegraph pole on one end, put it overside and it will float vertically, bobbing much less than a boat. A long enough "pole," getting nearly all its buoyancy from the tranquil deep layers of the sea, would hardly move at all. If it were thick enough, it could become a small chunk of terra firma — to be used to run salt fountains or Claude plants, provide a mid-ocean harbor to shipping and even, Isaacs has suggested, serve as a resort and fishing platform for sportsmen prone to seasickness.

He can seldom resist a constant urge to venture beyond his field. "Nine times out of ten, you make a fool out of yourself with dubious ideas," he confided to me, "but the tenth time, you won't." He has stuck out his neck all the way into the earth's mantle and up into space. In 1964, Isaacs enlisted the aid of Dr. Hugh Bradner, a Scripps geophysicist, to try to explain how the earth's interior is heated. The usual answer is radioactivity generated by the rocks in the mantle, but Isaacs and Bradner queried it. The flow of heat from beneath the ocean floor and from the continents is almost the same. They gently pointed out in the *Journal of Geophysical Research* that this is "difficult to explain." Under the continents, there is a thick mantle of radioactive granite; under the oceans, a thin layer of basalt. It is hard to make this similarity of heat flow stand up, they said, "without invoking a miracle of distribution of radioactive materials."

So they looked elsewhere for a source of heat. They came to the neutrino, that neutral particle whose existence was first postulated by nuclear physicists when they found that the electrons emitted by a nucleus during radioactive "beta decay" did not account for all the energy released. Something else was being emitted too, and it was eventually found: the neutrino, a particle with zero mass and no electric charge. The sun is probably the main source of neutrinos that the earth receives from outer space, but according to nuclear physics, they go right through our planet and come out the other side. Isaacs and Bradner speculated that if neutrinos lost from 1/300th to 1/8000th of their energy on the way, they could account for the generation of heat within the earth. Physicists maintain that this is highly unlikely, but the two Scripps scientists, reasoning from what has been found on the sea bottom rather than in a laboratory, provocatively left the matter there.

The most notorious of Isaacs's "dubious ideas" is the skyhook, which was described in *Science* under his signature and those of Bradner and Dr. George E. Backus from Scripps, and Allyn Vine of Woods Hole, who often gets such inspirations himself. They began with a synchronous satellite always remaining over the same point on the earth's surface. Such a satellite could, in principle, be extended to the earth by a tapered cable. (I spared myself their explanation of the principle, and the analysis of possible materials for the cable.) Then loads could be sent along the cable, which would be attached near the equator so that the energy of the spinning earth would drive them up. Such an installation, the authors emphasized, could be very useful to maintain observatories, fuel spacecraft and "support very tall structures on the earth's surface." The skyhook was inevitably shot down by a letter writer to *Science* and, just as inevitably, put right back up by the authors in their reply. They did grant that "we are quite aware that the engineering problems inherent in this system could be answered only by a program commensurate with some of the large contemporary projects." So far, there have been no takers.

Isaacs will not shun an idea merely because it happens to lie within his own field and costs less than a manned moon landing. One of his most appealing suggestions is based on the ability of the albatross to cover thousands of miles without ever moving its wings. The bird actually surfs in the air above the waves of the deep-ocean swell, which move at 70 miles an hour in much of the Pacific. Isaacs thinks that it should be possible for a "ground-effect vehicle" like a hovercraft to imitate the albatross riding the wave-driven air, and use its engine only to hover. He dashed off a short paper on this nearly ten years ago and he had apparently gone farther with the idea, for he politely refused to tell me anything more about it.

The man is not just a dreamer or a prophet. Throughout his career at Scripps, he has turned to the exasperating problems of work in the sea and come up with some elegant solutions to them. One of the earliest was a device intended to tell the oceanographer when an instrument has reached the bottom. If something has been lowered on 15,000 feet of wire from a drifting rolling ship, a winch operator cannot be expected to sense the bottom at once when the wire slackens. So Isaacs and Dr. Arthur Maxwell invented a signal. It consisted of a pointed piston that hammered into a hollow glass sphere when it hit the sea floor. Water pressure, running to thousands of pounds per square inch, did the rest, collapsing the sphere with an enormous bang that could be heard on the surface with a hydrophone. At least, that was what it was supposed to do. The first spheres tested proved astonishingly resistant. Glass in a sphere gets stronger when it is compressed, a characteristic that led Isaacs and Maxwell to predict its use as a likely material for the inner hulls of deep-diving research submersibles. Even a 25-watt light bulb, they found, often did not collapse until it went down to 2,500 feet. As for the spheres, some would only chip, bending the piston point. Only after such bugs were chased out of their device did Isaacs and Maxwell proudly offer it to seagoing scientists as . . . the ball-breaker.

More recently, Isaacs and his group at Scripps have been working in a direction taken by modern oceanography everywhere. Ships are expensive to run, too expensive to keep tethered to a wire while a recording instrument runs for hours or days on the bottom. Scientists also can think of more fruitful ways of spending their time. Yet the greatest gap in our knowledge of the sea is a lack of information about what happens over a long period at a fixed point. Meteorologists know the hourly variations of temperatures in New York over the past one hundred years; but there are parts of the ocean where extrapolations must be made from measurements taken years apart. (Fortunately, the ocean is less flighty than the atmosphere, or no extrapolations at all could be made.)

There are two different approaches to planting relatively permanent stations in mid-ocean and they are intended for different purposes. One is to drop an instrument overboard, steam away, then return later when it bobs up. Even when a ship remains in the vicinity, this eliminates the tedium of lowering a few miles of wire (and adds to the chances of losing the instrument). The other is to hang instruments on and below a buoy to measure, let us say, temperatures at intervals between the surface and the bottom. Days, weeks or hopefully months later, a ship can return and pick up the record.

Scripps and other research centers work on both approaches. Fundamentally, anything that can drop to a preset depth and return when its job is done is nothing but a balloon in reverse. Over ten years ago, Isaacs's group was sending down fish traps hanging from gasoline-filled floats to operate at 12,000 feet. They popped up when seawater had eaten through a magnesium link, releasing their ballast. Then, on the surface, they indicated their whereabouts with the help of a small buoy carrying a light and the type of radar reflector that the Navy puts on its life rafts.

To Isaacs, these were vehicles that could do a great deal more than catch fish. Two of his engineers, George Schick and Meredith Sessions, refined them to the point where they could take down delicate current meters that revealed the circulation of very deep water. Others could carry a camera with a chunk of bait to lure subjects. In the first tests of the camera, it stayed on the bottom from 30 to 60 hours, snapping pictures every fifteen minutes at depths as low as 11,200 feet. One of the shots showed a "marine monster" that was later identified by Scripps's marine biologists as a 22-foot Greenland shark. The shark had its picture taken in the tropical Pacific off Baja California, but it was swimming in deep water only three degrees above freezing, its own Arctic Ocean. The camera's shutter remains open all the time; pictures are shot when its flashtube flicks on, surprising whatever is in the vicinity. At the time I saw Isaacs, he was not quite convinced that this monster was merely a big shark and he wanted to get another look at it. He was thinking of ways to sink a large enough piece of bait, something like a dead horse, and make it worth the monster's while to come back to the camera for another sitting. Grandfather Isaacs would have approved. Recently, Isaacs has been able to photograph at least six more specimens off Hawaii in 6,150 feet of water. One was at least 30 feet long.

The second approach, that of putting instruments on anchored buoys as a permanent automated observation post in the sea, involves a project that has been close to Isaacs's heart for a long time. There are years when the North Pacific seems to go mad. One case occurred in 1957 and early 1958, and Isaacs has described it in these words: "One of the deepest and most prolonged meteorological lows on record developed off the state of Washington, remaining for three months. A strong, narrow countercurrent developed off the west coast of the United States, carrying subtropical organisms as far north as Oregon. Southern fish visited Alaska, the desert isles of the central Pacific became clothed with green, the heaviest rains in a decade dampened California." The first hint of the change came with an unusual wind pattern in the winter of 1956–57 when warm central Pacific water was driven all the way to the Aleutians, far north of its usual position.

A symposium held at Scripps in 1959 brought in thirty scientists from the United States, Japan and Peru to discuss what happened. From the Gulf of Alaska to the coasts of Peru, sea temperatures were much higher than normal, but unusually cold from the Bering Sea south to Japan. The sea level was six inches higher than normal on the California coast, where sport fishermen caught ten times as many barracuda and yellowtail and a hundred times as many mahimahi. Tropical forms of marine plant life were collected from Scripps Pier. Sardines spawned off Southern California rather than the Mexican coast of Baja California. According to a report written for *Science* by Isaacs and Dr. Oscar E. Sette of the U.S. Fish and Wildlife Service at Stanford, 1958 appeared to resemble the unusual years of 1926, 1931 and 1941. But the symposium was stumped by how it all really started and could only emphasize the need for more measurements in the deep ocean. It warned too "that local changes of conditions cannot be studied provincially but are part of Pacific-wide or possibly world-wide changes."

To Isaacs, there is no "mysterious communication" between changes affecting Japan, the American west coast and Peru during the same year. They are simply an expression of something occurring on a very large scale. But what does occur? Which factor is the egg and which factor is the chicken? Is there some unusual movement of water masses over vast distances? Or a change in the cloud cover or the exchange of heat between ocean and atmosphere in that no-man's-sea where an observation is the exception? Such are the questions that Isaacs has asked and is now trying to answer, knowing quite well there is no single reply.

First, he and his ocean engineers had to develop a tool. He believes they have it in the form of a strange twin-hulled twelve-foot craft moored to the bottom by a taut nylon line. More than fifteen years of trials and errors have gone into it. Since a buoy must remain comparatively fixed in relation to what it is seeking to measure, it cannot drift around at the end of a slack anchor line as ships do. Nylon under tension took care of that problem, but there were others. Experiments showed that fish, particularly sharks, were less tempted to bite a gold-colored line than a white one. They also showed that fishermen and passing ships were less likely to examine, board and "recover" an ugly catamaran buoy than the sleek fiberglass boat originally used. A deck had to be flat enough to enable instruments to be serviced, but uncomfortable enough to discourage seals and sea lions from climbing aboard, demolishing equipment and capsizing the whole affair. These are only a fraction of the problems that beset ocean engineers and, as Isaacs once remarked, cause them to smile when landlocked colleagues suddenly worry about plant roots cracking pipes or starlings getting into jet engines.

The Scripps buoy first carried an instrument panel with a dozen dials that gave readings from its sensors. They indicated air temperature, sea temperature at six depths between 3 and 450 feet, wind direction and speed, compass heading (so that the true wind direction can be calculated), tension on the anchor line and the time. Every hour, a camera took a picture of the panel and it had enough film to go on doing so for 83 days. Isaacs preferred to use a camera at first, instead of directly recording measurements on magnetic tape, not only out of atavism but because he still had to be convinced of the complete reliability of so-called digitized systems at sea.

Ultimately, Isaacs wants to put down more sophisticated buoys as a network across the North Pacific in water as deep as 18,000 feet. He sees the start of the program as a "hand-held pilot study" with a cluster of buoys recording what is coming into their area from above and below and what happens to it while it is there.

In his pilot study, he particularly wants to catch the sea red-handed in the act of heating, much harder than trying to detect cooling. "It's like warming a pan of water from the top with a blowtorch," he said. "To raise the surface temperature of a reasonably calm ocean one degree, only ten or twelve feet of water need be heated. But to lower it one degree, 300 feet of water must be cooled." This, he believes, is why monthly observations by ships detect the process of cooling but often miss the development of heating.

With luck, he will be ready for the North Pacific the next time that it misbehaves, assuming that its changes are misbehavior. Isaacs does not — his mind is completely open to the possibility that it is the normal conditions that are unstable. They have been defined as the norm by man, and Isaacs never accepts such pat packages wrapped up in an "anthropocentric viewpoint," whether they contain the weather of the North Pacific or anything else.

"We cannot pick out any specific activity without judging it by its benefit or disadvantage to mankind," he has said. "We can visualize the extinction of some obscure species without a qualm unless its racial demise were likely to produce a miasma, reduce the catch of a food fish or rob some biological specialist of specimens upon which to work. The grudge against the Russians for the destruction of Stellar's sea cow seems mainly based on some indefinite revulsion and on a very definite yen of some to dissect an unavailable creature that had a magnificent hindgut, the longest of any mammal."

Isaacs loves to sink anthropocentricity. In his ringing, rotund phrases, he once wrote:

"Man's hope for guidance is to sup fully, confidently and wonderingly of the rich experience of man and of nature and to learn: an erupting star could inseminate space with the substances of life, a planet could bring forth cells, a clam could develop perfect eyes and jet propulsion, a porpoise could develop an advanced brain and conversational rapport, a medieval European could see farther than the Pillars of Hercules, and blasé modern man can sail out from his Mediterranean and discover a new world."

No one will see his way out of the Mediterranean if he is blinded by neo-scholasticism. Isaacs has some views on that, too. "Every so often, I am depressed when I see a big fruit orchard. They want an orange that ships well and sells in a grocery store. Some seedlings may have the capacity to fruit with the nectar of the gods, but the growers decapitate them and graft them on a useful product. God knows what potentials are hidden beneath the ground, never to fruit.

"The education of human beings is carried on commercially in the same way: it seeks to replicate the people of the past with reasonable improvements. But where are the new varieties? Let many of the seedlings grow, even if nine-tenths of them are wizened. That's what a university should do, and does do — in its horticulture department!"

My talk with Isaacs ended there, though it could have gone on indefinitely despite another delegation outside his office. Later, I ran into him as I was rushing to an appointment. The sandals I had hastily bought to blend with the Scripps environment were slipping off my feet and I was making my way semi-barefoot. Isaacs, well-dressed as usual, said hello to me and remarked in passing:

"Must you really look like everybody else around here?"

5. The Fish Business

John Isaacs's picture of a generous sea pouring protein into the mouths of my ten billion descendants made my own mouth water, so much so that I decided to carry my research farther. As a first step, I went to one of La Jolla's seafood restaurants, whose name I would rather not mention. If they think the shoe fits, let them put it on.

There, getting a meal from the ocean was not as easy as Isaacs had led me to believe. It was Mother's Day. Hatted, permanented, sunglassed, the matriarchs from the surrounding hills had been towed in by their children. The chances of getting a table before Father's Day seemed remote indeed. At the cashier's desk, my name was placed on a list as long as the Domesday Book and I was transferred to a cocktail lounge to be stacked along with other hopefuls. We sat there like jets waiting to land at Kennedy. By the time my name came up, I had absorbed so much gin and tonic from the environment that my numbed palate was unable to get through to the subtle flavor of the abalone, the big snail-like mollusk that is the most touted dish to come from California waters. I prefer to suspend judgment on the abalone until I can try it without mothers on the side.

Despite its dead end, this had not been a completely unprofitable line of inquiry. Waiting customers had spilled into the cocktail lounge and onto sidewalk benches because seafood was special food. They were willing to pay a good price for it; the market was tailored to their demands. It supplied them with California halibut, Florida pompano and South African lobster tails at the culmination of a complex and costly system processing food as smoothly as the restaurant had processed them. As I picked up my check, I could not help but think that this was no way to try to feed ten billion people. There would not be enough gin and tonic to go around.

No one plans to feed them this way. One does not find salmon or turbot on the menus that are being prepared for the year 2000. Instead, there are such delicacies as *Pandalid* shrimps, *Pleuroncodes* red crabs, *Euphausia* crustaceans, lantern fishes, hake, herring, anchovies, and tropical sardines. They will be served neither broiled, boiled, fried, canned nor on canapés, but as an odorless, tasteless powder called marine or fish protein concentrate. Whether MPC or FPC, it will be nothing but the American chicken's old friend, fish meal, without the fishy taste and smell. If current plans materialize, it will be incorporated into flour or breakfast foods and will provide ten grams of animal protein a day at a daily cost of seven-tenths of a cent, according to the U. S. National Academy of Sciences. Or it can be fed to chickens just as it is being done nowadays to an extent that has led one authority to remark: "If you had an egg for breakfast this morning, you've eaten seafood today."

The authority is Dr. Wilbert McLeod Chapman, of the Ralston-Purina Company's Van Camp Sea Food Division in San Diego. Chapman is a big, bulky, graying chain smoker who turns up at oceanographic meetings everywhere to keep them from straying too far from what he considers the point. When the talk drifts into geostrophic motion or the displacements of the Gulf Stream countercurrent, Chapman can always be relied on to rasp a reminder that fishermen merely want oceanographers to tell them where they can find fish. This, he seldom fails to add, would be an improvement over the present situation where it is the fishermen who tell the oceanographers where the fish were found.

For a man his size, Chapman flits around the country like a leprechaun. From the seventeenth of March to the seventh of April, in a typical year, he had participated in a conference at Ohio State University, a symposium in Washington organized by the National Fish Meal and Oil Association, and another on "The Ocean from Space" at Houston. I had no chance of being in the same place at the same time as Chapman, but he had thoughtfully sent copies of his papers to Scripps, where I was able to pillage them at my leisure.

Chapman, like Isaacs, is deft with zeroes. According to his own estimate, the ocean is producing "at least 2 billion tons per year of organisms which have a size and form that render them capable of practical harvest by man with known technology." To each his own estimate. Walter R. Schmitt has calculated that the ocean's potential productivity of animals — not plants — is about 4 billion tons per year. The biggest number of all comes from Dr. B. G. Bogorov in the Soviet Union who has set the ocean's stock of phytoplankton, mainly one-celled algae that drift on or near the surface, at 1.5 billion tons at any given moment. To maintain such a stock of plants that live only for a few hours or days at the most, the ocean must produce 550 billion tons of them every year.

That is a lot of food, but it all comes in microscopic sizes. Even when plants bloom to the point where they stain the sea red, brown or green (the clear blue sea is a desert), Chapman notes that there is no way to harvest them without straining astronomical quantities of water at an equally astronomical cost. This is the reason why all speculation on the sea as a future source of food is confined to animal proteins. Carbohydrates are much more easily obtained from land, where in fact there is no shortage of them.

At the present time, the numbers assigned to the ocean's productivity shrink woefully when one turns from promises to performance. By 1948, the world's fish catch from the sea was up to 18 million metric tons (a metric ton is ten percent heavier than a 2,000-pound ton) and barely over its prewar level. By 1966, it stood at 48.4 million metric tons and it was rising at eight percent a year, faster than the world's rate of population increase.

About all that the experts agree on is that it will not keep rising indefinitely at such a pace. Some think that it can only be doubled, others see it quadrupling and no more. Even 200 million tons of fish a year is a long way from the multi-billion estimates of a Schmitt or a Chapman. The difference lies in the definition of fish. If we stick to the Mother's

Day menu in La Jolla, it would be optimistic to expect even a doubling of the ocean harvest. Delicious sea tigers like the tuna or the salmon are already being taken in amounts that shave the line of overfishing as closely as possible. The near-tripling of the ocean fish catch in less than twenty years was accounted for mainly by increases in landings of sardines, herrings and anchovies and other small herring-like fishes that flourish in great quantities and obligingly run in schools so they can be easily caught.

Even such sources are not bottomless. Catches of anchovies off Peru peak at around 8 million tons a year. Figures culled by Chapman show that the limits of herring production in the Atlantic and around Scandinavia seem to have been reached, as well as in the Pacific off Japan. The South African pilchard is weakening, the California sardine is mainly a memory.

Then where will all the protein come from? Chapman shrewdly observes that the bigger the fish, the smaller the total catch. Fishermen traditionally go after fish more than ten inches long, the ocean's carnivores that must live on smaller fish. They are easy to handle, look well, taste well and can be presented whole to the consumer. Smaller species, though more abundant, are hard to preserve. In a hot climate, they can even liquefy on deck under the weight of a big haul. Marketing is a problem: as Chapman points out, the can that contains anchovies, sardines or herrings is often worth more than its contents. It was only when the chicken-feed market opened up that fishermen found it worth their while to land fish between five and ten inches long.

There is nothing wasteful, despite prejudices to the contrary, about feeding anchovies to chickens in the form of fish meal. Chapman seldom fails to remind his listeners that the final output of animal protein in the form of meat and eggs is higher than if the anchovies had been converted to tuna through intermediate stages. A chicken turns thirty percent of an anchovy diet into protein; a tuna only one percent.

The next big jump in oceanic production will come, he believes, when fishermen turn to the size between one and five inches that covers mainly crustaceans like shrimps and crabs rather than fish. The smaller the animal, the closer it gets to the 550 billion tons of plant plankton that the ocean grows in a year. Among commercial fish, only the prolific anchovies actually graze on plants, while the sardines and the herrings are small-scale carnivores.

At this level of the ocean's food pyramid, the picture grows foggy. The pyramid itself collapses into crisscrossing patterns so complicated that they are preferably described as a food web. Some animals feed only on plants; others will eat plants, animals and each other. Barging into the web like an elephant in Lilliput is the whale, the biggest animal that ever lived, taking as its diet one of the smallest. In the Antarctic, the whale feeds on a small, shrimp-like euphausid known as lobster krill or *Euphausia superba*, a plant-eater that can reach a length of two and a half inches. It does so with enviable efficiency. Dr. Theodore J. Walker, Scripps's most assiduous whale-watcher, has described what happens when a whale runs into a mass of krill: "The whales need only swim back and forth through these cloudlike aggregations to fill their mouths quickly with water and shrimp. With each mouthful, the water is expelled between the jaws through a mat of fibers which hangs down from the upper jaw. The shrimps, which are retained on the mat, fall down onto the tongue and are swallowed. The work of pushing out several tons of water with each feeding is done by the tremendous tongue."

The krill is there in masses. Among the many scientists who have been tempted by this possibility of perpetual rations is Dr. Willis E. Pequegnat, a former professor of zoology at Pomona College in California and now with the National Science Foundation in Washington. About ten years ago, he added up some figures based on the energy requirements of a ninety-ton blue whale and published his results in the *Scientific American*. His totals showed that a growing blue whale needed three tons of krill a day during its six-month feeding season in the Antarctic Ocean. From here, he went back to an estimated whale population of half a million in the Antarctic in 1910, before whaling was begun there with a vengeance. The whales were gulping 270 million tons of krill a year and Pequegnat guessed that this was only twenty percent of a total annual production of 1.35 billion tons in this ocean alone. That is a lot of krill and there are no longer half a million whales to take it. Hunted almost to extinction, there is not much left of the whale except a lesson: hunger on the scale of a ninety-ton blue whale or a dense human population can be appeased by the sea only as far down as possible on the food web.

Pequegnat was much less precise when it came to the palatability of krill. He ventured only to report that samples had been pilfered from his laboratory freezer by nonzoologists who mistook them for shrimp. The krill-poachers never told him what they thought of it, but at least they didn't die. Pequegnat himself was not tempted, despite "the appetizing appearance of these bright red animals."

He foresaw the possibility of krilling to replace whaling in the Antarctic. The Russians are working on such a possibility, an artificial limb as a substitute for the amputated whale in the food web. They have tried a trawl net with a pump, a seagoing vacuum cleaner that slurps krill into the hold of a ship. If the Russians succeed, they will have scored quite an achievement. The harvesting of krill has been pooh-poohed as science fiction for a good many years because of the amount of power that would be needed to filter seawater as the whale does so naturally. One expert totted up the bill and concluded that it would cost $5,000 to fish a ton of krill. Experts can be wrong.

As for Chapman, he does not stop at krill. He hints that another protein source may lie in the "deep scattering layer." This is one of the most intriguing features of the ocean. Its existence became known with the invention of the echo sounder after World War I. Until then, the only way to measure depth was to heave a lead on the end of a wire. The echo sounder does the job by aiming a ping at the bottom and clocking the time the noise needs to make the round trip. Since the speed of sound in water is known, the elapsed time indicates the depth.

When echo sounders came into general use, chart-makers were puzzled by reports of shoals in water supposedly thousands of fathoms deep. Not only that, but the shoals would come and go, depending on the ship making the measurements. With more refined instruments, an explanation was found for what had been politely called "phantom shoals" so as not to offend shipmasters. Pings from the echo sounder were bouncing not on the bottom, but on some kind of layer thick enough to scatter sound but too thin to be sampled. By day, such layers occur between 900 and 1,200 feet, then rise to the surface at night. This indirect evidence led biologists to suspect they may be composed of small animals that come up at night to feed on plant life, then drop by day to hide from enemies. It is this "elevator" capability that complicates the study of plankton — a term derived from the Greek word for wandering, and used to designate plants and animals that drift. By changing depth, plankton is borne by different currents, making it all the harder to track.

Up until now, the deep scattering layer has been mainly a headache to hydrographers trying to keep their charts straight, and a nasty problem to naval antisubmarine forces probing into the ocean with sound beams. Chapman regards it as a resource: he thinks that when it rises at night, it brings up lantern fish and deep-sea smelts which are feeding on its members. There is no reason why we, in turn, should not feed on the lantern fish.

He does not regard these fish as a delicacy any more than krill. What is important is that a ton of such untapped species contains just as much protein for future conversion into fish flour as a ton of sturgeon. At the protein level, no fish is more equal than any other fish, whether the anchovy that brings $10 a ton in Callao or the bluefin tuna that sells for $3,000 a ton in Tokyo. At the economic level, the cheap species are the most useful, for fish protein must be inexpensive enough to face competition from vegetable proteins like enriched soya.

Cheap protein will not come from aquaculture, which Chapman dismisses in this respect as "a fashionable subject just now among uninformed dreamers." These are harsh words for any dreamer to swallow, but there is more than a kernel of truth in them. Farming of fish in the open ocean is unworkable under property laws that boil down to finders-keepers. No farmer will raise calves, then turn his cattle loose unbranded to roam for thousands of miles. This applies to the fishes of the sea except for species like the salmon that return to their birthplaces in what has been neatly termed a built-in roundup. Aquaculture in closed waters is a costly business turning out a costly product. Chapman foresees that, while greatly expanded, it will be pursued in the immediate future much as it is today: either to grow food to be eaten on the spot without expensive processing and transportation, or to produce such tidbits as oysters, mussels, clams or shrimps, for which the customer gladly pays all the expenses. The raw shrimps that appeal to the Japanese gourmet, who eats them while they are still quivering, can fetch their farmer over $3 a pound.

This is not the market that the U.S. Bureau of Commercial Fisheries had in mind when it went to work on upgrading fish meal for chickens into fish protein concentrate for humans. The main snag came in getting approval for the final product as human food. It had to be tasteless, odorless and free of potentially rancid oils as well as any unwanted substances, such as hormones, that could lead to side effects. The Federal Drug Administration in Washington approved fish protein concentrate in March 1967, thereby canceling its previous ruling that it could be shipped only in sacks labeled "not fit for human consumption in the United States." That was not the best sales pitch abroad for a product that already generated resistance among consumers who did not particularly care for tasteless, odorless food. The Bureau of Commercial Fisheries has gone ahead cautiously with a Pacific Coast pilot plant that is to process 50 tons of hake a day into powder. On the East Coast, Alpine Geophysical Associates diversified its activities to include the production of fish protein concentrate, opening a factory in New Bedford, Massachusetts, to convert 100 tons of fish per day into 16 tons of human food.

By 1971, the United States hopes to export the technique, so that a plant capable of giving ten grams of animal protein per day to a million people will be operating in at least one protein-short country. This demonstration project is being managed by the U.S. Agency for International Development. Along with the building of processing plants, AID also wants to improve local fisheries and marketing methods. Distaste for a tasteless powder may well be outweighed by the advantages of putting fish into a form where it can neither be spoiled by archaic transportation nor tabooed by prevailing customs.

Whether they wind up in a powder or a *paella*, fish are the basis of all these projects and forecasts. A mere doubling of the present catch would not make them a weighty factor in future diets. While reading Chapman's papers, I saw that one of his most optimistic sources was close at hand in the person of Dr. Milner B. Schaefer, director of the Institute of Marine Resources of the University of California on the Scripps campus. He was shortly due to leave for his present position as science adviser to the Secretary of Interior in Washington. Schaefer's appointment is another fortunate example of how oceanographers are infiltrating our affairs.

His office was appropriately located above the Scripps aquarium, with a fine view of Baby Jean and the porpoises, their backs looking like sea serpents coiled in the outdoor pools of the Physiological Research Laboratory. To pass some time before my appointment, I wandered through the aquarium, which really does not end — at its exit, a sign informs visitors that they can continue to satisfy their curiosity in the Pacific Ocean, 300 feet away. It was a splendid day and I regretfully disregarded this advice.

But Schaefer proved as stimulating as anything I might have encountered in the sea. He is an odd combination. There is Professor Milner B.

Schaefer, chairman of the National Research Council's Committee on Oceanography, high-ranking member of half a dozen scientific societies, associations and institutes, former director of the Inter-American Tropical Tuna Commission, author of nearly 100 papers, which deal mainly with the dynamics of fish populations (and containing such recondite remarks as "Saetersdal and Validivia (1964) have fitted a von Bertalanffy growth curve to their data for this species"). There is also Benny Schaefer, a roughhewn native of Cheyenne, Wyoming, where he was born nearly sixty years ago, who can speak about the ocean with a fisherman's viewpoint and vocabulary. I talked to both.

It is Schaefer whom Chapman quoted as stating: "I have concluded that, at a conservative estimate, the world fishery production may be increased to 200 million metric tons per year with no radical developments, such as fish-farming or far-out new kinds of fishing gear." Schaefer is less gloomy than Chapman about the availability of fish in standard sizes. He sees large stocks of unused species, even on such heavily exploited grounds as the North Sea and particularly in the open ocean. In Antarctica, he notes, we catch only whales; the tropical sardines of the eastern South Atlantic are almost untouched; the western Pacific is fished mainly for nearshore species. His ideal example of an underexploited area is the east coast of the Arabian peninsula, where fishermen using beach seines haul in 100,000 tons of sardines a year — and feed them to camels.

Much of Schaefer's optimism probably comes from his own experience with the Peruvian anchovy fishery, whose dynamics he has thoroughly studied. In 1951, 7,000 tons were caught; in 1964, the peak year, 8.9 million tons. Peru had become the world's biggest fishing nation, with a fleet of 1,900 modern ships manned principally by Indians who had come down from the Andean highlands. This story is well worth pondering when one tries to set limits for the future on the basis of what has been done in the past.

Peru had always regarded its local variety of anchovy, *Engraulis ringens*, as food for the seabirds that covered offshore islands with heavy deposits of guano, highly valued as a fertilizer. Though the development of chemical fertilizers cut heavily into the use of guano by Peruvian agriculture, there was still opposition to anchovy fishing for fear that it would starve the birds. Schaefer and others working on the problem have had to juggle the requirements of the birds, the fishermen and the anchovies themselves, which just cannot keep hatching more and more children if too many parents are caught. With some delicate figuring, he has concluded that the annual harvest in the Humboldt Current is 10 million metric tons; 7.5 million going to the fishing boats, the rest to the birds. This could be increased to 9.5 million tons for man if the birds were cut from their present population of 16 million, a number that Schaefer considers more than sufficient to preserve them. As soon as the total harvest by bird and man goes over 10 million metric tons, the fishermen are faced with diminishing returns. Long before this figure is reached, the size of the anchovies in their nets gets smaller.

"It's the same with fish as it is with people," Schaefer told me. "When the mortality rate is higher, the population becomes younger. The fish business is a game. Like most games, the more you play it, the more sophisticated the arithmetic gets."

As if the vested interests of the guano industry were not enough to complicate the Peruvian anchovy game, there is *El Niño* to be put into the equations as well. The anchovies swarm off Peru's coast because the cold Humboldt Current moving north to the equator is driven offshore by the southeast trade winds. When this water moves away from the coast, something has to replace it and deep water does, upwelling with the nitrates and phosphates that fertilize the anchovies' feast of plant plankton. Every year during the summer, the trade winds weaken, allowing an offshoot of warm equatorial water to penetrate down to northern Peru. About every six or eight years, this warm water travels nearly 400 miles farther south than usual. Heavy rains flood the usually parched Peruvian coast, the marine plants fail to bloom, the anchovies shun the warm surface waters, the guano birds die by the millions and fishermen may return to port with empty holds. The catastrophe is known as *El Niño* (The Child) because it usually strikes at Christmastime.

As a hardheaded adviser to Peru and other nations on fishery dynamics, Schaefer seemed less sanguine than as a forecaster. Granted that there were other Peruvian El Dorados in the ocean, it was still hard to see how he had arrived at an estimated "conventional" fish catch of 200 million tons, twice as high as most other predictions.

First of all, Schaefer is wary of conservative figures. With barely concealed glee, he once wrote how an expert at a United Nations conference on national resources in 1949 anticipated that the catch might go up another 4 million tons in the far-off future. And so it did — only a year after the conference proceedings were finally published in 1951.

Secondly, he is wary of a fundamental figure: the assumption of 10 percent efficiency between each strand of the food web (the sempiternal example of 1,000 pounds of phytoplankton yielding 100 pounds of zooplankton yielding 10 pounds of herring, etc., which I had quoted myself). Nature does not necessarily follow a decimal system, handy though it may be for scientists.

"I think that 10 percent efficiency may be low," Schaefer said. "It's based partly on a theoretical example and partly on experiments with animals in captivity. Petersen at the Danish Biological Station at the end of the nineteenth century made some theoretical illustrative calculations for the demersal [bottom] fishery of the North Sea. He decided to assume a 10 percent efficiency and it got into the textbooks. Slobodkin [Professor Lawrence B. Slobodkin of the University of Michigan's zoology department] and others, experimenting with various animals in the laboratory, came up with 10 percent, too. The trouble is, he's cleaning the feces out of his aquarium every day. In nature, this is all recycled. In many areas of the ocean, the number of predators at the top of the heap is too big to be accounted for by a system running at 10 percent efficiency. All this crud is coming back down into lower levels and then used again. I prefer to use 15 percent, and I think 20 percent should be possible."

Schaefer has published the implications of his estimate. If 15 percent of each level of life in the sea is found in the one above it, the numbers sing a different tune. Instead of 19 million metric tons of tuna and other king carnivores being produced every year, there are 96 million; and the figure becomes 304 million if the biggest aquarium of all is running at 20 percent efficiency.

"My own end of this racket is easy," he continued. "I'm looking at the dynamics of the fish at the top. There are a hell of a lot of fishermen working for me. I've got 1,900 boats giving me figures in Peru alone. Phytoplankton is pretty well in hand, too. You can grow it in the lab. But it's the zooplankton that gives trouble. It's not easy to grow in the lab, it's not easy to sample at sea. The middle cut of the fish business is the hardest of all. Somewhere, we hope we'll be able to meet."

Schaefer also thinks that fish-farming in the open ocean to feed the hungry is "a long way down the trail" and he sees no real need for it. "In Peru," he told me, "you're laying down anchovy from the open ocean for ten or twelve bucks a ton and it's pretty hard to raise animals for that price. Cows cost about two or three hundred dollars a ton. No, aquaculture is not the answer for protein concentrate. But it's a good way to make more money, such as by raising pearl oysters or expensive fish and shrimp."

As far as feeding himself is concerned, Schaefer thinks anchovies should be eaten fresh. He gave me the address of a place in San Diego that served them and I promised myself I would try it the next time I happened to be in the vicinity on Mother's Day.

My talk with Schaefer had led to some more signposts for my journey through Scripps, which had now begun to resemble that of a billiard ball on a table with countless corners. I rebounded from Schaefer to Dr. John MacGowan, a compact black-bearded marine biologist whom I had already noticed at lectures and meetings. In a somewhat querulous tone, he invariably asked the speaker describing a research cruise if any zooplankton samples had been taken. MacGowan was much less aggressive in private conversation, and he explained to me his Cato-like insistence on samplings. "What I keep trying to convince the physical oceanographer is that he is looking for only one or two properties, but the biologist is looking for a couple of thousand," he said. "There is just no comparison between his sampling problems and ours. He's now got thermistors that record temperature continuously. They represent progress over the bathythermograph that gives you a curve of temperatures as they change with depth. The BT represented progress over putting bottles down on a wire. But if you want to sample zooplankton, you can still only do it with a modified butterfly net."

When I asked MacGowan what he was doing, he steered me into his laboratory and asked two graduate students to tell me what they were doing. One of them, Peter Wiebe, was chasing zooplankton in a computer. Wiebe, a young man emulating MacGowan with a scrubby growth of embryonic beard, first pointed out that "sampling" does not have the same meaning when it is applied to zooplankton rather than people. With mathematics on his side, a Gallup can just about hit the nail on the head when he announces what 200 million people are like, on the basis of a sample amounting to no more than a few thousand. Wiebe is a long way from that enviable stage.

"The area in the Pacific covered by the California Cooperative Fisheries Investigation has been sampled more intensively than any other in the open ocean," he told me. "Every forty miles, stations have been taken with towed nets filtering 500 cubic meters [a cubic meter is a metric ton of water] down to a depth of 460 feet. Yet they were sampling only 1/500,000,000th of the area."

What Wiebe has done is to put into a computer numbers representing a box of water 1,000 meters long, 50 meters wide and 50 meters deep. Scattered at random inside this box are patches of plankton. Then, having set up the rules of his game, Wiebe plays it by telling the computer to tow a net through the box of water. In this way, he computes the factor of error that can be expected in an actual tow at sea, and as he explained, he can learn what happens to this factor when the size of the zooplankton patches is changed. Wiebe has one big advantage over the shipboard biologist: he invents his own patches.

Instead of modeling the ocean in a computer, Charles Miller, the other student fed to me by MacGowan, had gone to the opposite extreme. I was puzzled by a flat red metal pill on his desk. "Oh, that's part of a model zooplankter," he told me. Under questioning, Miller confessed he was trying to duplicate the habits of *Limacina inflata*, a snail living in the open sea.

First, he started with a parachute drogue or sea anchor attached to a buoy. This is a parachute that can be lowered to any desired depth, where it will drift with subsurface currents, towing the floating buoy. Physical oceanographers have used drogues to track such currents, but Miller had a more complex case on his hands. Like other zooplankton, *Limacina inflata* migrates vertically, coming to the surface at night. To induce his snail to behave the same way, Miller added the flat red pill, a buoy six feet in diameter, and equipped it with a winch to raise and lower the drogue.

"The winch is controlled by clockwork," Miller went on. "At first, we thought of putting a photometer in it so that it would respond to light like the snail, but that was too expensive. Then we thought of using radioactive zinc on the plankton layer in the sea to make it hot enough to trace. But we found that it meant too much radioactivity, five or six curies, and that's hard to handle. So our snail runs by clockwork."

At sea, Miller puts his ringer overside when a layer of snails is found. Then the drogue drifts down below with the layer, the red pill giving away its position and that of its neighbors. Every two hours, a sampling net is towed alongside the pill. "It's a way to key towing to the daily life of the zooplankter," he said. "You can tag a population as soon as you find it."

"You mean, you had to imagine you were a zooplankter to think this up?" I asked him.

Miller looked startled, and to change the subject, he showed me his collection of bottled euphausids, smaller relatives of the whale's krill. About half an inch long and no thicker than a piece of string, they had shrimp-like bodies and round black protruding eyes. "I've eaten euphausids raw," Miller said, anticipating my question. "They're too small to peel, so I ate them whole. It was a sickening taste, very fishy."

He put an end to our chat with some relief. I later learned that he was worried about me. After I left his lab, he asked MacGowan: "Who is this guy that thinks I'm a zooplankter?"

There are more ways than one to catch zooplankton. Like Miller, one can tiptoe up alongside it, make friends with it, be accepted as one of the bunch and then politely intrude a net into the conversation every two hours or so. Or one can burst in with a swooping net, scoop up specimens and leave the premises as quickly as one entered it. This enables the biologist to move around the ocean at a much greater rate than that of a drifting *Limacina inflata*, but he usually must lose precision to gain speed. He wants to know not only what small animals live in the ocean but also at what depths, temperatures and salinity conditions. Only then can he have an inkling of how life varies with the changing sea.

One of the most ingenious devices for sampling zooplankton over a large area goes back to the poetic, pre-electronic days of oceanographic instrumentation. It is called the Hardy plankton recorder and it was developed by one of the great figures in marine biology, Sir Alister Hardy, in the late 1930's. It consists of an open-ended tube that can be towed through the water at a speed as high as 15 knots. This forward motion spins a propeller that unwinds a roll of gauze across the tube. The plankton that enters the tunnel is picked up on the gauze, which is then wound into a storage tank of Formalin where the samples are preserved.

The great advantage of this device is that it can be put aboard cooperative merchant ships, lowered overside and swallow plankton over a distance of 200 miles. Here the biologist has been able to enlist the help of "ships of opportunity." The physical oceanographer has been doing this since the appearance of steam on the sea. Ships always record the temperature of surface water when it is taken into their engine rooms, and their logbooks are a precious source of data.

The Hardy recorder was developed to give the biologist such a source and to meet a situation where any information was better than none. Its main drawback, aside from the fact that the biologist cannot expect a 10,000-ton freighter to go back for another look at some interesting copepods, is that it sweeps a single depth and provides only a continuous streak of specimens.

Dr. Alan R. Longhurst at La Jolla is among several biologists who have been trying to combine the speed of the Hardy recorder with the precision of the butterfly net. Like plankton, Longhurst has been a wanderer: he was born in England, earned his doctorate at the University of London, and came to Scripps in 1964 after serving ten years with Nigeria's Federal Fisheries Service. He knows the fish business from the food web up to the operations of a fleet of trawlers.

I met him in his office in the Bureau of Commercial Fisheries building that anchors the northern end of Scripps's territory. The building is admirable: it perches on the cliffs facing the Pacific, with a carpet of wild flowers in front of it and creamy surf below. When I expressed my appreciation, Longhurst told me: "We're all waiting for the first big earthquake to see what happens."

A slim, deceptively soft-spoken man in his early forties, Longhurst has been taught to expect things to go wrong. He does not take assurances of architects or other experts at their face value. I mentioned to him the dramatic prospect of turning small fish into large quantities of concentrated protein and he looked at me wryly. "I'm all for it," he said, "but I do think it's dishonest to call it a big breakthrough. A decade ago, the South Africans decided to put fish flour into all the bread that they baked, and that didn't turn out too well because the people who needed the protein weren't buying bread anyway."

Longhurst could not help adding some realistic retouches to some of the bright pictures that I had been painting in my mind. One of them, which I had liked, was that of underfed peoples getting their own protein from the sea. "The trouble with such schemes is that they never work out the way they were intended," he remarked. "I sweated my guts out for ten years to develop local fisheries in West Africa. We rationalized methods, we worked on population dynamics, we produced data for the fishermen. But politicians got into the business. There was no regulation. Naturally, the catch went up, investments were made in trawlers and, just as naturally, everything collapsed because not enough fish were there. Fortunately, the Japanese and the Russians came in just at that time and offered cheap frozen fish caught off Angola. Even though the local trawlers had gone broke, the net result was that much more protein was going into the ports . . . which, I suppose, is what we were trying to do.

"To tell you the truth, most of the fish consumed in Nigeria is dried cod from Scandinavia, this Russian frozen fish from Angola and local dried fish from Lake Chad. We put a checkpoint on the roads from Lake Chad and counted what was coming out of it. You know, more fish were being caught on the lake by canoes made of papyrus reeds than by our local trawler fleet on the whole Nigerian continental shelf in the Atlantic."

Longhurst also penciled a few corrections to the menus I had visualized as having a plethora of such creatures as *Pleuroncodes planipes*, the red crab. He had done considerable work on *Pleuroncodes* in the California Current off the United States and Mexico. *Pleuroncodes* flourishes because it can graze directly on blooms of plant plankton near the surface. From an underwater observation chamber on a research ship, Longhurst has had the opportunity to watch it feed. He wrote: "The crabs graze with a casting-like motion of their fan-shaped maxillipeds while they are sinking slowly downwards with their legs spread out in the form of a parachute." This is how the red crab harvests one-celled plants from the sea. A human imitator would have to keep one other specification in mind: nature's model, though only two inches in diameter, gets its food by filtering 115 gallons of water a day.

Longhurst does not see the red crab as a vast direct source of protein, at least not off the California coast. The reason is that yellowfin tuna feed on it, taking 2,000 tons a day in the California Current at the start of the season and, for once, fattening themselves with great efficiency on the zooplankton area of the food web. Since the yellowfin is worth over nine times as much as red crabs on the market, Longhurst regards *Pleuroncodes* in this case as mainly a supplemental local fishery for Mexican ports. California food processing firms, however, are now studying it and Longhurst is sure they will do a thorough job. When it comes to exploiting the ocean's underused resources, he has a simple rule taught by experience: "If there is a buck to be made, someone will make it." Since talking with Longhurst, I have heard that Soviet factory trawlers have started making rubles with this species — in their first season, they caught 5,500 tons.

As for Longhurst, he prefers to leave economics to others and to continue his various scientific pursuits, among them the building of a better zooplankton trap. While this is not a full-time job, he enjoys it because it takes him from his desk to a laboratory a few doors away. He took me along with him.

In the lab, decorated with the usual clutter of electronics components, Longhurst explained to me the device that he and his associates have developed. Basically, they have taught a number of new tricks to the old Hardy plankton recorder. There is still the roll of gauze that traps the plankton like flypaper, but there the resemblance ends. Their device is fitted to the small end of a zooplankton net and is towed obliquely from the surface to a depth of 500 meters (1,540 feet) or more. Instead of continuously taking in specimens, it opens its maw only every ten meters as it is hauled up. Simultaneously, the water's depth, temperature and salinity are recorded along with each sample.

"It does mean an appreciable saving in time," Longhurst said. "If we take 50 sub-samples in a single one of our hauls, we have the equivalent of 50 individual net hauls, but we need take only 40 minutes of ship time instead of perhaps six hours. We gain more than time, too, because no one can expect the plankton to stay still while a ship is on station that long!"

On a table in the laboratory, the samples from one haul had been laid out, 50 bottles in a row representing the Pacific Ocean's zooplankton population from 500 meters to the surface. "You can tell at a glance that it was a night haul," Longhurst said. "We got those lantern fish up near the surface. By day, they're far down."

A girl was busy counting the specimens that had been taken, the most tedious task in marine biology. "Oh, there are ways of speeding it up," Longhurst remarked. "One way is to tick off the ones that interest us with an electric probe that counts them automatically. Or else we can blow the plankton through a tube and measure the changes in electrical conductivity that occur as organisms of different sizes pass by. That, I am afraid, is as far as we are likely to go right now, and even that is pretty tricky. No one will ever get a computer to recognize the shape of one spine on the fifth leg of an *Undinula*."

All is not for the best in the best of all electronic worlds. Shrimp-like copepods do not merely wait in the water to be caught. "If I put a copepod in an aquarium and gave you a pipette, you'd probably never catch it. They move fast. They can't go far, but they have great acceleration. When they feel the pressure wave of a net towed through the water, they can leap yards out of its way."

MacGowan has reminded Longhurst that the little fellows can make the biologist's life miserable even when they are caught napping. They may land on the side of his net, cling to it for dear life as it rises a few hundred feet, and then slide into the recorder to be registered, processed, bottled and counted — all at the wrong depth.

"There are six of these recorders in existence," Longhurst said. "There are other types, too, but too many are built by technicians who never go to sea, and those types don't work. Though I'd like to improve ours, I'm not devoting my full effort to it. I'm a naturalist, not a gadgeteer."

He glanced at a photo over his desk of the *Kiara*, his old 80-foot research vessel that was still being operated by a Nigerian scientific party. His eyes hesitated, then he went on:

"With all the great song and dance about improving methods of zooplankton collection, you can still do a lot by hauling a simple net through the water. Using classical methods, one can learn community structures and relationships between different levels of life.

"We've just completed a classical net survey of *Pleuroncodes* larvae in the California Current. We found a variation of from 20,000 larvae to none at all in a cubic meter of water. This tells us much about where breeding and mortality occur in the ocean. You know, we can't all drop butterfly net methods and wait for something better, or we'll do no biology for ten years."

6. Sex and the Copepod

Longhurst was only one of my teachers at Scripps belonging to a new school of biology less interested in naming things than in learning how they work and what position they play on the team. It is a dynamic attitude that runs counter to the old stereotype of the taxonomist, merely collecting and classifying. It is a practical attitude, too: taxonomy becomes frustrating near the lower levels of marine life where larval and adult or surface and bottom forms of the same animal are often identified erroneously as different species. The new school is particularly concerned with the initial strands of the food web, in which the energy of sunlight is converted into organic matter by plants and passed on to minute animals grazing on them. While knowledge of such a process can be acquired on land just by watching a cow eat grass, it is sorely lacking in the sea.

In the first place, the cows are small, no more than a millimeter or two in length. In the second place, as one of the scientists at Scripps who is most concerned with the problem has observed, their patch of grass has an inconvenient tendency to move over into the next county overnight, splitting up into several small plots as it does so. If only it could be made to keep still, he reasoned, then one might stand a chance of learning the number of cows a patch of grass will support and perhaps the number of cow-eaters as well. So Dr. John D. H. Strickland left the eternal changes and the sublime upheavals of the ocean to the poets and the romantics. He set about to find ways of getting it to stay in one place. He began in Canada by wrapping up a piece of the Pacific in a seaborne plastic bag, like tomatoes in a supermarket.

Strickland, who is head of the food chain research group of Schaefer's Institute of Marine Resources, has the bristly personality that many biological oceanographers adopt as protection against onlookers who ask them when they expect their first breakthrough. He flaunts a red beard and a disdain for academic niceties in order to increase his chances of being left alone so that he can get on with the job.

The job has been a long one. Strickland got to Scripps by the roundabout ways I soon came to expect in my fruitless attempts to classify oceanographers. He had started life as a chemist, earning his degrees at London University, and did research on armor-piercing alloys during World War II. In his mid-thirties, he was an Englishman and a metallurgical chemist. In 1952, he left home for the University of British Columbia, to become eventually a Canadian and an oceanographer. Strickland has literally worked his way up the food chain. As a chemist with the Canadian government's respected oceanographic center on Vancouver Island, he became interested in the natural fertilizers in seawater. Having ingested sufficient nitrates and phosphates, he went from the inorganic to the organic and bloomed into the next stage, that of phytoplankton. He spent a year reading up on the subject and wrote a review on production of plants in the ocean.

Here, his background as a chemist got the better of him. Strickland has never been able to accept the idea of sampling the ocean at random with nets or bottles and working only on the basis of such techniques, valuable though they may be. "I have a reputation for being a controlled environment nut," he told me in his office at Scripps, "but I can't help that. Being a chemist by training, I get emotional when I see something that I can't manipulate." Since laboratory conditions in the test tube can never duplicate those of the living sea, Strickland decided while he was in Canada to try experimenting with a larger and more representative slice of ocean.

He and his associates took a big plastic bag, twenty feet in diameter. On a calm bay off Vancouver Island, they filled it with 35,000 gallons of seawater from which all life had been previously filtered. The largest laboratory container ever immersed in the sea floated within easy reach; then it was sown with some unfiltered seawater. Soon Strickland found that he was raising a crop of marine plants on an experimental farm.

Patiently, he ironed out a few kinks in the operation. The Fraser River, thirty-five miles away, occasionally poured large quantities of fresh water into the bay, making it less salty and consequently less dense and lighter than the packaged ocean, which promptly began to sink. Above his farm, Strickland had to put out a device, an airbell, that could be filled with air or flooded, depending on how much buoyancy was needed. It led to another hazard. Water skiers could not help seeing how close they could come to such an irresistible target.

Despite the wear on his nerves and the appearance of a few more bristles on his personality, Strickland was able to run his farm for 100 days. He correlated the growth rates of his plants with an analysis of the nature and quantity of the mineral nutrients they were using and also with changes in sunlight and temperature. Once the plants had exhausted the natural fertilizer in the bag, Strickland covered it with black plastic to blank out the sun. He could then watch the decay of the dying plants as they decomposed into mineral nutrients.

Satisfactory though its results may have been, the method had limitations. It could only be used in very calm water, of which there is none around Scripps. And it begged the issue of what happens to the plants when they are not protected by a layer of polyvinyl chloride from hungry zooplankters. Here, the food web becomes a tangle and the laboratory worker throws up his hands in despair. He has never been able to raise and keep a herd of cows in a beaker. Only certain varieties of zooplankton found near piers or in salt marshes will cooperatively reproduce in a container holding a few quarts of their environment. The type of copepod frequenting the high seas may be no more than a very little shrimp, but it knows what it needs to breed. Strickland wishes he knew as much, for then he would be able to fulfill an often-expressed desire to write a Kinsey report on copepods. Once they began to increase and multiply, he could determine such factors as their fertility and birthrates.

At Scripps, this urge led Strickland from a captive ocean to a private inland sea. It consists of a tank, ten feet in diameter and thirty-three feet deep, inserted into a concrete pit. Lined with inert plastic to prevent contamination, it holds 70,000 liters (18,000 gallons) of seawater, making it by far the biggest test tube anyone has used for the purpose. A pole planted in the middle is used to measure temperatures and take water samples. Portholes are spotted in the side of the tank so that a reasonably agile researcher can crawl down a ladder outside the tank and peer at what is going on inside.

For once, the ocean is under control. The tank can be chilled to the temperatures of polar seas and stirred with compressed air to simulate the turnover of the real thing. Even the sunshine it receives is man-made. While La Jolla is smog-free, it has its share of cold fog brought in by the Pacific, and Strickland did not wish to lose time waiting for California weather to live up to its advertisements. So he hung his own sun over the tank. It begins with a World War II surplus antiaircraft searchlight. With a mirror five feet in diameter, it is mounted on the ground 100 feet from the tank, next to a generator. Excess ultraviolet radiation and heat from the searchlight's carbon arc are filtered by a glass screen with a sheet of water running over it. The cooled beam then strikes a mirror hinged at a 47-degree angle and is deflected down into the tank. To run the artificial sun, the generator uses 50 gallons of gasoline a day. Strickland shudders when he thinks what copepods will cost per pound.

Having eliminated heavy seas, Strickland encountered interference from another quarter. "We had some trouble when we tested the searchlight at night. People could see it in San Diego and they thought it was a movie premiere. We were invaded by drunks and kids. That's why we try to avoid publicity in the local press."

He had been describing his plans in his office when he suddenly interrupted himself: "Oh God, it's Monday. It's my turn to change the record on the drum." I followed him up to the roof of Sverdrup Hall, where an automatic station for measuring radiation energy was keeping tabs on the real sun. He removed a chart from the recorder, added fresh paper, put an eyedropperful of ink into the apparatus and wound it up.

Then he took me to the tank, which was dry after having passed its first test. It had been seeded with a marine plant known as *Ditylum brightwellii* that had been grown for two weeks. "It's an interesting little thing. It's fairly hardy and it has unusual floating ability. Its density is almost the same as that of seawater. When we shut off the compressed-air flow, it still didn't settle."

Almost unlimited samples can be drawn from the big tank. Another advantage over smaller containers is the opportunity it offers to study vertical migration of plant and animal plankton alike. Strickland suspects that copepods may find this a congenial feature when they are ready to breed. But first, a generation must be brought in from outside.

"We now have forty huge carboys of algae, a dirty-brown culture of *Ditylum*," he said. "What we want to do is add them to the tank, catch a few hundred fertilized female copepods from the sea, and build up a generation of our own. We have 70,000 liters of water and we'd like one animal per liter. It won't be easy — that means 70,000 of them. What we want to raise is called *Calanus helgolandicus*. It's a copepod about a millimeter long, and a common herring food in the North Sea."

He sketched it for me: two splayed antennae on a carrot-like body.

"The trouble is, it's a delicate beast. It goes through no less than ten molts, and its mortality rate is very high. People have been able to get gravid females to lay eggs, but *Calanus* won't breed properly in a few quarts of water. Perhaps it needs the ability to swim up and down to copulate.

"After *Calanus*, we'd like to add the next stage, a carnivorous zoo-plankter. We're thinking of *Euphausia pacifica*, and that will be really complicated. It's omnivorous. In fact, one cannot classify these things by what they eat. Zooplankters eat like people. If there are no plants around, they're not such clots that they would die rather than eat meat.

"Ideally, it would be nice to get three 'trophic' levels in the tank, but it's horrendously difficult. The whole thing can go wrong."

To hedge his bets and also to amortize the considerable investment in his synthetic sea and sun, Strickland uses the tank as a general facility. Among the other experiments he had in mind was the creation of an artificial "red tide" by growing dinoflagellates in it and studying their vertical migration.

"Oh, that's an animal, isn't it?"

He looked at me with the expression he reserved for water skiers: "No, it's a plant. There's no reason why a plant can't have flagella and use them to swim up and down. Flowers on land open and close, don't they?"

Not wanting to sidetrack the conversation, I neglected to tell him I had done some homework before coming to his office. In one glossary, I had seen the dinoflagellates defined as one-celled plantlike animals; in another, they were cautiously termed a bridge between the plant and the animal kingdoms. In any case, they get their name from the two whip-like flagella which they use either to rotate or to move vertically.

Dinoflagellates are responsible for most red tides, the most dramatic instance of marine plants running rampant. Under certain conditions and notably in warm waters off Florida and California, they flourish to the point where they turn the sea rusty red. Just as weeds destroy a garden, they consume nutrients, leaving nothing for other forms. They can be deadly in two ways. When they die and decay, they consume so much oxygen that masses of fish suffocate. Or in certain cases (among them, a dinoflagellate known as *Gonyaulax*), they produce a toxic substance concentrated by shellfish, which then become poisonous to man. A red tide can render mussels lethal. Strickland's group has been trying to learn what brings it on.

"Off Southern California, it can occur in patches and streaks, seldom more than a mile or two from shore, but it can extend 200 miles from Los Angeles to San Diego and beyond," he said. "Every few years, coastal towns get red tides and fish-kills in their harbors. The chambers of commerce become disturbed, there is a big clamor to do something about it, then everyone loses interest when it goes away. Some people tend to blame red tides on sewage outfalls pouring mineral nutrients into the sea, but that's hogwash. This coast had red tides before it had sewage systems. Sewage may trigger a red tide, but I doubt that it causes it."

What does?

"I think it's a combination of several factors. What may happen is this: an upwelling brings nutrients to the surface. The diatoms, a form of phytoplankton, grow and consume them. At the same time, a small popu-lation of dinoflagellates grows up. The diatoms slowly strip the nutrients from the top of the sea, then they die and sink. But the dinoflagellates can better survive a food shortage. If another upwelling comes along, they are on hand to profit from the next slug of nutrients all by them-selves. Then they flourish to the point where they turn the sea red.

"We think the dinoflagellates can move vertically twenty or thirty feet a day. They go down for food and up for sunlight. We hope to be able to test this in the tank and learn their migration rates. We'll make our own red tide."

Despite its 18,000-gallon capacity, the tank cannot be expected to hold all the factors that cause a red tide in the Pacific. Since Strickland is dogmatic about controlled environments only up to a point, his group was also running a survey of the full-sized ocean off Scripps to see if they could monitor physical, chemical and biological properties leading to a red tide. Even if no such thing happened during the eight months of their survey, they would still have a much clearer picture of the sea's behavior over a long period in the same place.

"We call it a red tide study, for publicity purposes," Strickland confided, "but basically we're trying to find better ways of looking at the productivity of the environment *in situ*. We go out every Wednesday. Why don't you come along? I'll be around to get you at your motel at eight."

Strickland turned up the following Wednesday in his tired Mercury just as the clock in the steeple of the little village church of La Jolla Shores would have finished chiming its eighth stroke — if La Jolla Shores had been that kind of a village. Instead, the manager of the Speedee Mart around the corner on Avenida de la Playa was opening up to sell his first hero sandwiches of the day to the floating population of surfers.

As Strickland drove, he gave me a few details about the program. "We've got the *T-441*, a converted Army workboat," he said. "I bought her for eight months, for fifty grand out of my budget. She has a crew of three. They take her out of the Scripps marine facility on Point Loma at seven in the morning. Then they meet us at Mission Bay, where I'm driving you now."

Mission Bay, lying between La Jolla and the center of San Diego, is a body of water devoted mainly to pleasure craft, and marinas where such ordinarily prosaic structures as offices and storage sheds are housed under Hawaiian roofs. The effect would be startling to anyone who had any capacity left for being startled in this part of the world.

"The ship goes out three times a week," Strickland continued. "Twice a week, Dr. Michael Mullin takes zooplankton hauls for a study in population dynamics. Then on Wednesdays, we have our plant productivity study. I was responsible for running field programs for the first three or four years of my group's existence, but now Dr. Richard Eppley is in charge of this program. He's a plant physiologist who changed over from big seaweed to phytoplankton. Our zoologist is Dr. Jack Beers, from Harvard. He's studying very small animals, not the usual little zooplankters, but the very small ones — an important missing link in the food chain. Our chief chemical analyst is Lucia Solorzano. She came along to me from Ecuador on a fellowship from FAO, the Food and Agriculture Organization. Then there's the most valuable one in the whole bunch, Charlie Stearns. He's a good marine technician, and technicians in general are the salt of the earth. He can mend anything on a ship."

It was only a few minutes to Mission Bay through La Jolla and Pacific Beach, the latter a much sloppier and more relaxed place than its prosperous neighbor. Strickland parked the car at the marina and introduced me to my future shipmates for the day. They were already lugging their gear to the dockside, to be ready for the ship when it arrived.

"What we do every Wednesday is run a standard transect from eight miles out at sea into the beach," he explained. "We take three stations: at eight miles, two and a half miles, and a half mile from the beach. We take the last one off Torrey Pines State Reserve because we know there are no submarine canyons there and we can anchor. We will just go out and run our analyses until a red tide or something else of some interest happens. It's not very exciting, but oceanography rarely is when you really get down to doing it."

At dead slow, the *T-441* hove in sight and nudged the dock. A strict speed limit is enforced in Mission Bay to protect its population of small sailboats. It is the only sheltered body for miles around where Sunday navigators need not brave the open Pacific.

The *T-441* certainly did not look as if she was worth $50,000 of Strickland's budget or anyone else's. She was a stubby craft, sixty-five feet long and painted in the workmanlike gray of Scripps's research vessels, with a yellow stripe on her stack. The yellow stripe, so I had learned, was all that remained on Scripps's ships of a commendable scheme to paint them gold and gray, the colors of the University of California. At sea, the gold did not glitter long, and it was devalued to a yellow stripe.

The *T-441* is listed on the roster of the institute's vessels as having originally been a cargo and passenger boat for the Army, all sixty-six tons of her. It was a good description, for the Army always considers passengers as cargo. Yet this little floating chip of steel had made several trips to Baja California, and she occasionally ran on research cruises as far as 300 miles due west into the Pacific. As I went aboard, I recalled an international meeting I had attended, where the representative of a small and not very seafaring nation explained that his country would need a research ship at least 100 feet long to work more than ten miles offshore. If a donor ever gave him one, it would have been a poisoned gift. There are a number of such vessels lying in the harbors of small countries for prestige purposes. When they are used for any other purpose, they cost so much to run that two weeks of cruising engulfs a year's oceanographic research budget.

On the *T-441*, so much scientific cargo had been taken aboard that there was not much room for an idle passenger like myself to stay out of anybody's way. So I proceeded to make a nuisance of myself, prowling around the deck and through the aftercabin, which was packed with equipment for chemical analysis. We had now cleared Medanos Point at the entrance to Mission Bay and the ship's diesel engine snored noisily as it drove us along at ten knots. We had a voyage of an hour and ten minutes ahead of us to the first station, marked by a red plywood float three feet tall and anchored to the bottom in 200 fathoms (a fathom is six feet) of water by a few sections of railroad rails. I did not see how anything that size could be found in the foggy Pacific, but Captain Joe Mehling was not flapping. He steered for it on a compass heading of 307 degrees magnetic, he told me. Even if he missed it on the first try, he knew that it lay along the 200-fathom contour line on his chart, which he could follow with an echo sounder, while scanning the surface with his radar, the way airplane pilots used to follow rivers. Since Mehling did not need my advice, I wandered into the laboratory. Lucia Solorzano, a dark bouncy girl in slacks, was setting up the ship's autoanalyzer, an automated chemical laboratory.

The autoanalyzer was the heart of the red tide study. At each of the *T-441*'s stations, a pump would be lowered at the end of a rubber hose. As it was gradually hauled up, it would send water into the laboratory for immediate analysis by what Eppley called the robot chemist. "It enables us to see what the water is like when we're there, not when we're back on shore," he explained.

One hose from the pump ran into the lab. The other snaked over the lab roof to the stern, where Beers was setting up his gear on the open fantail. His apparatus looked much more homemade than the autoanalyzer. From what I could judge, he had started with a steel rack, which he then covered with a plywood top pierced by two holes. In the holes, he had placed two nylon cones, screening their open ends with flat nylon disks. Under the cones were two plastic garbage pails. Beers wasted few motions as he went about his preparations while the ship rose and dipped to an easy swell. He remarked that he was not always so lucky with the weather.

While he worked, he explained to me how his apparatus would operate. It was designed to capture the microscopic forms he wanted to examine. A net towed through the water could not get at them, for it would be quickly clogged. Instead, Beers would use the *T-441*'s submerged pump to "tow" water through his nylon cones, actually extremely fine nets.

From the pump below the surface, water was piped over the lab roof to his table. First, it passed through the flat screens above the cones. They were made of nylon mesh with openings 202 microns wide (a micron is a thousandth of a millimeter) to bar the way to "big" organisms. Then it streamed into the cones of fine nylon gauze, its openings only 35 microns wide, where his specimens would be trapped. I could not see any difference in the openings of his two grades of nylon mesh. I couldn't see any openings at all.

He would use the first cone, Beers told me, to sift water from the euphotic layer of the sea, where sunlight is strongest, and switch to the second as the pump dropped farther down. To learn how much water he had examined, he only had to read the meter, a household water meter that he had bought in a shop and converted to read in liters (a liter is roughly 1.06 quarts) instead of cubic feet.

Beers was a quiet man in his early thirties who answered my questions with great patience. "The purpose of this," he said, "is to get at a whole level that no one has ever looked at, a mixture of plants and animals." I may have looked puzzled, but he had no time for further explanation. The *T-441*'s engine was now idling, for we had reached our first station. It was just ten o'clock.

There had not been much of a leisurely shipboard atmosphere on the *T-441* during the trip out. There was none now. Strickland first put a thermometer on a wood float overside to take the surface temperature. It read 17 degrees C. (62.5 degrees F.). Then Beers hooked a BT fish to the cable of a high-speed electric winch. This was the bathythermograph MacGowan had mentioned to me. It had been born in 1938 as the brain-child of Dr. Athelstan F. Spilhaus, now author of a comic strip, dean of the Institute of Technology of the University of Minnesota, and another of the creative inventors that the ocean keeps spawning. It looked like a small brass bomb about two feet long. As it dropped, a stylus inside the fish would move in response to temperature and pressure changes with depth, expressing them in a single line scratched on a gold-plated glass slide.

Beers let the BT dangle just beneath the surface for a few moments to equilibrate it with the water temperature. Then he signaled to Stearns, a bustling young man in dark glasses and a yellow sou'wester, to release the brake on the winch. When the winch meter read 450 feet, the dive was stopped and the fish hauled back. Beers opened it and removed the glass slide. I could see the scratch. From the top of the slide, it slanted at a slight angle, then bent sharply downward. The bend represented the thermocline, the level where the sea's temperature suddenly drops. Its exact depth could be determined precisely by examining the slide under a scale graduated in depth and temperature.

The bathythermograph, Strickland remarked to me, gave a general profile of the temperature structure, but more accurate information was needed. Next came a Nansen bottle cast. This device has been the standby of the oceanographer ever since it was developed by Fridtjof Nansen, the great Norwegian explorer and statesman, who drifted across the Arctic in the ice-locked *Fram* just before the turn of the century. The "bottle" is a bronze tube, holding about three pints of water, with plugs on each end. It is lowered into the sea with the plugs open, and when it reaches the required depth, a messenger weight is sent down the cable to trip the bottle. It flips, the plugs close and a water sample is taken to be analyzed later for salinity. At the same time, a reversing thermometer outside the bottle turns over, breaking its mercury column and giving the temperature at this depth.

Sending down Nansen bottles is the old handmade way of doing oceanography. A deep cast can take hours and is far more time-consuming than present methods of lowering electronic instruments that instantaneously record temperature, depth and salinity. But the Nansen bottle is a reliable way to check these instruments.

Stearns used the cable on the ship's big winch for the bottle cast. He first attached a seventy-pound weight to the end of the cable and signaled to the winchman, Cap Selser, to lower away. Selser was the grizzled, loquacious first mate and chief engineer on the *T-441*. When he saw me noting his name, he said: "That's Cap like a hat. Don't give anybody the idea I'm striking for the old man's job."

When the winch stopped, Stearns clipped the first bottle to the cable. Selser paid out 25 meters from the winch. (The reader will excuse me for shifting measurement systems without constantly converting. I am just trying to let him look over my shoulder into my notebook, where fathoms, meters, feet, liters, Centigrade and Fahrenheit stand as testimony to human irrationality. A meter, once more, is about three inches more than a yard.) Stearns and Selser repeated the process until five Nansen bottles were clipped to the cable at 25-meter intervals, starting at 75 meters from the surface and going down to 175 meters. The winch stopped and Stearns let his string of bottles hang.

"We have to wait three minutes for the thermometers to stabilize," he said.

"You know, I've been writing about oceanography and I've never seen a Nansen bottle cast," I told him.

"That's not as bad as the companies that make oceanographic instruments and never see the sea," he said, consolingly.

The three minutes were up, the temperature of the patient had been taken. Stearns slipped the messenger, a small brass weight, onto the cable. As it raced down, he kept his hand on the line. I did, too. First I felt a singing vibration, then a double nibble as if a fish had struck a hook. The first strike came when the messenger hit the bottle, the second when the bottle tripped and sent another messenger down to the next bottle on the line. By counting the strikes, Stearns could tell if each bottle had functioned.

He signaled to Selser to start the winch. When the first bottle, which had been planted 75 meters down, could be seen as a yellow streak in the water, Stearns yelled: "Sight!" When it broke water, he called out again: "Surface!" The winch stopped just long enough for him to free the bottle and place it in a rack on the side of the wheelhouse. "The trick here is to not run the bottle through the sheave of the winch. Sometimes you can lose 12,000 feet of cable if you do that."

Stearns and Selser went through their routine smoothly until all five

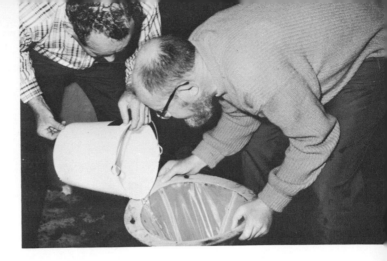

AT WORK AT SEA

Above, aboard T-441 *Pacific water is strained for plankton. At left, project director John D. Strickland records an observation. Below, marine technician Charlie Stearns pays out hose to sample the ocean with a pump.*

Nansen bottles had been taken off the cable. Beers read out the temperatures and depths while Strickland marked them on a chart:

DEPTH in meters	TEMPERATURE in degrees C.
Surface	17.0
75	9.68
100	9.53
125	9.67
150	9.20
175	9.10

"I don't like that temperature inversion at 125 meters," Strickland said.

"It's the thermometer on the third bottle again," Beers said. "It's been giving us trouble."

All this work had been part of the constant cross-checking inherent in seagoing research. Results of the bathythermograph and Nansen bottle casts could be compared with each other. Then they would be stacked against the readings of the automatic temperature and depth recorder attached to the pump.

Before the pump went down, Eppley made a cast with a Secchi disk. It was simply a white disk, about ten inches in diameter, attached to a handline like the ones used on Mark Twain's steamboats, except that the marks were in meters. He let the disk drop until he could no longer see it. He had 20 meters of line out. This indicated to him how far sunlight was penetrating the sea. The rule of thumb, he told me, is that phytoplankton stops growing at three times the Secchi depth.

The pump was now ready to go. Stearns put it over the weather side of the ship, facing the wind. It was not the pleasantest side to work on in rough weather, but comfort was less important than the instrument. On the lee side, the ship might have drifted over it. Stearns kept the pump about two yards below the surface for a few minutes to fill the system. Then he sent it down with a hydraulic winch that inched out the thick red rubber hose at a meter a minute crawl.

At the rate of 22 liters a minute, the pump was sampling the Pacific from the surface down to 100 meters. First, I followed the hose that led into the laboratory. Readings from the temperature and depth recorder on the pump were being traced on two charts. As for the seawater, it passed into the slender plastic tubes of a peristaltic pump that works almost exactly like the human heart. Rollers were pressing the tubes just as the heart puts pressure on the arteries.

The robot chemist was versatile. To determine the plant plankton content of the water, it measured the amount of chlorophyll present. Into a sample it beamed ultraviolet light, which then emerged as red fluorescent light. The more fluorescent the light, the more chlorophyll in the sample. A fluorometer decided this matter and put its findings onto a graph.

Lines were being traced on two more graphs as well. They showed the quantity of mineral nutrients available for plants. The first recorded how much phosphate was in the water; the second showed nitrate and silicate content, using red and green lines respectively.

At a depth of 12 meters, the chlorophyll chart showed an increase. "That's living phytoplankton," Eppley said. "When you get higher values lower down, at 30 or 40 meters, it's probably plankton two or three days old that is settling and decaying."

Eppley and Lucia did not take everything the autoanalyzer told them at face value. Before starting the pump cast, they had run a sample of "standard seawater" through it to check its performance. Lucia now went out of the cabin to the stern, where she took a sample of the water pouring into Beers's apparatus. She knocked on the cabin window, and Strickland, who was inside, glanced at the depth chart and noted where the water had been taken.

The nonautomated Beers had not been wasting his time either. After fifteen minutes, the mesh on the top of his first cone was covered with copepods too big to interest him. They looked like grains of sand, but they felt soft to the touch. "When the chlorophyll peters out at three times the Secchi depth, I'll switch to the second cone," Beers said. I let him work in peace on the fantail. It was a busy moment and he needed room.

Inside the lab, the steel walls were vibrating to the din of an auxiliary generator. Strickland told me that the silicate and nitrate content of the water was starting to rise. "The plants in the top part of the water have used up the nutrients," he said. "We're getting below that layer now and that's why there are more silicates and nitrates left in the water." At 30 meters down, I could see a jagged line on the chlorophyll chart and I asked him what it meant. Strickland swore and said: "Must be a loose connection. The pen moves when the ship rolls and gives us a jagged line. It takes years to debug this stuff so that it will work at sea."

Strickland stepped outside for a moment, returned and noted in his log that the pump's hose was at a ten-degree angle from the vertical at a depth of 39 meters. I went aft again to see what had happened to Beers. It was 11:13, and he was just switching to his second cone as the pump went below 50 meters. His household water meter showed that he had filtered 550 liters of Pacific Ocean from the surface down to this depth. While the pump sent water into his second cone, he hosed down the first one with filtered salt water so as not to contaminate the sample. Then he drew off the sample into a bottle in the plastic garbage pail under the cone.

"We'll get bigger copepods below 50 meters, but they don't interest us," he said. "We catch all kinds of things. The intake on the pump is three-quarters of an inch in diameter and there's no filter on it. We just hope that a fish won't sneak in and wreck the whole system."

Beers finished his second cone as the depth recorder down on the pump showed signs of temperament. Stearns took a wooden meterstick to check the length of hose that the hydraulic winch was feeding out. "We've got $300 worth of electrical tape wound around that hose to protect the wires of the temperature and depth recorder," he said. "But you can't expect it to work forever."

When the pump reached 100 meters, Cap Selser reversed the winch and began to haul up the heavy hose. I told him he looked like he was fishing. "Yes, fishing for knowledge," he said solemnly. "First time I ever went out on a research ship was in the central Pacific. They did long-line fishing for tuna. Never caught a thing. I told them it wasn't right to waste the taxpayers' money like this. Then I found out they were trying to find places where there were no fish. So they could test atom bombs."

After the pump came aboard, Selser changed roles from winchman to chief engineer and the *T-441* rattled off to our second station. It was the nearest thing to a break during the day. Scientists and crew drifted into the galley, where the cook had steaks in gravy waiting for them. The combination of a calm sea and cool air kept appetites high. It had been a long morning, and I relished my steak and gravy as much as the captain's dinner aboard the *France*. I washed it down with black coffee. Operated by the University of California, Scripps's ships are dry.

At 12:55, we sighted an orange buoy marking the second station.

Strickland wrote in the log that the surface temperature was 17.3 degrees C. and the wind was coming from the southwest. "You never know, ten years from now, someone might want to know what the wind was doing here today." He glanced up at the sky where the sun was just starting to burn a hole in the mist.

"Usually, a Cessna comes over at one o'clock," he said. "Bob Linn, my marine technician, goes up every day to see if he can spot a red tide on the water. I don't think he'll try today, it's too foggy."

The team went through the same preparatory steps at the second station. This time, the thermometer on the third Nansen bottle was behaving properly and the temperature profile looked normal. But Stearns had to go into the lab to look at the chlorophyll chart on the autoanalyzer.

"We never get a situation where everything works at once," he said.

"Very rarely," Strickland commented. "It doesn't work in space, either. It only works in movies."

He peered at the graphs from the first station. "Judging from this," he said, "there's less upwelling and the plant material in the water has decreased. But I won't have a chance to look at it until some time next year. We're just finishing up the experiments we ran in Peru last year. In any case, there's much less plant material than we had last week."

"Will this show up in Beers's animal collection?" I asked.

"Not necessarily. There's a lag. Plants live a day or two, animals a month or two. That's the problem, we don't know the life cycle of small animals."

On the stern of the *T-441*, Beers showed me a gelatinous patch on the "coarse" mesh over his cone. "At first, I thought I'd take it back," he said. "It looked like the young of *Velella*, the by-the-wind sailor. But it's only copepods and I really don't have time for them. The trouble is, we have a mixture of single-celled and multi-celled plankton. The most abundant forms are the ciliates, a one-celled protozoan in a vase-like case. This is my sixth trip this year and I've only been able to study four samples."

Suddenly, I wondered what a submarine commander would have reported if he had surfaced behind the *T-441*. Red hoses wound over the roof into T-joints, from which smaller lines ran to Beers's table. The whole system was held together by clamps and tied with rope to steel beams projecting from the lab cabin. Filtered water from the nylon cones was trickling into the two garbage pails beneath the steel-and-plywood table where Beers presided like a frantic bartender.

Eppley had a quieter time, for he was only interested in plants. He removed a box from the cabin roof. It contained three one-gallon jugs. "Later, we'll take a water sample and let it incubate in one of these jugs," he explained. "Phytoplankton will keep growing in it for forty-eight hours and then we can look at it in the lab. It's hard to come to conclusions, though. Everything is too complex and dynamic here. Even a lake is better than this. At least, you're working with the same water from one week to the next."

Strickland sympathized with him: "That's the Factor X that bugs everybody. There are things in seawater we can't explain. You can take a bucket of seawater and grow a weed in it. A month later, you can take a bucket from the same place and the weed won't grow. The trouble is, you never know. We're getting a very low nutrient content today on the autoanalyzer. It may be that big plankton blooms used up all the nutrients or else we're looking at new warmer water. We should be doing this seven days a week, but it would take too much manpower."

At any rate, the Pacific was more barren than it had been the week before. When we reached the third and final station, Eppley put the Secchi disk overside and lost sight of it at 9.5 meters. On the previous Wednesday, the Secchi depth had been only 5 meters here because the water was teeming with life. We were a half mile off Torrey Pines State Reserve. Mehling had found the station by taking a bearing on the towers used to mark the Navy's measured mile. Behind the shore, I could clearly see the cliffs, creased by their dry canyons. With not much more than 60 feet of water under the *T-441*, drifting on station was out of the question. Selser went up to the bow, let go the anchor and jumped up and down on the chain to see if it was holding. He turned to Mehling in the wheelhouse and first held up one finger, then two crossed fingers.

"What's that?" I asked.

"It means I've put out a shot-and-a-half of chain," he said. Another measurement system for the notebook: one shot of anchor chain equals 60 feet.

The routine changed at this station. Since the pump could only be lowered 20 meters, there was no need to make a Nansen bottle cast to see what the water was like further down. The bathythermograph dived to the same depth. When it came up, the slide showed it had barely caught the level where the temperature dipped. Eppley then ran another experiment. He started by putting a photometer overboard, a device that looked like the rim of a bicycle wheel with a depth recorder hanging from it. With this sophisticated version of the Secchi disk, he was trying to find the depth where sunlight was reduced to 10 percent of its level on the surface. To no one's surprise, the depth recorder did not work. Stearns's faithful meterstick did. The dial on the photometer showed that it had reached the 10 percent light level at a depth of seven meters.

Eppley then lowered a Van Dorn bottle, made of plastic to protect phytoplankton from the effects of metal poisoning, and took a sample at this depth. Once animals had been filtered out of the water, he would add nutrients and radioactive carbon-14 to it. He would let it incubate for forty-eight hours in his gallon jug and then use a Geiger counter to see how much carbon had been taken up by the plants. "This way, we can give the zooplankton buffs an estimate of how much phytoplankton was in the water and we can calculate its initial carbon content," he said. From the third station, he expected mainly negative results. The chlorophyll chart on the autoanalyzer was showing 100 times less phytoplankton in the water than the previous week, and Beers's nylon mesh looked clean.

The sea may not have been very populous at this station, but the sky was. Gulls screamed around the ship and the rumble of invisible Navy jets from the Miramar base never stopped. Beers quickly finished his work, for he only needed one cone in such shallow water, and Selser heaved up the anchor. At ten knots, the *T-441* headed back to Mission Bay to drop the scientific party. The pace aboard ship finally slackened. Beers tidied up after his last cone and showed me the results of the day. On three stations, the pump had been hoisted through 220 meters. What he had strained from its hose was now contained in five small bottles.

When I said good-bye to Beers and the others at the Mission Bay dock before Strickland drove me home, their work had only begun. A few days later, I dropped in on Strickland, and Beers was in his office. He invited me to see what his cones had caught.

"It wasn't much," he said apologetically. The zooplankton had apparently vanished along with the plants. He showed me his log for the first cone on the second station. What he strained from 500 liters of seawater had been placed in a bottle containing .632 liter. From this bottle, he had taken a 3-milliliter sample, a tenth of a fluid ounce.

"How do you know you're getting a representative sample?" I asked.

"We just shake the bottle for ten seconds in a random fashion," he said. The resultant drop of water had been transferred to a slide, and once more Beers ran transects over the sea, this time with a microscope. It took him four to five hours, he told me, to count a sample. From the surface down to 50 meters on the second station, his 3-milliliter model of the Pacific yielded the following census: 54 nauplii (a larval form of copepod), 36 foraminifera (single-celled animals with calcium carbonate shells, one of the most abundant forms of marine protozoans), 11 copepods, 22 radiolarians (another protozoan with a silicate shell) and one bivalve larva, a future blue mussel. In Beers's microscope, I could see tubes of various shapes with pointed ends. They were tintinnids, a form of animal plankton, he said.

Strickland shook his head wearily as he watched us. "Counting samples is our worst bottleneck. We're now looking into the possibility of using holography, 3-D laser photography. All the light waves reflected from an object are frozen onto a glass plate. You get the sides as well as the front. Then when you look at the plate, you can see everything that's in the frame as if it were really standing there in front of you. When you look at a hologram with a microscope, it's the damnedest thing you ever saw. You have to focus individually on everything that's on the glass plate, just as if you were looking through a telescope at objects at different distances.

"Some day, we hope to take holograms in the sea. You could merely lower the apparatus slowly and look around on all sides. You could even put it on a buoy and take time-series photos.

"But first, we'll try it in the tank. It's a ten-grand piece of equipment and we would hate to drop it. In the meanwhile, we'll have to go on slinging butterfly nets through the water. One problem is to catch enough copepods for breeding purposes in the tank; another is to catch a representative sample of copepods so that we can estimate their numbers *in situ.*

"If we can solve these problems and if we can take holograms in the tank, we might be able to write that Kinsey report yet."

7. Sound Sees the Invisible

The Scripps scientist was something of a crustacean himself. Before one could get at the meat, an outer shell had to be pierced. Ninety-nine times out of a hundred, his wary reaction upon learning that a book was being written about oceanography was either "What, another?" or "I'm writing one myself."

Not the hundredth time. During a sunny lawn lunch with the usual mixed sample of table companions, I had been introduced to John Tyler, a placid fatherly-looking gentleman who was with the Scripps Visibility Laboratory. Tyler followed the conversation for a moment, then blurted out: "I've got something for your book. Do you know that you can read a newspaper by daylight 2,000 feet down at the bottom of Crater Lake?"

There was no need to ask which paper. It had to be the New York *Times*. Inhabitants of Scripps make a fetish of picking up their air-delivered *Times* at a friendly liquor shop in La Jolla Shores that sells it as a community service. On Thursdays, when the Sunday paper arrives five days late by the overland trail, they look forward to it as expectantly as South Sea islanders awaiting the arrival of the mail schooner.

No doubt I would have filed away this information about Crater Lake along with other morsels like the ocean's greatest depth (35,800 feet in the Mariana Trench, 200 miles southwest of Guam), if my recollection of the *T-441*'s one-day voyage had not been fresh. Six miles from where we were sitting, Eppley had lost sight not of newsprint but of a big white Secchi disk just thirty feet down in clear undersea weather. It was hard to imagine how anyone could see in the sea, and Crater Lake sounded like an unusual body of water. I wondered aloud what Tyler had been doing there; it is in the Cascade Range of Oregon and nowhere near the ocean. He invited me to drop in for an answer at his office and warned that he did not have much else to offer.

Tyler was grappling with the opaqueness of the ocean, which he measured against the clarity of Crater Lake, his criterion. "It's the cleanest water we know," he said. "Strong blue light penetrates all the way down to the bottom at 2,000 feet. But the ocean is not that simple optically. It's full of biological and mineral particles that scatter and redirect light, just like fog. In clean water off Coronado Island in Baja California, you can see only 35 feet horizontally. But in San Pedro Bay next to the sewage outfall, you can't see your hand in front of your face."

Confronted by such variations, Tyler was not at all enthusiastic about the possibility of using light to identify many of the ocean's features. "The Russians have tried to describe currents optically," he remarked. "They lowered instruments a thousand meters down, then brought water samples up from greater depths and made charts of equal light-transmission levels. Other workers have tried the same thing. But I don't believe such charts have real meaning. We tried it once . . . we couldn't agree on the interpretation of the data.

"Off San Clemente south of Los Angeles, I made a calculation for an oil company on the detectability of a 100-watt light bulb. The idea was to try to locate the bulb by means of a scanning photoelectric gadget in 250 feet of water. The oil company wanted to see if they could return to a drill hole on the bottom. I never heard from them afterwards, so I guess they must have found a better way."

Tyler was a mild, self-deprecating man who used his dry humor to undersell himself consistently. I don't think he was being fair to John Tyler. He had not gone stale during his fifteen years at Scripps. A few years ago, he had taken a plunge with John Isaacs into planetary optics. Together, they published a paper on an optical method of proving the existence of sand dunes on other planets, which led to their constructing a cylindrical model of Mars. Now he had turned to the same sort of biological problems that Strickland was attacking, only from a different quarter.

"That's what all this stuff is about," he said, waving at the equations on the greenboard behind him. "We've worked out a theory that shows a relationship between the transmission of natural light by water and the water's chlorophyll content. What we are trying to do now is to estimate the phytoplankton concentration.

"We can do this if we can determine the concentration of plankton on the basis of chlorophyll content. That part isn't too bad. But now, we want to go to sea and test our method. We've obtained the use of a ship and we plan to work in the Gulf Stream off Bimini. With Crater Lake water as our base point, we hope to be able to tell if the Gulf Stream water is clean or if it contains chlorophyll."

Tyler almost sighed: "Oceanography has one good point. If you go out on a ship and gather data, no one can ever go back to exactly the same place, nor can he ever hope to have the same conditions. Consequently he can't prove you were wrong."

Even the mighty laser meets its master in the sea's light-scattering particles. At a distance of 100 feet, Tyler told me, a laser beam can be merely a diffuse glow. As it draws closer, it concentrates into a single beam, like the headlight of an oncoming motorcycle in a fog. Dr. Seibert Q. Duntley, the head of Tyler's Visibility Laboratory, has been conducting experiments in optical attenuation, with lasers at Lake Winnipesaukee in New Hampshire from an underwater house, a steel caisson sunk in ten feet of water with a window at the six-foot level. Outside the window stretches a horizontal track 100 feet long, where divers move a laser back and forth for his experiments. To keep out unwelcome natural light, the apparatus is run only on moonless nights with a black canvas cover floating on the surface over the track.

Such work has to be done on a lake to reduce the number of variables to a manageable quantity. "As for the sea, it's the most inhomogeneous place you can think of," Tyler said.

The visible light waves he uses to peer into the ocean are between 400 and 700 millimicrons long (a millimicron is one-billionth of a meter, and on this scale, Beers's animals are whales). At the other end of the wave spectrum lie radio waves. In the sea, they too are quickly absorbed.

Radio and light can reach out through intergalactic space, yet they face a near-impervious barrier in the ocean. So do the high-frequency radio waves used in radar.

Only sound waves offer a window of any consequence into the sea. Through sound, the oceanographer can not only hear but also measure, communicate, map and search. Since the underwater properties of sound offer both a way of hiding one's own nuclear submarines and tracking the other fellow's, it is also a window through which modern oceanography receives a great deal of money from the military. In 1968, the United States government budgeted $447,700,000 for marine science programs, and by far the biggest single item was $136,900,000 devoted to "national security." The National Science Foundation, in contrast, accounted for only $33,600,000 of the total. In its White House report on *Effective Use of the Sea*, the Panel on Oceanography of the President's Science Advisory Committee states forebodingly: "We must be able to verify that no presently unknown (to us) physical effects in the ocean environment make nuclear submarines susceptible to continuous tracking and location."

Happily, there is so much to be learned about sound in the sea that defense requirements are not incompatible with good basic science. My limited experience with basic scientists leads me to suspect that they use this factor for all that it is worth in terms of naval research grants and I also suspect that navies play along with them. In many countries, naval hydrographic offices are still the backbone of oceanographic research and they like to maintain this standing. Long before the exploration of outer space yielded improved frying pans, naval research was spinning off peaceful benefits. It was Matthew Fontaine Maury, an American naval officer in the days of sail, who produced the best wind and current charts of the Atlantic and fathered modern American oceanography when he published his *Physical Geography of the Sea* in 1855. Merchant as well as naval vessels made good use of his charts. Today, as I had already read, a fisheries expert like Wilbert Chapman can be attracted by the results of Navy-supported research on the animals that distort sound in the deep scattering layer.

If only layers of small animals distorted sound, navies could spend much of their research money elsewhere. In the sea, everything distorts it. One combination of variables can render a submarine "invisible" within torpedo range of a searching ship, another can enable a signal to be sent

10,000 miles. At frequencies higher than we can hear (the audible range for the human ear runs between 20 and 20,000 vibrations or cycles per second), sound is stopped by a school of herring, a fact of great value to fishermen. At low frequencies, it will go right through the sea floor to the earth's crust, a fact of equally great value to marine geologists. It is a window that clouds and clears, never remaining the same under different conditions.

Sound's whimsy is explained by its sensitivity to the temperature and density of what it is traversing. In air at zero degrees C. (the freezing point of water), it travels at 1,089 feet per second. At 20 degrees C. (68 degrees F.), it covers 1,130 feet every second, for its speed in air goes up two feet per second with a one-degree rise in temperature.

In seawater, sound races along roughly five times as fast as in air and it is affected even more by temperature: a one-degree centigrade rise accelerates it not two but fifteen feet a second. What complicates the study of sound underwater is that its speed also rises with increases in salinity and pressure, the two components of density in seawater. If the values of these components, along with that of temperature, varied at the same rate, the speed of sound could be easily plotted. They do not. Pressure is known, for it is dependent on depth, but temperature and salinity vary with a number of factors.

It is essential to know how fast sound is going to be able to determine where it will go. A sound wave, like a light ray, is bent or refracted when it encounters something that changes its speed. Light, for example, bends when it strikes glass at an oblique angle, for its speed through glass is slower. Sound behaves the same way underwater as it moves through colder or warmer layers in the sea. When a sound wave is sent down from a ship on a warm surface, it is refracted when it meets the sharply cooled water at the thermocline. Some of its energy is bent upward, the rest downward and the waves split into two paths. Behind this split is a shadow zone where much less sound penetrates.

From the surface downwards, two conflicting forces affect the speed and consequently the path of sound. Greater depths and hence greater pressures allow it to go faster, falling temperatures brake it. Temperature has the upper hand at first. In a typical ocean situation (the term is used for convenience's sake; no ocean situation is typical), sound moving at 5,000 feet a second on the surface has slowed to 4,900 feet a second at a depth of about 4,000 feet. Here the temperature decrease becomes very slight and the pressure accelerator takes over. At 16,000 feet down, sound travels 65 feet a second faster than on the surface.

To find and identify an object underwater, the exact speed of sound must be known. The naval officer works it out with the help of a handy little equation like this one (in which C is sound's speed in meters per second, t is temperature in degrees centigrade, s is salinity in parts per thousand and d depth in meters):

$$C = 1449 + 4.6t - 0.055t^2 + 0.0003t^3 + (1.39 - 0.012t)(s - 35) + 0.017d$$

Not so the porpoise: it "sees" acoustically as easily as we see optically without any knowledge of refraction or the relative speed of sound in air and in our eyeglasses. Experiments conducted by Dr. Winthrop N. Kellogg of Florida State University showed that Albert, a porpoise, used only sound to distinguish between the fish that he liked and those he disliked to eat. He emitted clicks and sorted out the different echoes he got back from different fish. The porpoise has no sense of smell and the experiments were run on dark nights. Albert simply had 20/20 vision when he saw with sound. He could detect differences in shapes, sizes and skin textures. As for the naval officer, he is not always sure of being able to distinguish between a school of fish and a submarine.

Albert was a better student than I was. Dr. Fred Spiess, associate director of Scripps and head of its Marine Physical Laboratory, had kindly given up his lunch hour to explain to me how sound behaved in the sea. He drew graph after graph with sinuous lines showing bulges and curves in the speed and path of sound. While he certainly encountered some high-density layers in my mind, I am afraid that the speed of penetration was slow.

Spiess erased the graphs and drew another diagram to explain how sound can travel around the world underwater. If it is moving in a minimum velocity layer (that is, a zone bounded above and below by layers where the speed of sound is higher), a noise will just keep on moving. Such a layer usually exists in deep water centered at a depth of 3,000 to 4,000 feet, for sound will travel faster in the warmer water above and in the colder but pressurized water below. It is known as the deep sound channel and its properties were used during the years immediately after World War II to save airplane pilots who had crash-landed in the Pacific. From his life raft, the pilot was supposed to drop a small bomb, which exploded in the deep sound channel. Hydrophones on Hawaii and the west coast of the United States could pick up the noise and thus determine his position. The SOFAR (SOund Fixing And Ranging) system went back into use in the Sixties as a way of locating missiles test-launched into the sea.

That is an obvious use of underwater sound. Much subtler ones are needed to map the relief of the sea floor. Like the porpoise's system of clocks, they are all based upon measurement of the time needed for sound to reach an object and for its echo to return. Each round trip is recorded with a stroke of a moving stylus on a chart. As the ship steams along, the stylus moves and produces a picture of the bottom in exactly the same way that a printed newspaper page is reproduced by a facsimile machine. If the measurement of the echo is precise enough, a picture of bottom features, either made by nature or left there by man, is revealed.

It is hard to obtain much precision with a sound beam sent down from a ship. This is akin to measuring the depth of a well with a rubber band while standing on a trampoline. To get the oceanographer out of such a predicament, Scripps's Marine Physical Laboratory had devised some ways to take the motion out of the trampoline, and that was why I had taken Spiess's lunch hour. Since he was thorough and serious, he first explained to me what he was trying to measure, before describing how he went about it.

Spiess's seriousness left room for more than a glimmer of fantasy. He had volunteered for submarine duty during World War II, and though he neglected to tell me himself, he had made a dozen patrols. He did tell me that his was the second generation in the family to listen to the sea. During the First World War, his father had been a seaman on a submarine chaser. Under certain circumstances, a whole convoy would come to a stop so as not to make any noise while the elder Spiess and others put stethoscopes to their ears and floated their listening elements to hear a U-boat. This was a wartime application of a technique that had been first used as a navigation aid. On certain buoys and lightships, bells were placed underwater so that navigators could listen for them with stethoscopes in foggy weather. Much the same principle is used today to enable submarines to get position fixes without coming to the surface. Acoustic beacons emit a signal that is heard by the submarine commander. When he recognizes the beacon's signal, he knows exactly where he is and he can correct his inertial navigation system. Similar beacons serve peaceful bents. In oil drilling on the continental shelf, they put a sound tag on a hole so that it can be relocated if the drilling vessel must run to shelter.

In his person-to-person lecture, Spiess made a careful distinction between active and passive use of sonar (SOund NAvigation and Ranging) beams, as they are called in the United States. The British call the device asdic (from Anti-Submarine Detection Investigation Committee). With passive sonar, the ship remains quiet and listens for the noise made by a submarine. With active sonar, the ship emits pings and tries to hear an echo off the submarine's hull. "The submarine has an edge in the game because he makes little noise," Spiess commented. "On a ship, you have to send out strong signals to overcome the background noise you are making with your engines. It is much easier for the submarine to hear the pinging of a searching ship. If there is a warm layer on the surface, sound bends sharply down, creating that shadow zone where the submarine can hide. During the war, this used to be called the 'afternoon effect.' On a sunny day, the surface was heated so much that destroyers could not detect anything. But some people claimed it was caused by the drowsiness of sonar operators after a big lunch."

Active and passive sonar alike are used in a device developed by Spiess's laboratory to map the sea bottom from a stable point. It has the unfortunate name of FISH, probably because of the laboratory's close association with the acronymia-stricken Navy. I guessed that FISH stood for "Finny Inhabitant of Saltwater Home" and I was wrong. It meant "Fully Instrumented Submersible Housing." In any case, it is a small FISH, only four feet long from its conical nose to the tubular tip of its body. It can be towed from a ship in water as deep as 15,000 feet and, in every case, far below the area disturbed by surface waves.

It explores with the whole gamut of seagoing acoustical techniques. To determine its depth, it focuses a sonar beam up at the surface, which, as Spiess reminded me, is much more suitable for such a purpose than the uneven bottom. To register echoes from the bottom relief, it looks down with another beam, a narrow one. Then it ranges as far as 600 feet on both sides with broad sound beams enabling it to pick out echoes from objects as small as six feet long. (The interest of the military in such objects is obvious after the H-bomb search off Palomares in 1966.) From the quiet depths, all this information gathered by sound is electrically fed into recorders on the ship along the coaxial cable that tows the device.

The FISH uses sound both to see and steer. A sound picture of a narrow canyon is not really useful unless its exact location is known. Under ordinary circumstances, the ship might have only an approximate idea of its own position and an even vaguer notion of where the FISH was swimming underwater at the end of two miles of flexible cable. Some kind of bench marks are needed on the bottom to keep track of the FISH. This is done with acoustic beacons, Spiess explained to me. Scripps uses a beacon that is powered by batteries and listens with passive sonar for a signal from the FISH. When it hears one on its hydrophone, it replies with a sound impulse of its own. The time taken for this exchange of messages indicates the distance of the FISH from the beacon, and this information, too, goes up the cable.

Unlike the modern musician, the underwater acoustician juggles frequencies to prevent sound from doing the unexpected. He must use a different frequency for each purpose or else he will achieve the cacophony of random music, with beacons replying at the wrong time to signals meant for something else. A beacon, therefore, is set to respond only to one frequency. "We can build acoustic circuits easily, but the trick is to get them to recognize noises," Spiess said. "In this instance, we turned the trick because our beacons reply only to the proper interrogation." In other instances, the porpoise is still ahead.

With a triangular array of beacons five miles apart, the position of the FISH can be determined with an accuracy of 30 feet. Spiess told me with pardonable pride that his laboratory's beacons survive for a year at a depth of 14,000 feet. Scientists can thus return to a site time and again to make a small-scale map of the bottom relief.

"I'm an experimentalist," Spiess went on. "I like two or three different payoffs, not just mapping. I like to get as much data as I can from a system without waiting twenty-five years for ideal subsystems." In other words, systems analysis showed that the FISH was good for more than taking sound pictures. Behind it on a cable, Spiess put a towed magnetometer to detect variations in the magnetic field on the bottom. Such measurements have been made for two decades by ships with surface instruments, but they are blurred by the intervening ocean.

"As long as we were down there, we thought we'd take some ordinary pictures, too. So we added a camera to the FISH and hung a light from it. The light stays ten feet from the bottom and the camera is at a safer distance, about fifty feet above it.

"Finally, we wanted to see through the sea floor. We added a low-frequency sound source and it gives us echoes from the structure 150 feet down into the bottom. For this, we use a frequency of only 3,500 cycles per second. Our echo sounder works on 40,000 cycles."

Spiess smiled as he saw my eyes glaze. Though I had missed lunch, it must have been the afternoon effect. He glanced at his watch: "Let's have a break. Then I think you might enjoy taking a look at FLIP. She's moored in San Diego. It will only take us a few minutes to drive there."

FLIP is operated by the Marine Physical Laboratory, and it was one of the principal reasons for my visit to Spiess. Isaacs had aroused my curiosity about this vessel, one of the strangest afloat (despite appearances, it does float). He had spoken of it as a steady piece of real estate in the middle of the sea, the precursor of floating islands and mid-ocean resorts. Spiess, who had led its development from the start, was much more interested in building a quiet listening post where he could study the propagation of sound. His towed FISH is protected from the restless sea by thousands of feet of water above it. FLIP stays put because its hull reaches 300 feet down into the calm layers of the ocean while its top decks emerge from the surface. Its name is both a description and, of course, an acronym: the FLoating Instrument Platform is towed out to station horizontally, and then flips into a vertical position to go about its tasks. The fourteen scientists and crew members aboard flip with it.

"It's really just a big spar buoy, a fence post in the water," Spiess told me as we walked to his car. "At first, we used submarines to study sound from a quiet, motionless point. You'd shut everything down, you'd get the crew into their bunks and you'd listen. But submarines are expensive, and besides it's hard to get them to hover at a set depth when they are not under way. We needed something with a deep enough draft to remain stable at sea, but we still had to be able to get it in and out of port and tow it. Dr. Fred Fisher and I spent days inventing things. We thought of hinged vessels, or of jacking devices up and down from a float. In the end, it was Allyn Vine at Woods Hole who had the idea of flipping an old submarine. We never tried it, but we went on from there. Fred and I were physicists, we weren't good enough as engineers. So we got a young consulting engineer, Larry Glosten from Seattle, to help us."

Spiess headed the car out Ardath Road to pick up the freeway into San Diego. Without freeways, it is doubtful that he could operate. His office was in the main administration building at Scripps, the Marine Physical Laboratory was inside the Navy's territory on Point Loma and FLIP was berthed at B Street Pier on the edge of downtown San Diego.

"We wanted FLIP so that we could look at fluctuations in the propagation of sound," he continued. "They're like the twinkling of stars, they're caused by irregularities in the transmission medium, water in one case and air in the other. Remember what I showed you on the board: you can't measure such fluctuations from a fluctuating platform. Ideally, we wanted something that would move less than three inches in thirty-foot waves. Our calculations showed that we would have to go 600 feet down to get this much stability if we kept to a straight cylindrical shape like a fence post. So we changed to a different design: a narrow waist at the waterline and a slightly flared bottom. I won't go into the mathematics of this, but it gives us the stability we need with only 300 feet of hull under water.

"That led to our main design problem. In the horizontal position, FLIP is 355 feet long, but her hull is only twelve and a half feet in diameter at that narrow waist which accounts for a third of her length. Yet, under tow, she had to be able to cope with a wave her own length that might make her sag or hog. A ship sags if only her bow and stern are supported by two succeeding waves; she hogs if only her middle is supported. In either case, she can break in two. We got around that by using high-strength steel.

"As an ex-submarine officer, I had a feeling for the ballasting techniques that we needed to bring her from the horizontal to the vertical and back up again. In the middle of the study phase, we built a model to a one-tenth scale and tested it in San Diego Bay to study oscillations and the time scale of the transition. It was 35 feet long and drew 30 feet. We had to make sure that the full-sized FLIP would not keep going down. You know, we were moving her center of gravity from the waterline at the start of the flip to a point 150 feet below when she was standing on end. It was like dropping a 2,000-ton weight down the hull.

"The model didn't sink when we put it down into a vertical position.

That relieved us, until we brought it back to horizontal. The model came up all right . . . upside down. We fixed that by putting fifty tons of concrete ballast in the bottom of the big FLIP, but we were uneasy when we tried her for the first time. That was in the summer of 1962 in Dabob Bay, an arm of Puget Sound. Everything worked just fine, but we still made everybody on board wear hard hats and life jackets, like drivers of racing speedboats, for the first twenty flips."

According to a leaflet Spiess had given me, FLIP had gone from horizontal to vertical 115 times during the first five years of her career. A flip takes fifteen minutes: for the first ten minutes, water is slowly let into her ballast tanks until she is down about ten degrees by the stern, her fifty-foot prow slanting out of the water. Then, in five minutes, she moves another eighty degrees and she stands upright, her former prow now her decks above the waterline.

I asked Spiess if a flip had ever alerted a passing ship. "No, but we always warn all ships in the vicinity that we are going to look like we're sinking. Most of all, we have to warn submarines. The biggest danger is that of a collision 300 feet down. A submarine never expects to find a ship there. You know, the Navy rates your importance by the draft of your ship. I guess I've had the deepest-draft command of any naval officer."

Spiess cut off the freeway to take Harbor Drive along the waterfront of San Diego Bay. Right before we reached B Street Pier, we could see the tall masts of the *Star of India*, an old square-rigger that was now a floating monument and tourist attraction. Her paint was fresh, her stays were taut and I caught myself nostalgically wishing that we could visit her instead of the prone fence post that was in store for me.

FLIP confirmed my nostalgia. She was lying low in the water with a maintenance barge moored alongside. Her fifty-foot prow (I knew it was the prow only because the leaflet said so) looked like the beginning of a ship that someone had been too lazy to finish. The flaring effect that Spiess had described to me added a hump, sprouting two strut-mounted propellers, halfway towards the stern.

Spiess read my thoughts as he must have read those of preceding visitors. "She looks prettier when she's vertical," he said. "She's more comfortable that way, too." He introduced me to FLIP's master, Captain Earl D. Bronson, who said he would be glad to let us go aboard. Bronson apologized for the disrupted state of his office on the pier. "We've just

FLIPped

FLIPping

FLOPped

had a herd of visitors, and NBC is doing a program on us," he said. "It's hard to get work out of a crew when visitors are around. We used to tie up on Harbor Drive near the *Star of India* and the tourists would come by. My crew are mainly ex-tuna fishermen and they're good sailors. But when girls are around in bathing suits, they won't do anything. They just watch."

According to the leaflet, FLIP had to be towed onto station and she could not move on her own. I asked Bronson what was the purpose of the propellers sticking up in the air amidships. "Orientation," he said. "We use them to maintain a particular direction when we're vertical. Otherwise, she always points her keel into the wind. Or else, we can 'cruise' by rotating in a small circle 100 feet in diameter."

Spiess and I went up the gangplank and onto the bow of FLIP. There are only three other vessels resembling her in the world, he told me as we set foot on what could have been either a deck or a wall. The Naval Ordnance Laboratory has SPAR, an unmanned craft of the same length, on the Atlantic coast. General Motors operates another, half the size, in the Pacific under the name of POP (Perpendicular Oceanographic Platform, heaven help us) and Captain Cousteau has one in the Mediterranean. Instead of a clever acronym, Cousteau's floating island boasts a two-man elevator for its crew and, Spiess added wistfully, a lovely even-temperature wine cellar below the warm surface layer of the sea. Vertical or horizontal, Scripps's ships are dry.

FLIP has no elevator and its personnel often feel they live like cliff-dwelling monkeys. Spiess told me of a plan to lay a track on the outside of her hull, along which a chamber could carry a biologist from the surface down to 300 feet for observations. Spiess regards FLIP the same way as the FISH: she is a 1,500-ton Christmas tree upon which any number of useful ornaments can be hung to add to her capabilities. She has been towed in a vertical position to make precise echo soundings of a narrow submarine canyon. She can double as a stake to measure surface waves in mid-ocean, or she can act as a relatively fixed point for tracking deep-ocean currents.

When we saw her, she sported a trio of booms that lowered temperature-measuring instruments into the sea to follow the rise and fall of internal waves. These long waves beneath the surface alter the sound-transmitting properties of seawater and they are identified by their temperature characteristics. In deep water, they can be hundreds of feet high. They are not felt on the surface, but they can affect a submarine. According to one theory, the *Thresher* was lost in 1963 when she nosed downward in an internal wave, racing to a depth where pressure caved in her hull.

With this gloomy thought, I entered FLIP, which resembles a submarine in its confined quarters but not in any other way. On board I could not help but recall the old practical joke of fraternities during the days of raccoon coats and hip flasks. I had read that, during a hazing, a pledge was patiently liquored to the point of insensibility. Then he was taken to a room to sleep it off, a special room where all the furniture was nailed to the ceiling. It was this that he saw, to his horror, when he woke up on the floor. On the FLIP, I seemed to be standing on a wall. A stairway ran crosswise over my head, one side attached to the roof. There was a railing on the roof, too, to prevent flies from falling overboard. On the wall, there was a capstan and a nonskid metal tread running straight up before my eyes.

Walking from bow to stern in port was the only way to visualize what FLIP looked like from top to bottom at sea. All the galley fixtures, including the electric stove and refrigerator, were on trunnions so that meals could be cooked in either position. So were the diesel engines used to generate power and drive the orientation propellers. Radar and electronics equipment was equally versatile. In the living quarters, sofas served as beds, their backs becoming mattresses when the ship went vertical. There were sinks for both positions, but the shower only worked vertically (probably there was not enough water available for it to be used as a tub). Storage space was designed to change from horizontal dressers to small vertical closets. "It's best to pack things in pigeonholes," Spiess remarked as we walked by.

Since I could hardly ask Spiess and Captain Bronson to tow FLIP out into deep water for me to see what life aboard was like, I had to recall some impressions I had heard from Robert Zalkan, a graduate student I had met around a coffeepot near my borrowed office. Zalkan is a naval lieutenant, taking his doctorate at Scripps. He thought FLIP had good and bad points.

"I've been on her five times," he had told me. "She's stable, even when she's horizontal. After all, she's just a big sewer pipe with a ship's bow on it. I once rode her to Hawaii for two weeks. We were being towed by a Scripps ship, the *Horizon,* and we were met halfway by the

Swan, a General Motors research vessel. In a high quartering sea, FLIP rolled eleven degrees, but *Horizon* was rolling thirty-one degrees and *Swan,* forty-one. I get seasick as hell, but on FLIP I just get heartburn."

He has been aboard FLIP when she stood on end in waves thirty-five feet high. The improvement was immediately noticed by his queasy stomach. "FLIP has three different motions when she is vertical," he said. "First, a heave. It's like pushing a stick into the water and letting it bob up and down. That motion is very small, and so is her rolling. Then there is a solid-rod type of motion. I mean, she wriggles. It's like being on the end of a pier when a big wave hits and makes it vibrate."

What were the bad points?

"Starting with Tank 10, she's got nine decks and you're going up and down all the time. There's the wet lab on top, then the electronics lab and the mess and berthing space. There is also berthing space next to the orientation motors, and you have to move when they're being run. They are needed for acoustics and internal wave work when you have to hold your heading to less than a degree.

"I've served in submarines, but FLIP is much more cramped. There's nothing to do on board when you're not busy scientifically. So you read, or you play poker and acey-deucey."

I had been curious about how FLIPpers adjusted from a supine to an upright way of life. "Oh, there's nothing to that," Zalkan said. "You're just a little disoriented at first. You have to remember that the door is at the other end."

Where Zalkan climbed, Spiess and I had to crawl. Soon we were on all fours in a tunnel three feet in diameter that could also be a vertical ladder. It led us through the air compressor room to the top of Tank 10. Beyond this point, FLIP was mainly a series of tanks that either remained closed for permanent buoyancy or could be flooded and blown clear. Spiess consoled me: "It's funny, but Tank 10 looks a lot farther away when we're vertical." He assured me that flipping did not require any gift for gymnastics. The ship's company just stayed out on deck on the bow and held on. Each man braced one foot on the deck and the other against the wall while they changed places.

FLIP was hot, for she was not air-conditioned at the time, and I did not regret the end of our horizontal climb back to the bow. When we came out on the control station, I could see the masts and spars of the

Star of India next to Harbor Drive. Spiess also looked at the lofty square-rigger.

Then he turned to me and said: "There's nothing really so unusual about FLIP. We tend to forget that men went to sea for a long time in deep-draft quiet ships with no engines. When they were lying on their bunks with their ears next to the hull, they heard sounds. That's where the old names of fish like croakers, growlers and drumfish came from. We only call it the silent sea because our ships are noisy."

8. *The Music of the Tides*

Of all the applications of underwater sound that I encountered at Scripps, the most appealing was its use in a project aimed at learning, among other things, how fast the earth's clock is running down and the moon is running away.

It is the tides that are slowing time. When they race over the shallow bottom of the continental shelf, the resulting friction acts as a brake on the spinning earth. It has been estimated by a British scientist, Professor K. F. Bowden, that the tide coming into the English Channel from the Atlantic reaches shore with only 13 percent of its original energy. The other 87 percent, 210 million horsepower in this case, is lost through friction on the Channel floor.

Since the earth's rotation is slowed, its days must necessarily lengthen. Its gravitational hold on the moon, governed by its rotation according to the laws of celestial mechanics (which I accept not because I understand them but because I am a law-abiding person), must gradually wane. Half a billion years ago, the moon was twice as close. Every century, it moves away 1/100,000th of its distance from the earth. Every century, too, an earthly day grows a thousandth of a second longer. Days just do not seem more endless than when we were young, they really are dragging.

A few billion years from now, a day will be a month and a half long and the moon will be gone from the sky, off on an orbit of its own around the sun. Exactly when this will happen is the kind of Mount Everest problem that always appeals to the oceanographer: he must solve it because it is there.

Astronomy tells him how much tidal energy is supplied by the pull of the sun and the moon. What happens to the energy on earth is not so precisely known. Some of it distorts the "solid" earth itself, which is actually about as elastic as a steel ball bearing. The rest goes into the tides, and as I learned to my great surprise, they have never been truly measured. Tide records on shore provide a blurred picture, thrown out of focus by the continental shelf, which is thrust wedge-like into the surging ocean. The tide in mid-ocean is known only from theoretical calculations. If it could be actually measured, the picture would clear considerably. The oceanographer could then set up a budget to show how the energy of the sun and moon is spent: so much on the deep ocean, so much on friction over the shallow sea floor, and the rest for the tidal "breathing" of the solid earth. He would know the elasticity of the earth. He would know whether or not the hands of the clock have always lagged at the same rate. If tidal friction is responsible, then this rate must have varied in the past with changes in the area of the sea floor.

I had heard of the tide-measuring experiment in various ways before I visited Scripps. In May 1965, a "working group on deep-sea tides," set up by the International Association of Physical Oceanography, met in Paris and suggested a seagoing international study to solve the problem as soon as instruments were available. My first reaction was bewilderment. "Deep-sea tides" sounded contradictory to the mind that can visualize the tide only on shore. There, in its impure form, it can vary from an almost imperceptible change in an enclosed sea to a spread of fifty feet in the Bay of Fundy, between New Brunswick and Nova Scotia in Canada. One of my favorite photographs of the absurd shows fishermen at low tide on the Bay of Fundy, standing on stepladders to gather their catch from nets strung high above their heads.

Historians of oceanography never neglect to mention how the effect of tides in shallow water was observed, to his discomfiture, by Caesar in

55 B.C. when he invaded Britain on the coast of Kent. Roman seamen, like the other navigators of the ancient world, were accustomed to the almost-tideless Mediterranean and they did not drag their beached ships far enough from the water's edge. In his *Gallic War*, Caesar reported, three days after his landing: "That night there happened to be a full moon, which usually made ocean tides very high; but our men did not know this. The warships which Caesar had used to ferry the army over and had beached became waterlogged, and at the same time, the storm buffeted the transports moored at anchor. It was impossible for our men to handle the ships or do anything to save them."

When he returned to Italy for the winter, he told his legates in Gaul to build ships for another invasion the following year: "To facilitate loading and beaching, he made the ships somewhat lower than is normal in the Mediterranean; he had observed that the waves were smaller because of the frequent ebb and flow of the tides." Caesar was better as a statesman than a scientist so he must be forgiven for jumping to a conclusion on the basis of insufficient observations. He was able to make some more, no doubt, when he lost forty ships in a storm during his second invasion of Britain.

Dr. Gunther Sager, a German oceanographer who studied Caesar's misadventure, has gone into the role of the tides in the history of northern Europe. He believes they would have foiled any attempt by Napoleon or Hitler to invade England. Neither had command of the seas and both had to load their supply and troop-carrying barges in harbors protected from the tide by locks. In such ports, locks can be opened and ships can sail only on high tide. This, Sager says, would have meant a fatal halt of half a day in the invasion wave across the Channel.

Deep-sea tides had never affected the course of history, at least not on a human time scale. It was only at the Second International Oceanographic Congress held at Moscow in June 1966 that I became convinced of their existence. Dr. Walter Munk, head of the Scripps branch of the University of California's Institute of Geophysics and Planetary Physics, gave a press briefing where he described devices to measure them.

Munk was the chairman of the working group on deep-sea tides that had first met in Paris. What he and a number of others around the world were trying to do was to measure the rise and fall of the sea in mid-ocean with the flow and ebb of the tides.

Obviously this could not be done as on shore by driving a stake into the bottom. Instead of measuring height from the surface, Munk's instruments sat on the sea floor and detected changes in pressure (which amount to the same thing). They could tell the difference between tides and storm waves. They were sensitive enough to register an extra half-inch of water on top of a column three and a half miles deep. Munk and his colleagues at Scripps were sending the instruments down in capsules named after their wives, recalling them to the surface by an acoustic signal. "It is the only time our wives come when we whistle for them," Munk remarked at the press conference.

Such a discovery alone would have justified a visit to Munk's laboratory, and I had placed it high on my itinerary for Scripps. Munk was not there. While I had not written him of my intentions, any scientist capable of detecting an extra half-inch of water from such a depth can sense an approaching writer and other disturbances thousands of miles away. To obtain the tranquility he needs to flesh out the skeletons of ideas like this one which have characterized his career, Munk was on leave for a few months at Massachusetts Institute of Technology in Cambridge. Temporary migrations are often used by scientists to get away from their telephones and administrative chores. That makes them hard to find, and as I had realized, this is the purpose of the whole operation.

At Scripps, Munk's colleagues admired him not only for his scientific stature but also for his temerity. Gossip had it that he was pitching an instrument worth over $20,000 into the ocean and relying on nothing more than a few feeble beeps to get it back. "It's like throwing a Rolls-Royce overboard," one oceanographer told me at a time when he himself was trading up to a compact station wagon. Since oceanographers have far less of the taxpayers' money at their disposal than space scientists, they are far more miserly in spending it. They complain of this at times, but I do not think it is an intrinsically bad thing, within limitations. My own slant on the matter comes from associating with neglected researchers in remote places where the breakage of a laboratory vacuum pump can be a disaster. Since their countries have no space programs, they usually single out the local oceanographers as targets for their jealousy.

Give or take a few ciphers, unmanned space vehicles and tide capsules have much in common. They are both launched to explore an unfriendly environment with a fair chance of never being recovered. Both are limited in payload. The size of the space vehicle depends on the power of the rocket that puts it into orbit. The tide capsule, or any other sealed device that goes into the deep, may appear unaffected by such a restriction. Instead of fighting gravity to get out to the job, it uses it to sink to the bottom at a gentle rate. But it must work against gravity to return to the surface. It can rise only by releasing weight, for there is no question of pumping out water ballast, as is done on FLIP or conventional submarines, against outside pressures of thousands of pounds per square inch. Reserve buoyancy is the rocket fuel that it uses to go back up to the surface. Here, the designer needs a delicate touch. Too little buoyancy will keep his device down below forever, too much will break it loose before it does its job.

Analogous terms like "wet space," "inner space" or "hydrospace" have been invented as attention-getters, but they can be misleading. The designer of the space vehicle has to worry only about the difference between zero pressure outside and something close to atmospheric pressure of 14.7 pounds per square inch inside.

The builder of the deep-sea vehicle is already coping with such a difference at a depth of 33 feet. His rule of thumb is that pressure trying to cave in the walls of his capsule will rise half a pound per square inch for every foot that he drops it. At the average depth of the ocean floor, roughly 12,000 feet, water is putting its shoulder against the door at a pressure of 6,000 pounds per square inch. No such environment is likely to exist anywhere else in the solar system.

Frank Snodgrass, an engineer from Montana who has worked fifteen years with Munk, was up against this environment in building the capsules. When I phoned and told him I was interested in how he was getting along with his project on deep-sea tide measurements and wifecalling, he said I could come over to the laboratory of the Institute of Geophysics and Planetary Physics. I accepted his offer all the more enthusiastically because the laboratory is one of the most attractive buildings on the Scripps campus. While it is the usual ubiquitous combination of glass and plane surfaces, some iconoclast had the idea of framing the glass not with concrete or aluminum but redwood. The effect is that of a log cabin redesigned by Le Corbusier. I appreciated it, and so did the indigenous bird population.

Snodgrass came to Scripps in 1945, when he first worked on oceanographic instruments to earn some extra money while he was studying on the GI Bill of Rights. He has been with Munk for fifteen years, somewhat in the position of a concert artist who specializes in the works of a single prolific composer. Getting the tide capsules to play has not been his easiest performance.

First, I wanted to know how they could detect the addition of what amounted, from where they were sitting, to no more than a few glasses of water. The problem reminded me of an upside-down remake of the old fairy tale about the princess who proved her royal birth because she was able to detect a pea beneath a mountain of mattresses in her bed. Snodgrass explained that he used a "vibrating-wire pressure transducer called the Vibrotron." When he saw with whom he was dealing (ocean-ographers are so close to their work that they often fail to realize that it can sound remote to others), he put it in another way: "It's like a violin string attached to a diaphragm. When a pressure change created by a high tide or a storm pushes the diaphragm inward, the frequency of the vibrating string changes." Any parent who has listened to an adolescent tuning a guitar knows what happens when the tension of a string is changed. Inside the capsule, changes in the frequency of a vibrating tungsten string are recorded on tape, to an accuracy of a thousandth of a cycle per second. With such sensitivity, an added .04 inches of water on top of a column 22,000 feet deep can be detected.

The length of the tungsten string is also affected by temperature, which must be determined as well. Snodgrass first measured it by putting a second vibrating string to his bow, to react to changes of a millionth of a degree centigrade. He now prefers to use vibrating quartz crystals that behave the same way.

Next comes the question of getting the string to play on the bottom and of recovering its taped recordings. The tide capsule is the answer. It consists of a pair of hollow spheres two feet in diameter and made of aluminum one inch thick to withstand an operating pressure of 8,500 pounds per square inch. They are mounted almost on top of each other, looking something like a sawed-off dumbbell. The upper sphere houses a radio transmitter that signals the capsule's position when it has returned to the surface. The busier bottom sphere contains miniaturized tape re-corders and the acoustic equipment that the capsule uses to carry on conversations. All of this is powered by eight or nine automobile bat-teries on an iron frame that work merrily in seawater and serve to an-chor the capsule tethered fifty feet above.

At the end of its assignment below, the capsule fires an explosive bolt to break away from the expendable batteries and starts its slow journey upward in a two-mile-an-hour climb. The batteries are cheap, and since they fill with seawater, they need not be pressurized. "They're not a good source of power, though," Snodgrass said, and added enviously: "The space people have solar cells."

Space people can command their unmanned vehicles and gather data from them by radio. Snodgrass only has sound to carry messages back and forth. He uses a code that, unlike Morse, is based not on dots and dashes but on pings and pauses. Each message consists of sixteen "characters" represented by a sound or a silence.

"At present, we have three commands from the ship to the capsule," Snodgrass said. "The first, and the most important, is to release ballast and return to the surface. It might be eight straight pings, followed by eight pauses. With the second, we ask it to make a status check of all instruments and devices to see that they're working: the tape recorders, the pressure and temperature gauges, the batteries. The third can tell it to do a particular experiment: lay a temperature gauge an inch off the bottom, operate a water sampler, measure heat flow from the bottom. Our main effort now is in tide research, but we consider the capsule as a vehicle for any number of possible experiments.

"As for the capsule, it can either speak when it is spoken to or send a message on its own initiative. Normally, it just acknowledges our commands. I mean, if we tell it to release ballast, it first responds that it has received the order, and then in a second message, that it has obeyed it. Or else it can alert us. For example, if battery voltage drops critically, it tells us. If it springs a leak, it will sense moisture and send up a message that might be eight pings alternating with eight pauses. Even if it does not receive a reply to this message, it will automatically cut loose from its anchor and come up to the surface. There, the radio transmitter takes over.

"We always have to strike a compromise. We don't want it to stay on the bottom no matter what happens, but we don't want it to come up on the slightest excuse, either."

Snodgrass was testing the acoustic equipment of a capsule and he let me listen over a loudspeaker. The ping, lasting a hundredth of a second, was more of a chirp and it seemed to harmonize with the birds outside in the driveway.

"The pulses are only a tenth as loud in seawater, but the ship can

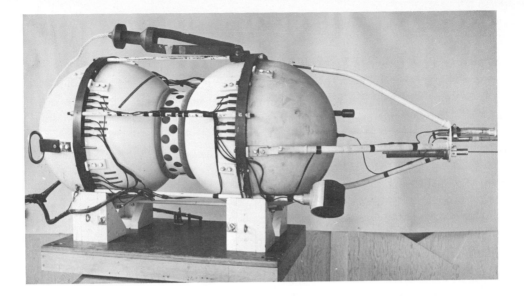

Add .04 inch to 22,000 feet of water, and the tide capsule will detect it.

"The traumatic moment when a third of our annual budget goes to the bottom": Walter Munk cuts his tide capsule free.

detect them five miles away," he remarked. "Some people say they can identify messages just by their rhythms." When he switched to an elaborate code, I did catch some kind of beat, but alternate pings and pauses sounded monotonously like a prisoner breaking rocks with a sledgehammer.

Indicating his capsule, Snodgrass said: "We're testing the circuits. Each capsule has about 400 logic circuits, and that's as big as an unabridged dictionary. We had some trouble with this one. It wasn't transmitting because of the logic in the system."

I replied with a pause of my own for digestion. I could hear the chirping of the pingers and the ticking of a recorder that was checking for moisture. Snodgrass explained that the spheres are dehydrated and filled with dry nitrogen before they are sent down. The moisture in air is enough to affect their circuits and probably render their systems illogical.

The first capsule was dropped into the sea in 1965 and, two years later, the longest any had stayed down was two weeks at a depth of 12,000 feet. Five in all have been built. They were named Judith (after Munk's wife), Kathy, Flicki, Josie and Dottie. I saw no sign of Dottie in the lab and I asked Snodgrass about it. "That's my wife's name. Dottie was the capsule that we lost right at the start, in December 1965. We lost contact with it after it reached the bottom. Either it flooded and it didn't come up, or else it surfaced and the radio beacon failed."

In the driveway, there was a big brown box, something like a packing case with a window in it. I tried to guess what it was, but I gave up. It turned out to be the Cape Kennedy of the tide capsules. "It's our portable shipboard laboratory," Snodgrass explained. "We tried to stain it redwood so that it would look better next to the building. When we want to go to sea, a truck picks it up and takes it to the ship. It only weighs 7,000 pounds, but we've got eight feet by fourteen feet of floor space. After a cruise, the truck brings it back here and we keep on working inside it. It used to take days to load or unload all this equipment. Now it's only three or four hours."

Snodgrass and I went in. The packing case contained the LORAN (LOng RAnge Navigation) equipment that brings the ship to within five miles of where it had left the capsule so that the pings can guide it the rest of the way. Kathy was in the lab for maintenance, and a dehumidifier was trying to get the best of the general moldiness left over from the last voyage. On one wall, a typewritten notice requested that the captain's place at the table be left vacant until he has eaten. Science had been containerized.

"If you've got some time, I can show you what the ship looks like without the lab," Snodgrass said. "I have to go down to the marine facility and see how they're getting along. We use the *Ellen B. Scripps*. She's only 95 feet long and 101 tons. But a big ship is a pain in the neck. Eighty scientists are always trying to use it and it's always scheduled months in advance. With the *Ellen B.*, we can go out for a week with our lab, then take it off and keep on working back here. We've been using portable labs for ten years, but we couldn't have anything bigger than six feet square without cluttering up the deck space. The *Ellen B.* was intended for just this sort of work."

Snodgrass and I drove to the marine facility on Point Loma, but I wish I could forget my impressions of the *Ellen B.* I think the generous lady is much more honored by a portrait in the Scripps library. Her soft eyes stare out from the frame that hangs above an intricate globe, on which the ocean floor has been modeled in physical relief under a transparent Plexiglass surface. She sympathized with me whenever I went to the library to try to keep track of what she and E.W. had started.

Miss Ellen deserves a more fitting memorial than the *Ellen B. Scripps*. That ship offends not only the eye but the ear as well: it is of a type known as a "botruck." Like the flat bed of a truck, the afterdeck of the *Ellen B.* is just an open space 22 feet wide and 45 feet long. When Snodgrass and I saw her, welders on her hot steel deck were removing winches used on a previous cruise. Everything had been cleared to make room for the redwood-stained laboratory and the track down which the capsules would be rolled into the sea. With that oblong box on her stern, the *Ellen B.*'s ugliness would go up by at least an order of magnitude.

She had accommodations, which I inspected politely, for eight scientists and a crew of seven. While I was at Scripps, destiny had taken the graceful *Alpha Helix* with its scientific *gemütlichkeit* to the Amazon and left me with such freaks as FLIP and the *Ellen B.* To make matters worse, the *Ellen B.* is floating on the wave of the future for small research vessels. As the converted yachts and wartime veterans used by oceanographic institutions reach the end of their lives, some will be replaced by seagoing mules with laboratory modules on their backs. The progress that the botruck represents becomes apparent when one reads how Sir Charles Wyville Thomson lived aboard H.M.S. *Challenger*, the 2,300-ton Royal Navy corvette that inaugurated the era of great oceanographic expeditions with a three-year voyage from 1873 to 1876. Sir Charles, as chief scientist, shared a 30′ by 12′ sitting room (three times the size of Snodgrass's portable lab) with the captain. When the *Challenger* sailed, she was given a send-off by a few visitors. Sir Charles recalled: "A party of sixty sat down in the handsome wardroom where we now have our general mess. We shall not soon forget the hearty British cheer of encouragement which rang out from a chorus of the voices which most influence the destiny of their country and their time." I felt like cheering myself when Snodgrass had finished his inspection of the *Ellen B.* and we were able to return to La Jolla.

Ugly duckling though she may be, the *Ellen B. Scripps* costs hundreds of dollars a day to operate. Such a figure, multiplied by the months of ship time that will be needed to measure the tides in the deep ocean, had tempted Snodgrass to concentrate on a capsule that could be left unattended on the bottom. He saw a psychological advantage, too: the kind of scientist who goes into oceanography is never enthusiastic about a voyage that involves mainly staying in one place to play nursemaid for weeks on end to an instrument.

Money is relative. Snodgrass may seem a pauper compared to the space engineer, but he is a rich American to the foreign oceanographer, for whom the $20,000 riding on Judith or Kathy or Josie when they go over the side is a tidy sum. The only others who have ventured into the measurement of deep-sea tides are the French, and they prudently tied a string to their instrument during its early stages. It was developed by Marc Eyries, chief hydrographic engineer of the French Hydrographic Service, and it works on the same vibrating-wire principle as the Snodgrass capsule. There, the resemblance ends. The wire vibrates on the bottom, but it sends its findings up a cable to a recorder on a surface ship. Despite, or perhaps because of, this built-in limitation, the French have been able to get more data from their instrument than Scripps had obtained when I saw Snodgrass. It was first tested in 1964 in about 2,000 feet of water, and the following year it took a plunge to 15,350 feet in the Atlantic off Morocco. In 1966, it even began to earn its keep, taking tide measurements on the continental shelf off Bordeaux that were used to study improvements in the city's harbor. Eyries, who manages his budget like a thrifty French housewife, later adapted his instrument so that the recorder would go down to the bottom along with the vibrating wires, leaving only a buoy on the surface to mark its position so that it could be hauled up. He keeps in close touch with Snodgrass.

Scripps and the French hoped to have their instruments ready for a meeting of the International Association of Physical Oceanography in Bern. This was part of the XIVth General Assembly of the International Union of Geodesy and Geophysics that drew nearly 3,000 scientists from sixty-nine countries to Switzerland in the autumn of 1967 and spilled over into four Swiss cities. At Bern, the oceanographers expressed unanimous enthusiasm over the ideas of a cooperative international survey of deep-sea tides and unanimous agreement that it would have to wait until the 1970's. The instruments were not ready. Both Scripps and the French reported they had been beset by "stupid failures." Their wires vibrated perfectly to the pressure of the tides, but external cables and connections were not performing satisfactorily. Water rammed its way into the slightest chink or air bubble. I felt quite humble when I saw that leaks and short circuits were enough to delay a project intended to learn what is making the world turn more slowly.

The survey will need instruments capable of working unattended on the bottom for a month. While this is tantalizingly out of reach at present, scientists from Britain, Canada, West Germany and the Soviet Union said they would be interested in buying tidal capsules from Scripps as soon as they work. Until then, efforts around the world will be concentrated on measuring tides over the continental shelf in depths of about 600 feet, where pressure is a much less formidable adversary and cheaper instruments can be used. It will be a step away from the shore and towards the deep sea. David Cartwright of the British National Institute of Oceanography announced at Bern that he is starting on his own what he hopes will become a modest international survey. He will record the tide above the continental shelf in an arc along the west coast of Britain. The strip could then be continued to the north by Norway and to the south by France.

Somewhat of an awed silence descended over the Bern meeting when it heard the description of a geophysical station that has been operating since May 1966 in the Pacific, 100 miles west of San Francisco, at a depth of 12,790 feet. Installed by the Lamont Geological Observatory of Columbia University, it is primarily intended to act as a seismological station and a watchdog to monitor nuclear explosions, but it also measures deep tides and currents. It sends its data over 100 miles of cable to shore. During the ensuing scientific discussion, one of the first questions the speaker was asked was: "How much does it cost?"

"That information is classified," he answered.

Unless someone can prove that the Martians are likely to beat us to it, such a hang-the-expenses approach could not be used for a world deep-sea tide survey requiring measurements in many places. Undersea cables, so I was informed, cost about $2,000 a mile, and there is no hope of hooking into existing ones to transmit data. They are filled to capacity with telephone calls almost before they go down. The oceanographers will have to keep writing prices into their equations for solving the tides.

The postponement of the world survey came as no surprise to Walter Munk, the father of the idea. He himself had described as "untypical" the results of a one-week trip early in 1967 when a capsule ran perfectly for five days at a depth of 4,100 feet for a floating session of his working group aboard the *Ellen B. Scripps*. He has learned by experience that technology often cannot keep pace with scientific creativeness.

In his career, Munk has explored the time spectrum of changes in the sea and the earth. He began with short ocean waves and went on to the daily and monthly peaks of the tides and the even lower frequencies of the currents in the deep. He has looked at changes on the geological time scale: the wandering of the poles as the tilt of the earth's axis changes, the waning attraction of the earth for the moon. Most oceanographers see different oceans, depending on the aperture in the time spectrum through which they are peering. It is like the blind men and the elephant: to the man studying wind-driven waves, the sea is shifting every few seconds; to another lowering current meters a few miles down, a cycle of change is measured in years. Munk is unusual in that he is still seeking new apertures in the spectrum. He once wrote: "If we could view the surface of the earth through time-lapsed photographs at intervals of one century, we would be impressed with the variability of surface features. Mountains rise, valleys broaden, and perhaps continents shift apart, with typical velocities of 1 centimeter per year. Modern gravimeters and associated instrumentation which were developed to measure the tides of the solid earth will soon be good enough to record changes even slower than those of the tides. It is here where ultra-low-frequency seismology turns into ultra-high-frequency geology."

Munk was born in Austria in 1917, but emigrated to the United States at so early an age that his native land — which he has described as "a country that boasts of several oceanographers but of no oceans" — left him with only a faint lilt of an accent that adds to his puckish charm. The more awards he is given, the more boyish he seems to become. He studied at California Institute of Technology, then took his Ph.D. at Scripps, where he was the disciple of the great Sverdrup. During the war, he and Scripps's Norwegian director worked together on the theory of waves. Munk has taken the torch from Sverdrup in a search for an explanation of how the ocean works, integrating all forces from ephemeral surface breezes to the steady rotation of the solid earth beneath the fluid sea. He is another of Scripps's living legends, although I was told by his colleagues that he is much less picturesque now than in the days when he lectured barefoot in torn shorts. A Munk lecture anywhere is an event. He has a disdain for jargon and a gift for deluding a listener into thinking that he understands the most abstruse mathematical reasoning in fluid mechanics, which Munk may call "the usual awful stuff of solving equations of motion on a rotating stratified sphere." Munk makes his audience feel they are geniuses.

He enjoys his work. A few years ago, he had succeeded in identifying waves raised by a storm in the Indian Ocean when they arrived on the coast of La Jolla on the other side of the world. To carry out his studies of how such waves move, he set up six stations on a line running from New Zealand to Alaska. Five of them were on islands and the sixth on FLIP, rearing its ugly head between Hawaii and Alaska. Munk wrote in an article for *Oceanus*, the bright quarterly published by the Woods Hole Oceanographic Institution, that he had expected to make his observations on "the remote island of Niue, where women are known to murder their husbands for eating too much." Instead, he had to settle for Tutuila in American Samoa, where he stayed 100 days, dressed most of the time in a sarong (since Tutuila's customs are not the same as those of Niue, he had his wife with him). His array of stations across the Pacific was able to detect waves from storms starting in the southern waters and to track them as they arrived in the north two weeks later. It was a long stride forward in the understanding of the ocean, but Munk could not resist the temptation to note disarmingly in *Oceanus:* "There is enough continuity in the field of wave intensity in time and space so that adequate predictions of surfing conditions at Honolulu could have been made on the basis of measurements at Tutuila some days in advance. From what I know of the surfing profession, I do not suggest this as a lucrative enterprise."

In person, Munk lived up to the advance billing of his written works. I finally tracked him to a refuge on Cape Cod where he was spending a few weeks during his stay at M.I.T. He and his family were living in a rustic motel on the edge of a forest, about as far from waves (and crowds) as they could hope to get on the Cape. He was now dressed not in a sarong or shorts but in faded blue jeans, a concession no doubt to increased age and distinction. As he talked, his strikingly handsome white-haired wife occasionally added an aside of her own. They are an inseparable couple and very pleasant to watch together.

Munk had just received a phone call from Snodgrass in La Jolla, who told him that a capsule had popped up prematurely once more, only a week after it had gone down. "Frank and I have learned an odd lesson," Munk said. "It's okay to do your damnedest with an instrument that has a thousand components, that is, a thousand connections. But when you have ten million components, you have reached a degree of complexity so great that you cannot just say: 'I am going to make it work.'

"So you can do four things. You can test every individual component; you can make systematic environmental tests like dropping the capsule on the floor or leaving it in a cold room; you can let it run for a month in the lab to check for physical failures; you can separate and analyze components, putting in redundancy to back up crucial parts that are not entirely reliable."

Mrs. Munk remarked: "You can say the hell with it."

"That makes five things," Munk said. "You know, there are times I think we may have started too soon and gone too quickly on the deep-sea tide survey. But we have time. At the rate that tidal friction is changing the configuration of the solar system, we have a billion years to finish our measurements before something happens."

What intrigues Munk is the part played by the tides in this happening. The present estimate of friction over the continental shelf is good only as far back as 10,000 years, when the seas assumed their present shape at the end of the last ice age. On the basis of the observed rate of the earth's slowing, a year should have lasted 400 days during Devonian times, 400 million years ago. Munk is bothered by studies of fossil Devonian corals that show this to be the case. Tiny striations in the corals indicate their daily growth lines, for they take up calcium carbonate only by day.

"I am suspicious because it came out so exactly," he said. "The fact that it agrees with the present rate of change seems to indicate that it is not the effect of the ocean, for we know the ocean has changed over the past 400 million years."

The possibility that a world survey may bring in a verdict of "not guilty" for the tides as a force of cosmological change does not disturb Munk at all. The tide capsule, as Snodgrass said, is only a vehicle. Munk wants to use it to get instruments to the bottom to measure any number of things that could help explain what makes the ocean run.

The flow of heat up from the sea floor, minute though it may be compared to what the sun pours in at the surface, is strong enough to create a temperature inversion just off the bottom, where water becomes slightly warmer. The capsules will be able to measure this heat and its variations.

Another problem he is thinking about is the generation of electric currents by the deep tides as they move through the earth's magnetic field like the rotor of a dynamo. These electric currents depend on two present unknowns: the deep tides and the conductivity of the earth itself. Once the tides have been measured, the conductivity can be estimated. Since conductivity is dependent on heat, this estimate can then be turned around to indicate how temperatures are distributed deep within the earth. In turn, if temperature distribution is known, it may be possible to chart the stresses that lead to earthquakes and volcanic activity. I remembered the temperamental capsules and their balky connections. For want of a nail . . .

Munk is happiest when he can sit alone and work, but he refuses to stay at a desk and let others go to sea for the data he needs. He manages to have his cake and to eat it, even if it means coming to grips with the frustrations of working at sea.

"I'm worried how to space those capsules when we make our tide stations," he said.

"Instruments are not Walter's specialty," his wife said. "He's really a sailor."

Instrumentation is only a means to an end. Munk has already thought out a further mission for the depth capsule. He wants it to carry down current meters to track the ponderous movement of the deep ocean.

Munk likes to remark that, in the past thirty-five years, oceanographers have been able to raise the record duration of deep current observations only from six to forty-eight days. "We need a year to make sense out of the deep currents," he said. "We have three priorities: long, longer, and longer records. That is why I am at Cambridge. I am trying to see what else can be done with these instruments.

"It may sound hard to put a piece of gear down, then pick it up a month later. It's an engineering challenge, but the intellectual challenge is just as great. The tide survey will lead to new problems that cannot be visualized.

"I'll bet you a bottle of champagne that we'll have those capsules out on an international tide study in ten years. But in two years, we'll have a couple of instruments just doing long recordings. What we are really trying to get at now are the long-time systems of currents. Remember, if we want to measure anything with a period of three days, we need 100 cycles — 100 little wiggles that will take 900 days to collect. If we can do this simultaneously in a few places, we will be able to solve a number of problems. I think that's how we'll spend the next twenty years before we get too sterile."

Munk smiled as boyishly as ever. He had not changed since the days in the Fifties when he did his own skin diving to investigate coral formations in the Pacific. He is considered one of the world's leading theoreticians on the circulation of the ocean. He runs a laboratory in La Jolla which consists of a dozen scientists — "eleven better than I am." He helped Snodgrass to nurse the tide capsule through its childhood diseases until it finally stayed down for a month. As a consummate diplomat, and an internationalist in deeds rather than words, he is mobilizing scientists from half a dozen nations for that deep-sea tide survey with its many implications.

But he makes it all sound so easy.

9. In Sight of Land

Meeting people like Munk was a stimulating but exhausting experience. To rest my weary mind, I got into the habit of taking long walks on the beach where I could go from sublime science to ridiculous sandpipers. Scurrying little birds with thin spoonbills and knees bent in reverse would escort me beyond Scripps Pier, the northernmost part of the La Jolla beach that can be reached on wheels. After the pier, everything belonged to the sandpipers. The boldest surfers thinned out in a couple of hundred yards. A mile farther on, a tumble of rocks marked the head of Scripps Canyon, diving steeply into the sea a quarter of a mile out. Only at low tide could the rocks be skirted by wading. At high water, they formed a crooked stile of misplaced stones, all at wrong angles. Beyond the rocks, the lonely beach spun out in the sun next to a parallel cliff. There must have been lawns, split-levels, golf courses and freeways lapping up to the brink of the cliff, but I made it a point never to find out. The firm sand gave me a free way of my own. Every now and then, to the snickering of the gulls, I would try to run on it (posters in La Jolla told me to "Run for Your Life"), and to my astonishment I could.

By the time I turned back, I was ready for another losing battle of wits with science.

If I had thought I was getting away from the concerns of oceanography, I was under a delusion. As soon as anyone sets foot on a beach and opens a bottle of suntan lotion, he becomes as important a "user of the marine environment" as the herring fisherman, the freighter captain and the offshore oil driller. Estimates on how much money the United States alone sinks into the ocean annually vary from $3 billion to $48 billion (if one includes the Navy). To simplify matters, the New York *Times* once came up with $10 billion and concluded that 20 percent of this was represented by "marine recreation." That would make $2 billion a year that Americans spend on everything from powerboats to snorkel tubes, and the sum is doubtless conservative. Without beaches and waterfronts, real estate values would drop several times this figure. A few summers ago, the city of New York spent $400,000 just to pump sand along thirteen blocks of Rockaway Beach, an item of offshore urban renewal amounting to $30,770 per city block. The highest figure I have heard for expenditure by Americans on the pursuit of happiness in the ocean is $8 billion, half on fishing, and half on boating (swimming is not even included). It comes from the highest source, Dr. Edward Wenk, Jr., executive secretary of the National Council on Marine Resources and Engineering Development set up by the White House.

The sea is the prime raw material of the recreation industry, a term that no Puritan or Victorian could have comprehended. It has changed the economic map of Europe. Every summer, the money in the chilly north empties as if a stopper had been pulled and drains onto the coasts of Spain, Portugal, Greece and Yugoslavia to buy sun. Leningrad on the Neva moves to Sochi on the Black Sea. Jets thundering into the airport on the island of Majorca make it Europe's busiest in August. As the beaches crowd to a point beyond the compressibility of human flesh, bolder souls strike out for the shores of North Africa and Israel. I know an island myself off the French coast where the vineyards run down to the pines, the pines run down to the sea, no planes can land and no cars are allowed, but I whisper its name only to close friends.

The greatest flotilla ever known is represented by pleasure craft. My friend at the Chase Manhattan Bank gave me an informative brochure telling me how to tie knots, run a channel, set a course, hoist a distress signal and, almost as an anticlimax, negotiate a boat loan. His smile probably would have chilled if I had told him I was interested in farming fish, mining gold on the continental shelf or tapping any of the other potential sources of ocean wealth described by the Sunday supplements. Right now, the most profitable species on and in the ocean is man.

He prefers to do his swimming and sailing in sight of land. For every Sir Francis Chichester bucketing alone around the world, there must be thousands of amateur seamen ready to fight for their freedom to tie up at a marina at the end of a day's outing. Space is as limited in harbors as it is on beaches. Frightful blunders have been commited in trying to extend it. In a formerly paradisiacal Mediterranean town I now avoid, the harbor was enlarged to the point where it polluted all the beaches, thereby sentencing so-called vacationers to two hours of daily commuting just to get a swim. The story is repeated in different versions everywhere. Human beings continue to dump their industrial and household waste into the ocean all week long and complain when they have to swim in it on Sunday.

Beaches are touchy. They change with the seasons, or overnight after a storm, or even by the hour with the tides and currents. In many places, beaches steadily recede before the ocean waves, to the despair of the human waves from land. They exist precariously, and where they do not exist, they are being invented. With their adjoining waters, they form what is probably the most valuable, but certainly not the most-studied, resource of the sea. Oceanographers forsake them as ships become more available to answer the call of the remote unknown. At the institutions I know, only a few scientists remain purposely stranded.

Dr. Douglas Inman is in this sedentary category at Scripps and likes it. He wears the healthy, bronzed look of a "specialist in nearshore processes." His childhood doubtless got the wanderlust out of his system. As the son of a Marine Corps officer and a schoolteacher, he was born on Guam and grew up in China, the Philippines and Nicaragua. He became a physicist, did some work on geology and sedimentation and found, like so many others, that such disparate interests could be best fulfilled in oceanography. He earned his doctorate in 1952 as part of the first postwar class at Scripps that now constitutes much of the marine scientific Establishment.

Inman quickly turned to inshore oceanography, attracted as he was by the "intense interaction of waves, currents and tides," on and off the beach. He was fascinated by their complexity, and he still is. "It's not just air-sea interaction, it's all interactions. It's the full spectrum and yet there are not too many men in this field. I'm here because people tend to steer away from it. I don't mind if they do. I think that 90 percent of all deep-sea oceanography is damn boring."

As a rara avis, the inshore oceanographer is too much in demand to be bored. Inman has been called by the Navy across the Pacific to investigate problems of artificial harbors, and by the state of California to a spot only a ten-minute drive from his office to advise on an artificial reef to attract first game fish and then sport fishermen. Kelp growers, whose harvest is best known to consumers as the algin that keeps their ice cream ice-free, ask for his help. Periodic crises arise when a tanker runs aground and threatens to spill oil on beaches.

Inman is much more flexible in his operations than his deepwater colleagues. Since his fleet consists of small boats launched from the davits on Scripps Pier, he need not schedule trips months in advance. He can walk to his station on the end of the pier where he measures waves with an electronic stake — a "digital staff" which records straight onto magnetic tape. He keeps trying to put arrays of these staffs in the surf zone to get both the power and the direction of the waves near shore, just as Munk tracked the swell of the deep Pacific from his island stations. Munk had his problems, Inman has others. Surfers and powerboats slam into the staffs and wreck experiments. "It's not sharks, wind and waves that are our worst hazard," Inman said. "It's people." Uncooperative though they may be, surfers are unwitting students of the ocean themselves. The wisest, or the laziest, among them use rip currents to carry them away from shore so they can get a free round trip. Water brought into the beach by waves first moves in a longshore current, then heads back to sea as a narrow rip current moving as fast as five miles per hour. This is the so-called undertow that actually exists only in the rip current zones. Experienced swimmers, unlike surfers, avoid it by simply swimming parallel to the shore until they are clear of the current.

Inman enjoys the advantage of dealing with a tangible quantity, the sand of the beaches. Several years ago, he and Dr. T. K. Chamberlain decided that two grains of sand need not necessarily be alike. They took about two pounds of sand from the sea floor off Scripps Beach, separated the quartz grains making up 68 percent of their sample, and mailed them off to Oak Ridge to be irradiated with phosphorus-32, a radioactive isotope that presented no apparent danger either to scientists or swimmers. When the sample came back from Oak Ridge, it was taken 750 feet offshore and spread on the bottom in ten feet of water by a diver.

To track the movement of the tagged sand, divers took down cards coated with grease and pressed them onto the bottom. The cards were then brought up and placed against photosensitive film, where the irradiated grains left their trace. This was done five times in twenty-four hours while instruments kept watch on waves and currents.

It was a calm day with waves only a foot and a quarter high. To Inman's surprise, the sand on the bottom was not at all quiescent in such gentle weather. The fingerprints that his divers took of the bottom showed that the marked sand had moved more than twenty feet during the first quarter hour after the sample had been opened. In twenty-four hours, the sample was spread over three-quarters of a square mile.

Inman and his crew can now actually watch the sand while it moves. Off Scripps Pier, they have set up what looks like a small section of fence on the bottom with lights hanging over it. The fence is a reference grid divided into rectangles. When the lights go on, a diver sprawled on the bottom makes a movie of the sand dancing in front of the grid. Instruments simultaneously record the strength of the waves that are making it dance.

If Southern California is not worriedly looking over the diver's shoulder as he takes his pictures, it should be. Multiply the dancing sand grains by an appropriate number and the result is Inman's definition of a beach on this coast as a "river of sand." He has divided the shoreline from Santa Barbara south to La Jolla into four such river systems, or "littoral sedimentation cells."

As he explained it to me, most of the sand on these beaches is supplied by erosion of rocks and soil far inland, an apparently limitless source of supply on a human time scale. Streams carry the eroded material to the coast to form the source of the sand river. The ocean starts the river flowing in two steps. First, waves pluck sand particles from the bottom and keep them in suspension, as the underwater movies show. The weak longshore current that drifts south along this coast could not move very much sand from the bottom, but it has no trouble transporting the grains obligingly suspended in mid-water by the waves. The sand river moves south, feeding the beaches that lie on its course. Finally, it meets the submarine canyon that marks the end of the cell and there it drains out to sea, lost forever to the beaches to the south. These beaches belong to the next cell that is fed once more by streams on land.

The littoral cell is one of those natural machines that work perfectly until human beings start tinkering with them. Such interference along the coast of Southern California has led to a tragedy of errors. If it continues, Inman gloomily foresees that "beaches around here will become something we remember from our childhood." The first act has usually been the construction of an artificial harbor whose breakwater slows the longshore current and cuts the flow of sand to beaches downstream along the coast. At the same time, the harbor is silted by the sediments that streams bring down from land and deposit behind the breakwater out of the longshore current's reach. In the next act, the streams on land are dammed to keep the harbor clear, thereby choking off the main supply source for the beaches in the cell. All that is left of the natural machine is the exhaust pipe, the submarine canyon that keeps channeling the sand, now a nonrenewable resource, into deep water.

As usual, my own observations did not appear to fit those of science. There was plenty of sand at La Jolla, and Inman himself told me that Scripps Beach was wider than it had been in years. The sand in my shoes was being supplied by a spate of new harbors to the north. In the short run, an artificial harbor may appear to improve the situation when sand removed by dredging operations is pumped onto the beach and placed in circulation.

"Unfortunately, we can't continue to build harbors forever," Inman said. "Sooner or later we will have to find a permanent way of replenishing our beaches." He could see several, to be used separately or in conjunction. In certain cases, submarine canyons could be dammed to stop sand from running away to sea and keep it moving past the beaches. Where such an engineering feat is not possible, Inman suggests that a detached breakwater be built upstream from the canyon. Unlike the more familiar variety, a detached breakwater is parallel, not perpendicular, to the shore. If placed close enough, it will cast a "wave shadow" on the coast. Behind the breakwater and in the shadow, the energy of the waves is reduced and sand settles to the bottom as it does in a sluggish river. Then the sand could be either pumped or hauled to the upper end of the littoral cells, where it could start its journey down again in a man-made cycle.

Inshore oceanography is practiced by Douglas Inman (below) in experiments to measure behavior of breaking waves.

Inman keeps emphasizing that any interference with a littoral cell, whether the building of an artificial harbor or the damming of a river, will imply such corrective steps sooner or later. "I am always struck by the way it happens. It's nothing but haphazard planning or none at all. Not so long ago, we decided to spend a weekend at Palm Springs for a change of climate. But so many swimming pools and circular sprinkling systems have been installed there that the place was humid and muggy. People were complaining about corrosion in the desert. These things are like Los Angeles. You wake up one morning and wonder what the hell you can do about it."

Even if he could, Inman would not stand in the way of California's march into the sea. Dissatisfied with what God hath wrought, the state is correcting the deficiencies in its coastline. Prices of acreage on land make artificial islands and offshore marinas a tempting prospect. Inman is all for them as long as they are planned properly. They could serve as detached breakwaters to protect beaches, but they must be far enough out so they will not halt his river of sand in the wrong places.

He is closely following the construction of Los Angeles's big nuclear desalinizing plant on an artificial island 5,000 feet from shore. An island, if properly designed so that it will not be chewed away by breaking waves, is ideal for an operation that requires an unlimited supply of sea-water and plenty of room to separate it from uneasy neighbors. The building of the nuclear plant means that a string of detached breakwaters should be placed in the sea to control water and sand circulation all the way to the end of this particular cell in Newport Submarine Canyon. Water must circulate to keep the sea ventilated. "Without ventilation, we will always get smog, in an oceanographic sense," Inman said.

The nearshore region is being changed to provide more facilities for fish as well as for people. Inman cooperated in the planning of a 1,200-foot artificial reef of rock, placed a mile out to sea just north of Scripps Canyon in 70 feet of water. Such reefs are a little-known but highly entertaining instance of how man has already begun to farm the sea, if only for fun. Fishermen have always known they can expect good catches over wrecks, and for centuries the Japanese have made reefs of rocks. The Second World War greatly increased the supply of wrecks off the coast of the United States, but there were not enough of them in the convenient places. Rather than start another war, which would be something like burning houses to roast pigs, American fish and game authorities in nearly a dozen states, including Hawaii, have been putting fish dwellings on the bottom. Almost anything will do: defective concrete pipe, junked car bodies wired together, retired streetcars, a sunken dry dock, loads of bricks, old tires weighted with concrete, and even prefabricated apartments for fish. A booklet written by Iris Unger and published by the American Littoral Society tells how a Florida fishing club put down a reef consisting of 60 car bodies, one bus body, a dozen stoves, a dozen engines, 40 refrigerators (not recommended — they can float back up), 30 truck bodies, and two tons of chain and pipe. Fish prefer rocks, but the possibility of beautifying land by dumping eyesores into the sea is an appealing one. Old car bodies do not last long in seawater and there is a steady market for them here, if nowhere else.

Placed on a flat sandy bottom, reefs of any material draw small fish seeking shelter from their big enemies, who in turn follow them there. Everyone lives happily on the reef until the sportsman drops his line, and then he lives happily. His fish have been concentrated for him at a safe point close enough to shore so that the risk is all theirs. Hemingway's old man would curl his toes at the whole business, but it's no worse than raising game animals in a forest and then turning hunters loose on them.

I had the impression that Inman did not have too much use for the crowd fishing the artificial reefs. He told me that the buoy over the one near Scripps Canyon had broken loose and the state fish and wildlife authorities had lost their reef. "I'm willing to find it for them, but I'll wait until they ask me," he said. Inman was not the only oceanographer I met who looks askance at the sport fisherman's insistence that the ocean be remodeled to suit his tastes. There were others who maintained that the sardine would still run off California if commercial fishermen had gone after the competing anchovy. Pressure from sportsmen "protected" the anchovy so that it could feed the tunas they wanted to catch. I sympathize with the oceanographers, but one must be open-minded: an estimated 17 million Americans fish for fun in salt water, while only 130,000 do it for a living. Such are the cockeyed economics of affluence.

Inman does not think that man-made structures offshore need be reserved for fish, nuclear desalinizing plants or owners of pleasure boats. Scientists belong on them, too, and he has devoted much thought to the matter. Scripps Pier frustrates him; it runs out 1,000 feet and ends in about 20 feet of water.

"If it were built out another 1,000 feet, the outer edge would be in

100 feet of water," he said. "Then Scripps would be not just a laboratory or a home for seagoing scientists, but a place where one could get into the ocean." If the pier were extended to 3,000 feet, it would overlook Scripps Canyon at a depth of 600 feet. Inman is willing to settle for 100 feet of water in a first stage.

As he sees it, the pier would be turned into a causeway leading to an artificial island. He thinks it would be simpler to build a cylindrical caisson that could be floated out to the site and planted on bedrock than to dump rocks in the sea as the Richfield Oil Company did when it created Rincon Island as a drilling site off Ventura, California.

Scripps Island could serve as a haven for small ships and a port of call for bigger ones, thereby cutting out much of the shuttling between La Jolla and the Point Loma marine facility. It could handle small research submersibles, lowering them into the water or storing them high and dry. Inman has a good talking point here. I never realized it, but one of the worst problems of the small submersible is getting it into and out of the water. The Navy calls this "going through the air-sea interface," an understatement of what goes on when a mother ship and its child are pitching or rolling at different rates and divers are scrambling between the two to get a line on the sub.

A major contribution of the island would be as a permanent base for man-in-the-sea operations. Divers could enter the sea from a lock at the foot of the caisson and carry out underwater experiments. Their range could be extended by small domes on the sea floor around the island, where they could plug into outlets of piped oxygen and recharge their breathing apparatus. After working in deeper water towards Scripps Canyon, they could stop at way stations on the bottom to decompress on their return to the island. Once inside the caisson, they could complete their decompression at intermediate points on the way up.

Inman visualizes the island with a diameter of 200 to 500 feet, depending on where it is placed. "It has to be out four or more diameters or else it will cast a wave shadow and ruin Scripps Beach," he explained, preaching what he practices. The island is little more than a gleam in Inman's eye at present because funds have yet to be allocated for a survey of the project. Several firms have expressed interest in the idea and he showed me a preliminary proposal by one of them, Ocean Science and Engineering, Inc., which is based in Washington, and headed by Willard Bascom, formerly of Scripps and now, as then, one of the most imaginative and colorful figures in the marine environment.

To package the facilities that Scripps wants, Bascom's firm has come up with an island resembling a nautilus (which also happens to be the firm's trademark). It foresees a spiral-shaped office building in the center surrounded by landscaped grounds, fish tanks, a training pool for divers, a parking lot and a heliport. In the drawing I saw, a traveling crane runs on tracks around the rim of the island to handle small boats. Into the lower deck of the island would be crammed more fish tanks, a marine biology laboratory, instrument rooms, and facilities for divers. It would lead out to berthing space for ships and a dry dock for launching research submersibles. There would be two ways of getting into the sea: a wet shaft for divers and a dry shaft at ordinary atmospheric pressure for observers behind portholes.

I would not dream of influencing Scripps's final choice of an island-builder, which probably will not be made for a few years, but I have a weakness for Bascom's presentation of the problem. He insists on aesthetics, with "a distinctive building to symbolize the 'more stately mansions' that lie ahead in marine research — surrounded by pools, plantings, and the Ocean." I foresaw the advent of the underwater realtor, and so did Bascom. His firm estimated that the island would create 74,000 square feet of land and 60,000 square feet of laboratory space. "If one values the new land at $100 per square foot (compared with values of $50 to $500 per square foot in choice business areas of large cities), the land alone is worth $7.4 million," its proposal stated. The new land might be worth more than the cost of the entire island.

Real estate was the last resource that I expected to come out of the sea, but it is already a precious one, at least around a megalopolis. I can almost see the time when courses at Scripps will include ocean business administration. As it is, Inman and his associates must flee to Baja California in Mexico whenever they want to study a natural beach untouched by human hands and cupidity. Like other species, the oceanographers are being driven to Lower California to seek nature as it once existed in Upper California.

If I wanted to know what offshore living would be like for scientists, I did not have to go very far. The Navy Electronics Laboratory on Point Loma, right next to the Scripps marine facility, has been operating an oceanographic research tower off Mission Beach since 1959. Inman, too, had thought of using a tower at first but decided that La Jolla needed a scientific marina, as well as a permanent oceanographic station. While the Navy's tower was not built as a model apartment for future subdivisions rooted in the sea floor, I was tempted to regard it as such. No doubt I had been reading too many books by writers worrying about where we will all live in the year 2000. One of them, a very serious work, was written by an Englishman who suggests that the only way to solve his country's space problem is to house the whole population off-shore, and reserve dry land for constructive leisure pursuits in a natural and uncrowded setting.

I had another reason for visiting the Navy tower. It had been con-ceived by Dr. Eugene LaFond, whom I had first met during the year he spent in Paris as deputy director of UNESCO's office of oceanography when he took leave from his job as head of the marine environment division of the Navy Electronics Laboratory. I got along with him very well and I still do, but he remains a mystery to me. He and his wife, Katherine, look like a sweet couple who should be concerned with gar-dens and grandchildren. She is actually a chemical oceanographer in her own right and they have sailed most of the seven seas together on re-search cruises. They both worked for Scripps during the hard times of the Thirties when, LaFond told me, the standard salary was $100 a month for everyone from the janitor up to, but not quite including, the director. Their idea of relaxation is to putter around Mission Bay in an old sailboat or spend a few days aboard a trailer in the desert. Bald and almost frail, LaFond is the most unmilitary of men, yet the sea view from his office on Point Loma is all battleship gray and I had to don a security badge to see him. I do know that he gave up a year of his inten-sive research on internal waves to come to UNESCO in Paris. I know that, as a Fulbright professor of physical oceanography, he gave up two more years to teach in Andhra University at Visakhapatnam on the east coast of India, the Bay of Bengal side of the Indian Ocean. I certainly did not hear this from him, but he is considered one of he fathers of Indian oceanography. During the International Indian Ocean Expedition, he was chief scientist of the American research vessel *Anton Bruun* on a biological cruise in the Bay of Bengal. He had toured univer-sities and research centers in India to explain the ship's program and se-lect Indian scientists to participate in it. Once, I asked him why he had gone to all this effort in a field so far removed from his own. He did not talk about the need to bring the light of science to the "third world" (he's done it so well precisely because he doesn't talk about it). LaFond spluttered: "Look, I'm a physical oceanographer. I've written 150 papers in physical oceanography. But now I want to do something for somebody. If I were a carpenter, I could build houses for people. But I'm not. Oceanography is the only thing I know."

LaFond has never shied away from new ways to study the ocean. With the development of the aqualung, he promptly became a scuba diver. Another means of doing oceanography under water was offered by the fleet submarine. He was senior scientist on the U.S.S. *Skate* when she made her first cruise to the Arctic and surfaced through the ice at the North Pole. Eight other surfacings were made through openings in the ice; otherwise, the submarine traveled in the Arctic under ice as much as 100 feet thick. With acoustic equipment, it was possible to determine the slope of the bottom of the ice field; other equipment allowed the measurement of light, temperature and salinity, and the collection of plankton and water samples while cruising underwater. LaFond, who made five cruises to the Arctic, has the distinction of having circumnavigated the globe in 20 minutes (that is, he sailed around the North Pole under the ice in a circle with a two-mile radius).

He is one of the few men in the world who have done thorough scientific work with small submersibles. He has made eleven dives in all, starting with the *Trieste* bathyscaphe. Nine dives were aboard *Deepstar 4000*, which the Navy chartered from its owner, the Westinghouse Corporation. About a dozen members of his laboratory and guest scientists were able to use *Deepstar* for studies of marine life, the structure of the sea floor and the properties of seawater. *Deepstar* is an appealing little craft that has been evolved from Cousteau's original *Diving Saucer*. It has the same basic shape of a slightly flattened bug, but it wears a brow that holds instruments for taking measurements and water samples. *Deepstar* carries a crew of three: a pilot and one observer lie on their stomachs with their eyes glued to portholes; a second observer sits and tends the recording instruments. I asked LaFond if I could come along on a dive and he turned me down. The cost of a day's operation of that waterbug would have supported my family for a respectable number of months.

LaFond feels that his laboratory got its money's worth from *Deep-*

star, both in data and in discoveries. On one dive off San Diego, he was gazing out his window when the pilot told him: "Look . . . look!" Coming towards them was a fish, its eyes "as large as dinner plates." The pilot later said it was 40 to 50 feet long. LaFond, whose reach was smaller, cut the estimate to 30 feet. It was a big one, gray-black and resembling a sea bass. It flicked its tail at *Deepstar*, close enough for both pilot and observer to agree at least on the size of the tail: four feet tall and frayed at the edges, a sign of age in a fish. On another dive, 3,000 feet down in the flat basin off San Pedro, LaFond found absolutely nothing, a lifeless desert. The bottom was covered with an unappetizing layer of "fine, brown, flocculent organic matter." Instead of the sea cucumbers, the snail-like gastropods and the sablefish he was accustomed to meet at this depth, LaFond saw only death. *Deepstar*'s camera caught a dead squid and a halibut-like fish that was already decomposing. LaFond released some dye into the water and it remained almost stationary near the submersible, enabling him to estimate that it was moving only about 50 feet an hour. Sixteen water samples taken by bottles on *Deepstar*'s brow showed too little oxygen to support life. The unfortunate squid and its neighbor had doubtless swum into the area and suffocated there. Even the worms were gone, although photographs showed tubes half an inch high on the bottom, left perhaps by a species needing little or no oxygen. LaFond noted that, according to unconfirmed reports, poisonous chemicals had been dumped into the area and a sewage outfall was nearby. He concluded that the desert was due mainly to the cuplike shape of the basin, creating a stagnant pool with not enough circulation to allow water rich in oxygen to enter. Decomposing animals that had fallen from the upper layers used up the small amount of oxygen available on the bottom.

The submarine desert and the old giant fish were bonuses for LaFond, who did not ride *Deepstar* just to look around. "When I am down there, I do three things," he said. "First, I try to measure current on the bottom. This is done by placing a current meter on the sea floor and recording the revolutions of its propeller. In addition, we release a fluorescein dye, as we did in the San Pedro basin, and this also shows us the speed of the current. Then we have a frame with streamers hanging from it. It looks like a jungle gym. The streamers give us the direction of currents and, with the dye patterns, show turbulence. Secondly, we do some precise chemical sampling. From a surface ship, I never know exactly where I'm sampling; I might be stirring up mud all the time. With *Deepstar*, I can close a sample bottle six inches off the bottom, then another at a foot and another at two feet." Big though the ocean may be, its most important areas are the slender boundaries where water meets the bottom or air meets the water. Analysis of the samples tells the presence near the bottom of more phosphates, nitrates and silicates, those fertilizing nutrients.

Finally, he measures the flow of heat from sediments into the water. *Deepstar* carries a three-foot proboscis, a probe sensitive to temperature changes of a thousandth of a degree, that it thrusts into the bottom six inches at a time. What LaFond hopes to find is enough heat from the bottom to start convection so that water will rise, just as it does when one lights a burner under a pot. The experiment requires *Deepstar* to lie quietly on the mud, its proboscis poised over the bottom. Then mercury ballast is pumped forward, *Deepstar* bows down and the probe goes in.

Deepstar's pilots can think of any number of things they would rather do than sit in the mud. On one dive LaFond described to me, the bottom temperature had been measured and it was time to go up. The pilot shoved a lever to drop a 70-pound ascent weight. Nothing happened. He shoved another lever to get rid of 140 pounds of trim weight.

"The motors were on, but we were barely rising," LaFond said. "We made it up to 2,000 feet. It was a long run and the batteries were getting low. The pilot was cussing me: 'When we hit the bottom like that, we pick up mud. We can't do your type of dive.' At 2,000 feet we were sinking again. I could see the little white particles of marine 'snow' — it's really organic matter — going up outside the window.

"The pilot called up on the acoustic telephone: 'We're sinking.' They ordered him to blast the brow off. I told him: 'No, my water samplers are out there.' I guess there was a big conference topside. We had been coming up for two hours. It was cold, too, though we were wearing sweaters. The temperature inside the sub was only 40 degrees.

"We had two alternatives; we could drop either our batteries or our mercury ballast. The pilot opened the mercury valve. Nothing came out. He hooked up a nitrogen tank and blew it out. We dumped 170 pounds of mercury at $10 a pound. It cost $1,700 to get the snow outside the portholes to go down again instead of up. When we reached the surface, we looked under the craft. All the weights we thought we had dropped were still there."

I think one reason why LaFond enjoys working for the Navy is that he will go to any lengths to get masses of data from the ocean and the Navy munificently lets him try. Since he succeeds more often than he fails, he is a good investment for his employers. His laboratory operates the *Marysville*, a converted escort vessel that I saw in dock on Point Loma. She carried a great reel near her stern, on which there seemed to be an oversized black garden hose. The hose was composed of a chain of metal links; it weighed 18 tons and was 900 feet long. Every twenty-five feet, an instrument that measures temperature electrically had been inserted into a link. At sea, the *Marysville* unreels the chain into the water and tows it along at six knots, its bottom end 750 feet down with a 2,300-pound weight to keep it there. The chain goes through the water like a knife, literally taking a temperature slice of the sea. Since 1961, LaFond told me, the *Marysville* has steamed 50,000 miles in the North Pacific from off South America to the Gulf of Alaska and westward to the Sea of Japan, dragging that chain like Marlowe's ghost. She has brought back a temperature profile of the Pacific that could be duplicated only by a ship stopping every 40 yards to lower a string of thermometers as I had seen done on the *T-441*.

A temperature profile meets the Navy's constant need to know how fast sound travels in the sea and where it is going. It also meets LaFond's need to know the movements of the crests and troughs of waves within the ocean, a subject on which he is one of the world's foremost authorities.

LaFond tried to explain internal waves to me a number of times. It was like trying to explain an Alpine glacier to an Amazon Indian. I will just have to take the word of LaFond and my other patient teachers that the ocean is not simply a tub of salt water but a cake of many layers, differentiated by their temperature and density. Winds, storms, tides, currents and changes in atmospheric pressure rumple these layers constantly by sending internal waves through them. LaFond has never seen a wave far below the surface, but he can follow its crests and troughs. Imagine a diver who decides that he wants to stay in water of 16 degrees C. (60.7 degrees F.) and takes a thermometer down with him to keep in this layer of the cake, the "16-degree isotherm," by swimming up or

Above, Eugene LaFond adjusts water-sampling bot-tles on DEEPSTAR 4000. *Below, the Navy oceanographic research tower off Mission Beach.*

down. LaFond does the same with an instrument preset to remain at a given temperature and suspended from a boom over the surface. If the water chills or warms, the instrument tells the temperature sensor hanging from the boom to move up or down. The sensor's depth — or the depth of the isotherm — goes onto a chart as a record of internal waves, a row of irregular humps.

They looked irregular to me. LaFond, driven to desperation by the most obtuse student he had ever had from La Jolla to Visakhapatnam, took a piece of paper and scribbled more humps over it, some smooth and others jagged. "These are surface waves," he said. "Surface waves are somewhat analogous to the invisible internal waves. They oscillate with the wind stress, with humps every eight or ten seconds. There are also groups of surface waves which have a period of around two minutes. They're caused by seiches, the same oscillating motion that water takes in a bathtub when you get out quickly — but in the small confines of the bathtub, the period is only about one second. Then, on the surface, we find waves with a frequency of around 17 minutes and created by storms and earthquakes. Other surface oscillations which are caused by the tide and sun have periods of 12 and 24 hours.

"Now, internal waves on the density 'boundaries' do not have short periods like the wind waves because the density difference between warm and cold water is less than that of the air and water boundary. The most common invisible wave recorded by temperature changes occurs as a hump every eight to ten minutes. There are also crests and troughs every 12 and 24 hours similar to the surface waves."

His pencil moved to a foothill that appeared every three to five days as the effect of weather. A monthly hump represented the internal wave driven by the high spring tides when the sun and the moon are in line and pulling in the same direction on the earth. Then a high peak and a low valley left by summer and winter, the wave whose crest comes by once a year. LaFond had sketched the imprint of most of the seen and unseen forces in the ocean.

To watch these forces for a year or more, he had to be able to keep his instruments in one place. An oceanographic research tower was the answer and he badgered the Navy into building one within commuting distance of his laboratory. Besides the study of internal waves, a host of other uses have been found for it, as is the case with any new technique. It has become a scientific settlement on top of the sea, with a floating population of oceanographers from the Navy and civilian institutions who can pursue a wide range of interests on and under it.

The tower stands eight-tenths of a mile off Mission Beach in 60 feet of water, a depth exactly halfway between the 20 feet at the end of Scripps Pier and the 100 feet that Inman hopes to reach with Scripps Island. The very fact that it stands there is an achievement. LaFond was determined to avoid any repetition of the "Texas tower" accidents during the 1950's when one structure was toppled by a storm. He planted his house on four legs, slanted outwards to give greater stability and welded to four steel pins driven another 63 feet down through soft sediment to bedrock. For nearly ten years now, it has stood up to the Pacific Ocean.

The Navy Electronics Laboratory began its colonization of the sea surface with a modest one-room outpost perched on stilts. To meet the needs of a growing population of visiting scientists, suburbs were added by building two more rooms, on the north and south sides of the original house. Three horizontal booms, the biggest 40 feet long, have further increased the area of the sea that the tower can cover.

In LaFond's eyes, the only disadvantage of the tower is that it can't move (although, as he says, this is an advantage for the study of internal waves). He presented me with a report he had done showing that the tower was built for only one-fifteenth the price of a research ship, and could be run for a year at one-eighth the cost of operating a ship. Clear and beautifully illustrated, the report reflected LaFond's original profession as a draftsman. He is another of the men who learned oceanography by doing it. His old skill at projecting on paper stands him in good stead when it comes to explaining his ideas to busy admirals who can scan pictures and drawings faster than banks of turgid scientific prose.

LaFond's report was the only prospectus I had ever seen for real estate 60 feet under water at low tide, but it sold the tower to me and I expressed a desire to look at my purchase. Nothing easier, said the report: it was only fifteen minutes from the station with a free bus service. The station was Quivira Basin on Mission Bay and the bus a Navy LCPL (Landing Craft Personnel Light, a ghastly name for a trim 34-foot launch impeccably maintained). The launch made four round trips a day, giving the tower better bus service than La Jolla.

I went out there one afternoon with LaFond on the one o'clock bus. Like the *T-441*, the Navy launch idled at one knot through Mission Bay and picked up speed only after it had cleared the channel, taking a few nasty rolls where the ocean waves hit the shallow entrance to the bay. Then the launch moved along at ten knots, quite fast enough for me but not for LaFond. He was trying to get a speedier boat that would be able to outrun waves stirred by bad weather. At present, he told me, scientists are marooned on the tower two or three times a year when the launch is unable to cope with heavy seas. Waves six feet or more in height stop the bus service.

We headed north after leaving the bay and I could see the tower, a cluttered yellow shack that had no business being where it was. This was also the opinion of the residents of Mission Beach, who had complained at the start of the project that it ruined their view of the sunset. No blacker pot ever could have insulted a kettle. Mission Beach made its presence felt on shore with the whorls of a roller coaster dominating its amusement park. "I complained to them that they were ruining our view of the sunrise," LaFond said to me. I looked east, I looked west, and called it a draw.

Now we were approaching the tower, and my dream of a manor house at sea faded even more. It greeted us with a sign "U.S. Government Property — Keep Off." Of course we didn't, since we were government property ourselves. The coxswain backed the launch up to the ladder on the bottom deck of the tower. Briefcases, packages and other encumbering objects were placed in a big canvas basket lowered from a boom and were then hoisted onto the tower, leaving our hands free for what was to come next. There was not much of a sea running and I declined an invitation to go up in the basket as an encumbering object. The coxswain tried twice before he was able to get the stern of the launch within reach of the ladder and, at the same time, poised on the crest of a wave, so that I could go through the boat-tower interface. A bus service is a good way to visit friends living offshore, a subway would be a better one.

LaFond and I climbed past the two lower levels until we reached the main deck of the tower. Two brooms and two mops stacked on the rail indicated that the Navy owned this part of the sea floor. There was an incinerator hanging from the rail, too. LaFond told me that nothing goes overboard from the tower, so as to preserve the sea bottom in its natural state and allay any possible protests from Mission Beachers enjoying unsullied nature beneath their roller coaster. Divers periodically scrape mussels and other fouling organisms from the tower's legs to prevent them from distorting the movement of currents. They take baskets down to gather the mussels and keep them off the bottom. The population around the tower has developed a Pavlovian reflex. When fish hear a diver hammering away at the mussels, they turn up to be fed.

James Cairns, a young physicist with LaFond's laboratory who is in charge of the tower program, told me that kelp bass and sculpin are the most abundant of the tower's permanent undersea residents. The sculpin is also known as the scorpion fish because of the poisonous spines on its dorsal fin. It lurks in corners under the tower and does not swim away when divers approach. It is the divers who swim away because, Cairns told me, a sculpin scrape can disable an arm for a few days.

Hammerhead sharks may turn up when the water gets warm. Divers on the tower see about half a dozen sharks every summer, running between eight and ten feet long. "These sightings became so numerous that, at one time, we started carrying an M-1 rifle in our diving boat," Cairns said.

The tower has six bunks, an electric kitchen and a wash basin. Some operations require the tower to be continuously manned for weeks, but with changes of scientists. The record for the longest unscheduled stay is held by Dale Good, an electronics engineer who remained on the tower for three days and nights during a storm. Cairns did not seem to mind an overnight stay every now and then. The isolation is only relative: radio links the tower to land, and electricity is supplied by cable by the local power company. LaFond had insisted on an outside power supply to eliminate vibration and noise from generators during laboratory experiments. There are emergency rations aboard and equipment for distilling seawater.

"I guess it's like Robinson Crusoe with 4,800 volts coming in from shore," Cairns said. "It's spooky at night. Usually I go into the galley and cook a big dinner for myself. That's one difference between the tower and a ship: we don't have stewards here and everybody does his own cooking. Then after dinner, you sit out here on the porch. You put your feet up on the rail and watch the lights on shore. If you're down on the lower deck at night when a really heavy sea hits the tower, you do feel insignificant."

There's always television, and a program was on during our visit. The screen showed a grid with streamers tied to it, a variation of the device that LaFond had used to track currents from a submersible. I was told to watch patiently and I was rewarded when a fish swam into the picture. The television camera goes down vertical railway tracks built on three sides of the tower where the camera can be dispatched with its lights to any desired depth. There is sound on the program as well. One of the many uses found for the quiet tower is to tape the background noise in the sea and, with the television camera, to show what makes it. On the site off Mission Beach, there is a twice-daily sound show put on at sunrise and sunset. It lasts for two or three hours, and credit for it is given to two members of the croaker family, the spotfin and the yellow-fin. Fish can be a good indicator of water turbulence as well. At times, the TV screen shows them swimming downward to hold the same depth, as if they had been caught in an updraft.

The tower has branched out on all sides. Seven hundred feet away, I could see a thin spar buoy that marked an underwater array of temperature sensors to record internal waves. This gear is serviced by divers who have telephone booths at their disposal on the bottom. Each booth is a 55-gallon oil drum cut in half. A diver enters the drum, blows air from his breathing apparatus into it and, once the air has forced the water down, picks up the phone and talks to the tower. He can also talk to a fellow diver using another booth, the call going through a switchboard on the tower.

I had lost sight of LaFond during my tour of inspection and caught up with him only on the roof, which the Navy calls the top deck because, I imagine, it has decided that the tower is a ship and not a house. He was standing next to one of those plastic owls that yachtsmen use to keep sea gulls away. "When we first put the tower up, the gulls thought we had built it for them," he said. The imitation owl did not work too well and it has been supplemented by four loudspeakers that broadcast the distress call of the herring gull every hour on the hour. I took note of this accessory for an offshore cottage. Not everyone will want to stand in his backyard and feed the gulls.

What LaFond really wanted to show me on the roof of his house was not sea gulls but external evidence of internal waves. "Look at those slicks," he said, pointing to glassy bands on the surface, moving towards the tower and into shore. They were formed, he told me, in the convergence zone behind the crests of shallow internal waves, where dead plankton and other oily organic material is concentrated in long rows.

The oil flattens the stippled effect of the wind, creating a smooth strip. On top of the tower's forty-foot mast, LaFond had planted a convex mirror, giving a 360-degree panoramic view of the marching slicks. A camera pointing up at the mirror took pictures every two seconds. Its film would then be played back at 24 frames a second, showing the direction of the internal waves and their changes in speed as they near shore.

The tower was quiet, just as LaFond had intended it to be, despite the amount of work going on. From the mirror on top of the mast to the big booms hanging like fishing poles over the surface and down to the television camera 20 feet below the waterline, information was pouring in from the sea. Some of it went into the digital recorders clicking away in two of the three rooms beneath our feet. Four Ph.D.'s had already been awarded for work done on the tower, the kind of victory that every oceanographic research vessel likes to paint figuratively on its side. Visiting scientists had come here from Britain, France, Japan and West Germany to work for weeks or months on end. That is the kind of atmosphere LaFond wants in his home on the ocean.

Like Inman on the end of Scripps Pier, LaFond keeps looking out to sea and wondering how to raise the money for another stride into deeper water. LaFond told me of his plans for a second research tower that would be another eight-tenths of a mile out to sea and in 100 feet of water. It would enable him to run a variety of experiments of interest to the Navy and to basic science. Effects of rough water on the transmission of sound could be studied with ships and submarines, impossible at present because there is not enough deep water between his tower and shore. A whole new layer from the ocean cake could be sliced up by his instruments. Divers would be able to work at greater depths. The biology and geology of another patch of sea could be looked at in detail and compared to what has already been learned off Mission Beach.

"It took me four years to get this tower," LaFond said on the roof. "We'll get the next one."

I think he will. People like LaFond and Inman can be very persuasive indeed when they talk of putting laboratories on artificial islands and taking the seasickness out of oceanography. The Navy should be prepared to add another stop to its bus line.

10. Ocean Capital of the World

The coelacanth is a homely fish about five feet long with two tails and fins sprouting from what look like the roots of limbs. I mention it only because it was believed to have been extinct for 70 million years. Paleontologists found its remains in some English chalk cliffs and wrote it off as an evolutionary dead end until, in 1938, fishermen off South Africa caught a live coelacanth in the Indian Ocean.

In my own researches, I came across another living fossil whose supposed demise, though more recent, was just as complete as the coelacanth's. The lone inventor who wired together an inspiration in a shed is as dead on land as the first Ford or the brothers Wright. In the sea, he prospers. From what I saw of the industrial side of oceanography, it is still the province of little fellows whose yearly sales seldom run over the $10 million mark. Even multibillion-dollar firms resort to a form of mimicry, turning over their seaborne activities to small divisions light enough to float. Size is not necessarily an asset in a market where every consumer has his own specifications for his own purposes. The individualistic oceanographer has to be convinced that manufactured equipment is as good as what he has been wiring together himself. It is an anachronistic situation that is bound to evolve in the next few years as industry climbs its rising growth curves. I was fortunate enough to see it before the change.

As in oranges, tourists, and eccentric politics, Florida and California are running a headlong race to lure ocean businesses. The Florida Development Commission peppers the trade press with advertisements headlined as "a message from the oceanographic capital of the world," where "the blessings of Nature and foresight of Science have been combined in projects whose possibilities are as exciting and fabulous as a trip beyond the moon." I was about to insert this information into my atlas when I came across a full-page display by California's Long Beach. A testimonial from as unquestionable an authority as the Real Estate Research Corporation declared that "Long Beach has the opportunity to become not just a center of ocean science but the national and perhaps the world center for this activity." In anticipation, Long Beach calls itself the "world center of oceanology."

San Diego adopts a softer sell, perhaps because it is already the home of Scripps, the Navy Electronics Laboratory, and a swarm of firms that have grown up in the usual symbiosis of industry and science. *Oceanics in San Diego, California*, a booklet behind a sea-blue cover, puts newcomers in their place by recalling that "nature began developing San Diego as a setting for oceanographic research about 20 million years ago," endowing it with a harbor, beaches, bays, and submarine canyons. With this head start, San Diego County has been able to attract about sixty firms in what the local Chamber of Commerce calls "ocean-oriented industries." The list runs from the American Agar and Chemical Company (seaweed extracts) through such brave names as Aquasonics Engineering, Decision Science, DoAll Science Center, and Oceanic Enterprises to the Westinghouse Electric Corporation. These are all either small firms or small branches of big ones. Only eight of them have more than 500 employees, and together they account for a total payroll of 6,800, barely half the size of the army that marches daily in and out of San Diego's biggest business, the Convair Division of General Dynamics.

Nearly a third of them have no more than ten employees. What matters in this industry is not the size of the staff as much as the number of Ph. D.'s and M.S.'s on it.

I began my sampling of oceanics in San Diego on G Street Pier, a man-made promontory occupied by Tom Lai's Restaurant, Olsen Ship Chandlers, the California Retail Fish Market (barracuda and yellowfin tuna at 35 cents a pound — whole), and the Hytech Division of the Bissett-Berman Corporation. Hytech began as a one-man operation and flourished to the point where it is now the country's major supplier of oceanographic instruments. Its founder is Don J. Cretzler, whose rise from relative rags to relative riches with the help of his relatives is a corporate epic in a minor key. It was related to me by Cretzler in an office that told me I was no longer in the Spartan halls of science. Eight sketches of dream ships, mostly twin-hulled except for one that was pumpkin-seed-shaped, hung on the walls along with three Rembrandt reproductions and a citation from an airline for hard traveling. The telephone sounded infrequently and only as a humble two-toned chime.

A big friendly man of forty-seven, Cretzler was as relaxed as the décor. Cretzler got into the sea as an engineer with the sewage treatment plant of the city of Los Angeles, his employer from 1950 to 1958. "In about 1952 or 1953 — I've not much of a head for dates — the California Water Pollution Control Board issued an edict related to cleaning up Santa Monica Bay. The edict provided the basis and stimulus which subsequently resulted in a bond issue, thus providing funds for the new Hyperion Sewage Treatment Plant. That's how I was introduced to oceanography. It became necessary to determine the extent of pollution in the bay by systematic sampling and analyses. In addition, current studies were made to determine flushing rates of the bay. I didn't know a Nansen bottle from a hole in the wall."

When Cretzler did get to know Nansen bottles and the other paraphernalia of the classical oceanographer, he was not impressed. He found them archaic and wondered if they could not be improved with the help of some dry-land engineering. First, he decided to learn something about the subject. He arranged to work the four-to-midnight shift in the sewage treatment plant so that he could get up at three in the morning and drive 120 miles to Scripps, where he was spoon-fed oceanography by James Snodgrass, a wizard with instruments, and Jeffery D. Frautschy, now assistant director of Scripps. Frautschy corroborated Cretzler's story: "His boss used to call us up and complain. He wanted Don to spend less time on instruments and more time at his treatment plant duties."

Touched by the zeal of their disciple, the oceanographers at Scripps suggested to Cretzler that he might try building instruments for them. An opportunity presented itself before the start of the International Geophysical Year in 1957, when Scripps decided to get water samples from most unlikely places by anyone who happened to be on the spot. Frautschy, who realized that a Nansen bottle could not be operated by an illiterate, designed a foolproof sampler consisting of a piece of pipe sealed with two rubber balls. Cretzler was then given the job of producing the Frautschy bottles and the gear to lower them. "Scripps needed a simple-minded, hand-operated winch that could be operated from a rowboat by a native. I sketched a winch with a wooden boom. For the drum, I used one of those medium-size spools that wire companies use. That was my first production contract and I'll never forget it, nor all of the people involved. I made about a hundred winches in my garage at Playa del Rey, working twenty hours a day.

"Frautschy and Snodgrass encouraged me to start a company. I cleaned out our garage, bought a lathe, a grinder and a drill press from Sears, Roebuck. I got a license and a letterhead, and called the company Mech-I-Tron, mechanics and electronics. I went to North American Aviation and bought a surplus IBM typewriter. I think I paid $39 for it, but you'll have to ask Marian, my wife."

(When I did ask Mrs. Cretzler, she told me they paid $25 for the typewriter, and told her husband: "You know we didn't have $39.")

A problem arose when the California Corporation Commission refused to accept the title of the company because it was too close to Mechtronics, a name already owned by someone in North Carolina. "We submitted five names," Cretzler said. "Hytech was one of them and they chose it."

One day, Cretzler walked into the office of Margaret Robinson, the guardian of Scripps's collection of bathythermograph slides. She has hundreds of thousands of them there, a record of temperature profiles in the Pacific Ocean going back twenty-five years. Cretzler heard her complain of how hard it was to work with the slides. "The slides were smoked with a flammable admixture of skunk musk. The slide coating was easily smeared, resulting in a high mortality rate of BT traces. I wondered if they couldn't be coated with something else. Margaret gave me a few boxes of glass slides and I went home to try. I tested everything: silver, lead, iron, gold. After working eight months in my garage with a vacuum plating machine, I decided gold was the most suitable material. It has remarkable resistance to corrosion and tarnish. The catch comes when you try to make it stick to the glass and not flake off.

"Margaret sponsored many at-sea trials and subsequently the flaking problems were solved. There is more than gold on the glass, but I am not at liberty to tell you what it is. Let's just say that we found something that sticks well to both glass and gold and made a sandwich.

"Through Scripps and Margaret, the slides were recommended to the Navy. I submitted specifications, and the Navy subsequently asked me to come to Washington to discuss the new slide coating. I'd never been there. Our income at this time was about $230 a month, derived solely from sales in oceanography. I didn't have the plane fare. However, my mother-in-law loaned me the money, God bless her.

"When I got to Washington, I stayed with my wife's cousin and his wife, Mr. and Mrs. Amidon, during the time I was showing the slides to the Navy. The Navy negotiated a contract for a sizable quantity of the new BT slides every year. However, they wanted me to reveal the process. The Navy has a good policy of never depending on a single supplier if at all possible. I refused to reveal the process, but I did say that they were welcome to copy it if they could.

"My wife, mother-in-law, and I began to turn out slides in the garage, and millions have been produced since then. The British and Australian navies buy them, too. The slides were a major factor in getting us out of the garage. I went into partnership with Bud Walker, another engineer at the sewage plant. We opened a small shop near Los Angeles with a total of eight employees."

Hytech was now branching out. The Woods Hole Oceanographic Institution asked it to build a hundred current-meter housings. In 1961, Hytech moved to the G Street Pier, taking over an old restaurant that had taken over an old boatyard.

Investors became interested in the little minnow that was getting bigger. In 1962, Cretzler sold his financial interest in the firm to the Bissett-Berman Corporation, thereby becoming part of a conglomerate. "We had ten employees at the time. They had about twenty-five," he said. Shortly thereafter a healthy $640,000 contract came in from

ASWEPS, the Navy's Anti-Submarine Warfare Environmental Prediction System.

Cretzler decided to beef up the scientific side of the company to meet the demands of the ASWEPS contract. At Woods Hole he had met an Australian scientist, Neil Brown, who is one of the world's experts at measuring salinity, not by chemical analysis but with a far speedier method based on the electrical conductivity of seawater. Cretzler wanted Brown to be his research director. Brown was back in Australia.

"We needed immigration papers for him in a hurry," Cretzler said. Once more, he enlisted the help of relatives. His wife's cousin in Washington had a wife of his own who was secretary to a Texas congressman.

"She had a girl friend who was the secretary to the head of the immigration service," Cretzler explained, almost drawing me a diagram. "Those girls walked the necessary papers through thirty-five signatures. We got Neil Brown and we still have him."

Hytech now has ninety-seven employees. Edward K. Dean, the plant's marketing manager, told me that volume had gone from $2.5 million in 1966 to $3.5 million in 1967 and is expected to run to nearly $10 million in 1969. Cretzler's first product, the native-powered winch of only ten years ago, has been replaced by the precision instruments that measure currents, pressure, wind, waves, air and water temperature, and salinity, among other things. In addition, they produce a SEAS buoy (a Sea Environment Acquisition System . . . like the hand winch).

Dean was optimistic about the buoy's future: "Everyone wants buoys. The Navy needs them, so do the oil companies and the fishing industry. I think every ocean-oriented federal agency in Washington has its own buoy program. One will talk about ten, another about hundreds. It's good for business and there really isn't all that much duplication. After all, the Weather Bureau isn't primarily interested in what is going on 3,000 feet down, even though oceanographers are. The Atomic Energy Commission and the Coast Guard don't have the same requirements. Nor do the Air Force and the Bureau of Commercial Fisheries. But they all see a need for buoys."

Cretzler suggested a look around the plant. It was soon to move inland to new quarters twice the present size. This will give it 32,000 square feet, compared to the 400 square feet of the garage in Playa del Rey. Hytech had remained true to the original Cretzler philosophy of doing everything under one roof. The cages in which its instruments go down were being welded outside on the pier, and all parts were manufactured in its own machine shop. Cretzler made a point of showing me the tank, 150 feet long, 8 feet wide, and 8 feet deep, in which current meters are towed for testing. "I dug it in two weeks with the help of two other fellows," he said. "We had a steel worker moonlighting on weekends to install the reinforcing steel for us. Then I arranged for a swimming pool contractor to come in and gunite it."

Hytech runs a small boat, the *Trio*, for testing instruments in San Diego Bay, and hitches rides on Scripps vessels when deeper water is needed. The oceanographers have a warm spot in their hearts for Cretzler, who shared their leaner days. He still moves constantly to keep up with them, but his traveling has broadened. Instead of shuttling between Playa del Rey and La Jolla, he turns up at such places as an oceanographic congress in Moscow or in the office of the assistant director of the Woods Hole Oceanographic Institution on Cape Cod. He is still learning.

The SEAS buoy that Hytech makes on the G Street Pier weighs less than 3,000 pounds soaking wet. The Monster buoy that is built by the Convair Division of General Dynamics a few blocks north on Pacific Highway weighs 100 tons. Convair itself is huge. It sits in vast buildings erected during the war and bordering Lindbergh Field. Here and in another plant outside town where it builds space vehicles, Convair employs 13,000 persons. Its economic health has been slowly improving since the early 1960's when it was the big loser in the winner-take-all contest for supremacy in commercial jet airliners.

As a division of General Dynamics, Convair now puts its eggs into many baskets. The Monster buoy is a small one that is being hatched by no more than 100 persons, including the factory hands who build it. At the entrance to the Engineering Building on Pacific Highway, the guard had never heard of the buoy. He passed me along to the next higher echelon, a receptionist inside the sanctuary who had a rotating file of telephone numbers at her disposal. She dispatched me to a room marked "Vendors" where I sat down on one of a row of chairs occupied by smiling men with attaché cases. It was there that I was salvaged by Robert Devereux, the manager of the Monster buoy program, who apologized profusely because we had missed connections at the gate.

I was in luck, he told me. A color film on the Monster had been produced and a showing was due in a few minutes. We slipped into a

Above, the Monster, with the Gulf Stream racing past. Below, the Jaguar that calibrated the buoy's wind gauges up to 75 miles an hour.

projection room and there we were able to see the buoy as it underwent a Gulf Stream test in the Straits of Florida. It was a big dish, forty feet in diameter, with a mast planted on top of it. Spokes radiated from the masthead and the total effect was that of a stylized tree planted in the ocean. The colors were beautiful: a red-and-yellow buoy driving a big white wake through the aquamarine sea (the Monster was standing still, but the Gulf Stream was racing past it at five knots, creating the impression of a ship under way). The sound was skillfully done, too. Every roll of the buoy was accompanied by the soughing of the waves in perfect synchronization. Devereux told me that one of the purposes of the film was to show it to the people at Convair and at the other General Dynamics divisions. It was the best interoffice memorandum I had ever seen. I thought it deserved a wider audience.

At first, I misjudged Devereux. He seemed bland and cool, the type of person one would expect to find as a cog in a corporate machine of this size. His suit was the proper shade of gray, his tie matched the black frames of his glasses and he began by preaching something called "systems integration" to me. I began to look for an emergency exit in his office. I had been on the fringe of systems analysis for weeks and I had managed to keep clear only with great difficulty. I knew that I would never grasp this form of reasoning the day I picked up a trade publication and saw a photo of the toilet in a research submersible with a caption under it: Waste Management System.

Devereux made me just as uneasy when we got into his car to look at the testing facilities that Convair had developed for the buoy. We drove interminably. It seems much farther than the distance from La Jolla to San Diego, but we were still on Convair property at the edge of San Diego Bay, the city's harbor. "Working for a big company has its advantages," Devereux said. "You've got a lot of real estate at your disposal. When we wanted to calibrate the buoy's wind gauges up to 75 miles an hour, we were able to do it with my Jaguar on company property. We had to use an old Navy airfield, though, to calibrate them up to 120 miles an hour. Surprisingly enough, this method is much more precise than using a wind tunnel."

Devereux, who was forty, had been with Convair since 1956 after spending five years at Scripps, where he became interested in problems of acquiring environmental data from the sea. He left before he became completely indoctrinated by oceanographers and he took some heretical ideas with him. "I think oceanography and meteorology are one and the same. They're just fluid dynamics. They study the two fluids that are the most important to us on earth, the atmosphere and the ocean. Of course, there are differences of density and viscosity, but their behavior is remarkably alike. The two sciences are becoming one."

At Convair, Devereux first worked on data acquisition in the F-106 delta-wing flight test program before he began the buoy program, which was undertaken in 1959 with a grant from the Office of Naval Research and the guidance of a committee composed of twenty leading American oceanographers. He and the Office of Naval Research were especially pleased at this first step away from the do-it-myself life of the oceanographer. "Much oceanographic equipment is still being designed by scientists," Devereux said. "This is beginning to puzzle me. Today in oceanography there are not enough gifted scientists to do the scientific work. Then why expect them to spend half their time doing engineering?"

Once more, I had to duck into my deep shelter as shells were lobbed over my head by both sides. I had heard Devereux's question answered many times by scientists fussing with solid-state circuits and pressure cases: "If we want instruments that work at sea, we have to make them ourselves." And I have heard manufacturers reply: "If there were money enough to build them so they'd survive being dropped on the deck, the instruments would work."

No oceanographer could have duplicated the facilities that Devereux showed me at Convair. A rig originally used to find the breaking point of the landing gear of the 990 jet airliner was torturing the Monster's Dacron mooring line. A hydraulic machine kept stretching the line with a stress equal to that of waves 50 feet high. With its points most likely to fray immersed in salt water, the line protested in alternate creaks and sighs as it withstood the ordeal. "We'll test here only to a million stretches, a million cycles," Devereux told me. "In a year at sea, the line would experience five million cycles."

Devereux then took me to Convair's 350-foot tow tank where a wind machine had been able to simulate scaled-down hurricanes for models of all kinds of buoys. It was here that various hull designs were put through simulated ocean waves until the final choice was made of a discus, flat and round so that it would hug the surface, stay upright and not impose too much of a drag on the mooring line. A spar buoy along the lines of FLIP had been considered but rejected when calculations showed it would have to be as long as FLIP to remain steady enough to support radio antennas for telemetry of data that the oceanographers required. Our visit to the tow tank was all the more fortunate because it enabled Devereux to go into a huddle for a few moments with some modelmakers. When he came back, he told me: "I realized I didn't have any money to take you to lunch. I had to borrow some." He was becoming more of a human and less of a system by the minute.

Seeing the Monster through to completion had been a job as big as the buoy. The Office of Naval Research had spent an estimated $6 million on the project, with some resentment expressed by those upon whom the manna had not fallen. "There are few who lament the old days when it took three years to work up the data from a one-month cruise," Devereux told me at luncheon. "People are beginning to accept the idea that arrays of buoys could provide more knowledge about one ocean in one year than we have gained about all the oceans in 75 years. A Monster buoy will cost between $200,000 and $500,000, depending upon mission requirements. That's far less than the initial cost of a research ship, and the saving is just as impressive when you look at the price of the results. We figure that our cost-per-data-point, let's say for one salinity determination, is 25 cents. It costs a ship between $2.50 and $5.00 to get a salinity point. A liter of seawater in a Nansen bottle is worth about $10 by the time you get it on deck."

Convair had to meet ambitious specifications. The scientific guidance committee of the Office of Naval Research insisted on measurements from at least 100 points above and below the surface. What they had in mind was an eventual fleet of buoys providing the oceanographer with something he has never been able to obtain: simultaneous measurements of ocean and atmospheric weather for long periods of time over a large area. The buoy, stated the committee, had to stay at sea for a year and survive waves 60 feet high, winds of 165 miles an hour and 10-knot surface currents. It had to be able to transmit information every six hours to a shore station as far as 2,500 miles away so that a central point on Hawaii, for example, could harvest data from a series of buoys distributed over an area of the Pacific 5,000 miles in diameter.

Devereux and his engineers found their answers in simple rugged techniques. Looking around for a hull material, they tried fiber glass but discarded it because of costs. They chose steel with an anticorrosion coating of inorganic zinc, the next best thing to gold plating, Devereux told me. They thought of fuel cells, nuclear reactors (fine in space but not on the sea, where ships might run into them) and even windmills as a power source. In the end, they met the buoy's appetite for a thousand watts of electrical energy by using an old friend, the internal combustion engine in a pedestrian version ordinarily found on farms. The buoy has two engines, which take turns running, and enough propane fuel to last two years. They breathe cooling air through the top of the mast and change their oil automatically when they stop after charging the buoy's nickel-cadmium batteries, another reliable solution borrowed from, of all places, the railroads. The best anchor for the Monster turned out to be nothing more than a long length of chain on the bottom, five tons in all.

Whether it was a buoy or an integrated system with subsystems from farms and railroads, it had to go to sea. Convair named its first buoy BRAVO and tried it in shallow water off Florida in 1964. In April 1965, it was placed in the Gulf Stream in the Straits of Florida, where I had seen it on the screen. From a scientific viewpoint, this is one of the most worthwhile places to measure the Gulf Stream because here it is literally a river flowing between two bodies of land, enabling its volume to be calculated more accurately than in the open ocean, where it is bounded only by water masses. BRAVO stayed in the Straits until January 1966, when it was towed to Bermuda for successful mooring tests in 14,000 feet of water.

The Gulf Stream experiment had some unexpected results. It created a rash of rumors about flying saucers and secret weapons off the coast. "The buoy's bow wave in the Gulf Stream was so big that it was always reported as under way by fishing boats," Devereux said. "We could never get a captain to realize that it was standing still. They insisted upon approaching it as if it were a dock. When they 'stopped' their boats in the water the buoy simply sailed away. It was their first and only visual reference of the Gulf Stream's speed. Out there, out of sight of land, the current runs swiftly."

Sports-fishing captains were reluctant to go out to the site, and on one occasion, they turned a Convair crew over to the local sheriff, who had to be convinced that the whole thing wasn't a weak cover for a trip to Cuba. Their navigation was a disappointment. Devereux cherishes a chart he has made of reports of the buoy being sighted by local salts in an area 30 miles long and 20 miles wide. "We made routine observations of the buoy with a Questar telescope. From its position relative to fixed landmarks ashore, we know that it did not move."

BRAVO stayed put during Hurricane Betsy on September 8, 1965, when it recorded gusts of up to 110 miles per hour. What still baffles scientists is the record of the strain on its mooring line. The buoy pulled less during the storm than in normal weather. One guess is that hurricane winds either slowed or displaced the Gulf Stream so that it was no longer exerting its six-mile-an-hour tug on the buoy.

At the time I saw Devereux, three Monster buoys had been built. The original BRAVO, towed home from Florida through the Panama Canal, was lying at anchor in San Diego Bay just off the old seaplane ramp that Convair uses for its excursions into the sea. Another buoy, known as Two Alpha, had been constructed at Groton, Connecticut, by General Dynamics and it was hard at work four miles southeast of Sandy Hook, where the U.S. Coast Guard had moored it to replace the old Scotland Lightship. Two Alpha has the same discus hull under a stubbier mast that supports a 5,000-candlepower light, a radio beacon and a fog-horn commanded from shore. Besides acting as a guide to ships approaching New York Harbor, it carries scientific instruments to serve as an oceanographic station.

The third and newest buoy was ALPHA, still propped up on beams next to the seaplane ramp, with two temporary plywood shacks on its deck. Devereux invited me into the Monster's maw and I was able to crawl around a few of its sixteen watertight compartments. At sea, no one crawls around them. The buoy is launched with its hatches welded shut and its interior purged of air and filled with dry nitrogen, like the Scripps's tide capsule. Instruments work better there than in an air-conditioned laboratory on land. Upon Devereux's urging, we squatted under the hull, where I was told to see for myself the flatness of the Monster's belly. "You see, the flat bottom couples the buoy to the sea surface," Devereux said. "It follows the wave slope and that lets us use the motions of the buoy itself to measure waves."

Next, we went back in Devereux's car for a look at the buoy's land-based mobile data center. On the way, I noticed *Star I*, the first of General Dynamics' small research submersibles, but Devereux was unable to tell me very much about it. Submersibles belonged to another of General Dynamics' watertight compartments. He did inform me that a little red teardrop next to *Star I* was a gravity glider, perhaps the forerunner of a new undersea sport. It could plane down from the surface like an aerial glider, but it had the added faculty of being able to glide up from the depths after releasing ballast.

I had now become so fluent in the patois spoken on Convair territory that I did not wince when the mobile data center was revealed to me as a secondhand Greyhound bus. "It was cheap, it cost us only $4,000, and the suspension is just what we needed for our radio equipment," Devereux said. The bus kept in touch with the buoy through two 50-foot antenna masts that could be towed behind it in knocked-down form. Instead of loping from Albany to Elmira, the old Greyhound ranged along the coast and inland to test communications with the buoy under all conditions. It was cheaper to drive a bus than to tow the buoy for such a purpose.

The bus had been converted into a "self-contained telemetry facility." It carried its own generating plant and a small digital computer to interpret the results radioed to it from sea on one of the three frequencies that the buoy can use. Frequencies are Devereux's biggest worry and he spends quite a bit of time traveling to international conferences to plead for space on the crowded airwaves for automatic buoys. Transmission of buoy signals by satellites may be the eventual answer.

The self-contained telemetry facility had sleeping capability, Devereux explained as he showed me bunks for the crew. "And here," he said, "is some of our life-support equipment." I looked and saw a compact galley complete with steaming coffeepot. What I really needed was a dictionary.

A short while after I saw ALPHA, the shacks were removed from its deck and it was launched for a test off La Jolla under the eyes of scientists from Scripps and engineers from Convair. Two Monster buoys are to be the hubs of a pair of clusters in the North Pacific, with four of John Isaacs's catamarans deployed around each of them. It is the first step in Isaacs's study, sponsored by Scripps and the Office of Naval Research, to learn how the ocean and the atmosphere act and interact over an area of four million square miles. The smaller and cheaper catamarans will measure surface winds and water temperatures down to about 1,500 feet, while the Monsters will also record a number of other factors like sunshine, rainfall, air and dew-point temperature, barometric pressure, wave heights and salinity, radioing their data immediately to land. I do hope that Devereux's Goliaths will hold the sea at least as long as Isaacs's Davids.

Goliath is perhaps an exaggeration. A two-column survey of Convair's operations published by a local newspaper mentioned the buoy only in the last paragraph, along with miscellaneous products like landing mats. Convair uses the buoy, as so many other large firms do, to keep its foot in the door of the ocean until the day the door swings open.

The most unusual corporate approach to the sea that I encountered in and around San Diego was that of Westinghouse, which has almost eliminated the profit motive in its operation there. It has created a miniature Scripps at an ocean research laboratory on the outer confines of San Diego County in the Sorrento Valley, whose solitude is broken only by a rare Santa Fe freight train.

The Westinghouse Ocean Research Laboratory should not be confused with the Westinghouse Ocean Research and Engineering Center in Annapolis, Maryland, where 700 of what the company calls "engineering and marketing personnel" are engaged in work with a clearly discernible profit motive. Annapolis hums with applications of marine science. It is there that Westinghouse develops its Deepstar submersibles. The *Deepstar-4000* that LaFond had used is only the firstborn of a family, and it is being followed by *Deepstar 2000* with a greater payload and more versatility for work at shallower depths. Emerging from the drawing boards is a third Deepstar that will be capable of descending to 20,000 feet. To give acoustic eyes to its own submersibles and other explorers of the deep, Westinghouse goes in heavily for sonar equipment. A big engineering effort is being devoted to the Cachalot, which, like its namesake the sperm whale (in French), is a highly perfected diving device. Its purpose is to spare divers the time they normally waste in decompression stages on their way up from the bottom. The Cachalot swallows up the diver like Jonah's whale and takes him to work in a submersible diving chamber. When he is through, the chamber taxis him back up, but with its interior kept at bottom pressure. The diving chamber is then bolted onto a deck chamber where the diver can remain under pressure until his next trip down. Only at the end of the workweek need he be decompressed in the deck chamber. The Cachalot and similar devices used elsewhere are being prepared for the expected rush to the resources of the continental shelf.

Dr. Roy Gaul, the manager of the ocean research laboratory in the Sorrento Valley, was not interested in underwater guided missiles or reactors for submarines, the bulk of Westinghouse's $50 million a year business in the sea. His suit was the wrong color for an executive and the three other young men in his office were in sports shirts. He introduced me to them: Dr. William Clarke, oldest man in the group at 37, biological oceanographer, studying the deep scattering layer and nearshore pollution; Dr. Tim Barnett, physical oceanographer, previously at Scripps, interested in waves and deep currents; Hugh Martin, physicist, solver of instrument problems. Gaul himself was fresh from the oceanography department of Texas A. & M., where he had earned his doctorate for environmental research conducted on two surplus Navy towers. A motley crew of businessmen, indeed.

"We've been having a great big flail with *Deepstar 4000* in the Gulf of Mexico," said Gaul, "but we've got some time for you. Ask us anything you please." Collectively, they explained their presence in Westinghouse. "What some of the big companies fail to do is separate church and state," Clarke said. "I was with one of the biggest. They used to send us forms asking what major breakthroughs we could predict for the next three months. Here, we're mainly supposed to keep Westinghouse abreast of what's going on in the world of academic oceanography." Barnett told me he had more salary and more worries at Westinghouse than at Scripps, but he didn't mind the latter: "I'm young, I want to do research. We're working with the German Hydrographic Office on waves in the North Sea. We go to the Salton Sea in the Imperial Valley to study how currents develop. We put down mid-water floats 500 miles west of San Diego to look at currents 1100 fathoms down."

Gaul listened to his colleagues, saw my bewilderment and threw me a lifeline. "I wanted you to see for yourself. We believe that a big corporation in the one or two billion dollar per year sales bracket should have an isolated pocket of longhairs in a protected environment. American companies in this category take two approaches to the organization of research. Some divide their research so that it is an integral part of each of their businesses. The other way is to put basic research together with most of the firm's applied research on an overall staff level, the way Westinghouse does. So do Bell Telephone, Shell and Standard Oil. I think the modern corporation must fight a tendency to put the best people on today's problems at the expense of development for tomorrow. If research is in a somewhat sheltered environment, it makes it tougher for the management of the operating divisions to put the finger on scientists.

"Westinghouse has applied research groups at component levels, but we're the only basic group for the ocean. Our home office is the Westinghouse Laboratories 2400 miles away in Pittsburgh. We can't be tethered with security red tape; it would restrict us. We're planted here to behave like scientists. We're money-consuming, not profit-making. One of our main jobs is to get the Westinghouse name on scientific papers related to the ocean. We're here so that the corporation can interface with specialized packets of intellectuals. We infiltrate the academic community from behind our apparent facade of corporate irresponsibility — that is, the lack of a profit motive."

Westinghouse has been doing basic research in its laboratories for more than half a century, Gaul told me, and he did not have very much difficulty in preaching to the converted. "I told my management back at Pittsburgh that we want to be the Beard and Sandal Country Club of Westinghouse. They loved it." They loved it so much that they gave Gaul a modest budget of $250,000 a year to keep him from growing too fat for his role. "It's not much, but we can do as we wish. We made our choice. With a big budget, we could be serene and fully staffed. Then we'd be static. This way, we're not static. We can grow or shrink as we please by taking on contracts. Our potential sponsors are the same as those of Scripps, the University of Miami or any other oceanographic institution. Mind you, we don't prohibit staff members *a priori* from doing useful work of immediate concern. The key is that they must want to do it and be competent to do it. If it goes beyond our funds, then they must find support. They're supposed to think of what they want to do. Any scientist can think up three lifetimes of work if he's worth a damn."

Gaul's laboratory was in its first year of existence. It had already acquired a research vessel, a 17-foot Boston whaler, anchored in a garage that also served as a locker for diving gear. Research was being concentrated on the nearshore area to get some benchmark data on marine animals and kelp beds prior to the construction of new sewage outfalls and nuclear desalinization plants pumping heat and brine into the sea. "The trouble with sewage and pollution problems is that we keep trying to solve them after the fact," Gaul said. "A monitoring program should have been carried out here for the past ten years so that we could know what has happened instead of guessing at it. Man must dispose of wastes and heat, true, but he should never forget the ocean is like the atmosphere. It is only a limited receptacle. The continental shelf is very easy to pollute. Things just don't keep going away to infinity."

Gaul sounded so much like an academic that I couldn't determine who was interfacing with whom in his laboratory. He would never do for making speeches to stockholders. "Some big corporations got into oceanography and then withdrew. I suppose they caught cold when they got their feet wet. The level of naiveté about the ocean among industrialists and bureaucrats is amazing. Five years ago, there was all that razzmatazz about the ocean being our new frontier. Then when industry looked more closely, they saw the available market was small. Dollars weren't becoming available nearly as fast as the publicity was growing. They still had to learn that oceanography is an interdisciplinary science in a natural and hostile environment. You don't just stamp out oceanographers. It takes seven to ten years to make one."

Gaul's corporate assets were the young men I met around his table. They need not show a profit, it is true, but they will be judged on how much of their work gets into the scientific press. "We've only been here nine months," Gaul said. "We haven't published anything yet. It's too soon. But, after two or three or four years, there will be a concentrated group of highly competent scientists here. Or there will be someone else sitting in this chair."

In my underwater business survey, I had the good fortune to be present in San Diego when the Marine Technology Society held its third annual conference there. The society has 2,700 members and its meetings are always an excellent opportunity to explore the industrial side of oceanography. (According to one survey I saw by the magazine *Science & Technology*, there are 1,000 companies in the United States alone that have gone heavily into the sea, and twice as many more that dip their toes into it at one time or another.)

To prove my theory about the ocean as a sanctuary for the small entrepreneur, I shied away from large firms and public relations men wearing their master's brands on their lapels. (The best way to prove a theory is to neglect whatever might disprove it.) This line of investigation led me to Dimitri Rebikoff, who was chairman of the Marine Technology Society's underwater photography committee.

He is also the president of Rebikoff Underwater Products, based in Fort Lauderdale, Florida, with sales of "under a million dollars a year," small enough to enable him to enjoy his work. Rebikoff was born some forty-odd years ago in Paris (his family came from Leningrad — which he still calls St. Petersburg) and he was brought up in France. He worked for the French Navy and the Institute of Fisheries before he founded a Submarine Research Institute of his own at Cannes with three scientists who had been studying the eyes of fish. They were seeking to eliminate the magnifying effect that occurs when the human eye or the camera lens looks through water from behind flat glass. The best way to solve the problem, they decided, was to enter the water and "start seeing, thinking and living like a fish." From this vantage point, they designed a lens to enable a camera to register the undistorted picture that a fish sees in water.

The products made by Rebikoff consist of cameras, lighting equipment and vehicles to take them into the sea. His Pegasus is a torpedo-like steed that a prone diver steers through the water at a three-knot gallop. For work beyond the depths that can be reached conveniently by divers, Rebikoff has the Poodle, a pilotless vehicle on a leash, that carries a television camera and is controlled from the surface.

He is much more of an apostle of underwater photography than a salesman of Rebikoff Underwater Products. His major competitors were mentioned and given their rightful due in a paper on the history of his subject that he had presented in Washington a few months before the San Diego conference.

Underwater photography is nearly as old as photography. Rebikoff credits its invention to Louis Boutan, a French zoologist, who first built a watertight housing for a box camera in 1893. By the following year, he had designed a camera of his own which he hung from an empty wine cask and used to take a picture of a helmeted diver holding a sign saying: "*Photographie sous-marine.*" It was also in 1894, Rebikoff notes, that Boutan devised a flashbulb, a strip of magnesium electrically ignited in a glass jar, so that he could work at night. Daylight was ruining his pictures by turning water particles into spots of light. Before he and his work were temporarily forgotten, Boutan succeeded in lowering a pair of arc lights and a camera in 1899 to a depth of 150 feet and took a picture once more of his *photographie sous-marine* caption.

Among the pioneers that Rebikoff mentions, the most imaginative was certainly Ernie Williamson, an American newspaper photographer, who first went below in 1913. He built a camera six feet high, big enough for him to go down inside it with his wife and child, and he used the technique for movies, shooting in 1915 what Rebikoff considers the best version of *20,000 Leagues Under the Sea.* He never went more than twenty feet down with his rig, but that was enough to work on coral reefs in the Bahamas and in the swimming pools of Hollywood studios.

After the First World War, underwater photography began to evolve from a stunt into an art and a technique. Progress in cameras and films was accompanied by the appearance of self-contained breathing apparatus and flippers for divers. Rebikoff insists on the importance of the skin diver as a photographer. Unlike the helmeted diver, he need not clump around the bottom in weighted shoes, stirring up clouds of sediment that obscure his picture.

The first photograph in the deep sea was made as early as 1939, a peek through a curtain that has now been opened by remote-controlled motion picture cameras, lighting systems and television cameras. Rebikoff thinks that the next logical step is to move from more or less random pictures of the bottom to photographic mapping. The width of the bottom strip that a camera can scan depends on its height above it, which depends in turn on visibility in the water. In the dirty water of the English Channel or Long Island Sound, the camera would have to go within two feet of the bottom and it could map in strips only four feet wide. But in clear ocean water, it could take in a width of 600 feet with Rebikoff's new 92° lenses. Stereophotographs giving the height of bottom relief could be taken by a pair of cameras. They should be mounted, Rebikoff does suggest in a commercial vein, on a vehicle like his Pegasus with a precise navigation system enabling it to operate like a plane taking aerial photographs over land.

In his inventory of the possibilities of underwater area mapping, he includes everything from the charting of canyons to the discovery of cached or lost nuclear weapons and Greek bronzes. He adds a category which he calls "all yet unknown and unexpected 'things' which may be totally unknown: sea monsters, remains from completely lost civilizations, or even maybe long-lost spaceships from outer worlds." In one of his papers, he has proposed to start "without further delay the underseas 'Lewis and Clark expedition' of the totality of the continental shelf everywhere in the world, beginning with two of the most important areas, the Caribbean and Mediterranean Seas."

After talking to Rebikoff, I went to the exhibit hall and drifted with the current of the crowd from magnetic correlators to acoustic transponders. I kept accumulating catalogs and specification sheets like barnacles until they slowed my progress and popped the seams of the sturdy envelope offered visitors by *Oceanology International*, one of several titles in the underwater periodical press (others include *Ocean Industry*, *Geo-Marine Technology* and *UnderSea Technology*). To my untrained and unappreciative eye, the trade literature merged into a blur. Then I happened to pick up a blue brochure from a table. The copy on the back cover began:

> *This is the ship of pearl, which, poets feign,*
> *Sails the unshadowed main —*

and ended with the verse:

> *Build thee more stately mansions, O my soul,*
> *As the swift seasons roll!*

On the front cover was displayed an X-ray photo of Oliver Wendell Holmes's chambered nautilus and the name of the firm, Ocean Science and Engineering, Inc. I recognized the trademark; I had seen it as a proposed design for Scripps Island. When I opened the brochure, I came across a message from Willard Bascom, the president of the firm, expressing confidence that Ocean Science and Engineering "will continue to grow like its symbolic nautilus."

It is difficult to say whether Bascom is the most literary of oceanographers or the most oceanographic of literary men. He has two books to his credit, one on waves and beaches, the other on the aborted Mohole Project, whose early stages he directed. He has contributed prolifically to magazines and he once took advantage of a nine-month stay on Tahiti to write about Polynesian history, even though the main purpose of his trip there was to install wave-measuring instruments. It is quite in keeping with the man that he chose five stanzas of verse as his corporate image. His *Waves and Beaches* is a sound piece of scientific exposition, but concludes by talking of "the inner peace that comes with the quiet contemplation of a beach on a still calm morning, or the feeling of exhilaration that comes from riding a great wave in a small boat."

Bascom's vocation came somewhat late in life. He was born in 1916 in New York, where, as far as I can gather, his acquaintance with the sea was limited to surfing in a canoe on the wake of Hudson River ferryboats. From New York, he turned not seaward but inland, learning geology in its applied and theoretical branches first as a miner, then as a student at the Colorado School of Mines. Before getting his degree, he quit school and went to work as a mining engineer, burrowing into the landlocked soil of Colorado, Idaho and Arizona. Not until 1945 did he see the Pacific Ocean, and then he was in it up to and above his neck at times. He and John Isaacs, his great friend and fellow engineer-poet, had the hair-raising idea of using amphibious trucks to make soundings of beaches in a research project for the University of California. Isaacs would stand on shore and take a sight on Bascom as the latter drove an Army DUKW through the surf, heaving the lead to measure depths offshore (echo sounders will not register through the bubbly froth of breaking waves). The purpose of the experiment was to check actual depths off beaches against their appearance from the air so that amphibious invasions of enemy beaches could be planned from aerial photographs. With the end of the war, the research was continued for purely scientific purposes. In his book, Bascom relates he was so unfamiliar with the sea that he thought nothing of surfing in a truck, its front wheels dragging in the crest of a racing wave. Only when the Coast Guard washed its hands of the project did he have some sobering second thoughts, but he was enjoying himself too greatly to stop.

From the beach, Bascom moved to deep-sea expeditions with Scripps, where he remained until 1954. Then he joined the staff of the National Academy of Sciences in Washington as executive secretary of its Maritime Research Advisory Committee. He was also executive secretary of the Academy's committee carrying out the preliminary phases of the Mohole Project to drill through the sea floor to the earth's mantle. In 1962, he left the Academy to found Ocean Science and Engineering.

In the firm's brochure, I had seen a picture of Bascom in a Windbreaker against the background of a stormy coast. I had no trouble spotting him in the exhibit hall. He was as taut and lean in a business suit as in his promotional literature. I wanted to talk to him in particular about a report that his firm had found undersea diamond fields off South Africa that were now yielding $15,000 a day. He looked despairingly at the crowd and suggested slipping out to lunch — which we did, accompanied by his wife. Rhoda Bascom was a tall willowy girl with the sense of humor she needed, no doubt, as the spouse of a man who has proclaimed in the public print that his only love is the sea.

Once we had found a table in a seafood restaurant on the edge of San Diego Bay, I asked Bascom about his diamond strike. "We've never done any actual diamond mining, we only did prospecting. We have mapped puddles of diamonds, but it's not yet an economic proposition to mine them. In 1965, all the diamond dredgers off South Africa were losing money. What's the good of taking out $15,000 a day if you're putting in $16,000?" He stopped and gestured at the view from our table. "It's a question of ocean engineering. Properly managed, those diamond fields should make money. But the dredgers are stubbornly sticking to old systems and they lose money. The ocean isn't like this bay. If you're swinging heavy weights in high waves, you can knock a hole in the side of a ship. Making things bigger to do a job in the ocean only makes them more expensive. It's no answer."

Bascom told me that his company's volume went up from $150,000 in 1962 to $3 million in 1967, 2,000 percent in five years. "We're the broadest-based company in oceanography. We do everything. And we've got competitors everywhere." The firm's home office is in Washington, where its cable address is OCEANS, and it has impartially located its American division offices at Long Beach, California, and Palm Beach, Florida. It has spawned three mining companies and two others to own and operate research ships that it builds itself. It has bases in Thailand, Malaysia, Tasmania, the Philippines and Vietnam. It charters research vessels to universities without a navy of their own. It devises its own winches, cranes, buoys and tools for sampling the bottom. It has developed, as an offshoot of the Mohole Project, a dynamic positioning system that enables a ship drilling in deep water to stay on station without anchors, using only its engines. According to its literature, its investors include Du Pont, the Anglo-American Corporation, Southern Natural Gas Company and the Aluminum Company of America. "You can insert 'among others' in that," Bascom said.

His company is well in the forefront of the rush for minerals on the continental shelf. It claims "tens of thousands of square miles of undersea property holdings" and this is a game fully as heady as driving a DUKW through the surf. Once a concession has been granted by a government it has to be mapped and surveyed within a year, then cut to a tenth of its original area. Ocean Science and Engineering holds 10,000 square miles around Tasmania and 1,000 square miles off Queensland, in Australia. It has gold beaches on the coast of Alaska, a good geological gamble, for chances are high that the mouths of rivers will contain placer deposits similar to those found upstream on land. Bascom told me he was making applications for tin concessions off Indonesia and Malaysia. He has his eye on Korea and Central America as he keeps looking for the "highest-priced minerals in the shallowest water." He and his staff of 150 deal with the complexity of terrestrial politics and regulations. He has estimated that to obtain an offshore mineral exploration lease in the Philippines, a man from Ocean Science and Engineering must sign 20,000 official forms, a month's hard work at the rate of 1,000 signatures a day. In Thailand, another of his agents has been obliged to hire elephants at $50 a day to reach remote provincial capitals where offshore leases must be filed.

Bascom's firm does not limit itself to resources on the bottom. It was involved in the establishment of a fishmeal processing plant in Western Australia as early as 1964 and it is considering possible research on new fisheries and methods of catching fish. "Many people say there are no fish in deep water. We don't. I've got a list of thirty possible projects that I've given to my chaps. Sooner or later, I think we'll be in the fish business in some way. But remember, we have to make money for our investors and our clients. We deal basically with money people. They couldn't care less if they get a return by making fishmeal in Australia, building more tables in this restaurant or buying a stove company in St. Louis."

Bascom was more reticent about discussing the Mohole Project, whose beginnings and background he has described in his highly readable book, *A Hole in the Bottom of the Sea*. Over coffee, he told me: "Originally, it was a perfectly clear plan, a series of logical steps with, as their culmination, a hole that would reach the mantle. The book came off the press while we were out drilling the first hole. Everything happened as I wrote it."

11. The Birth and Death of
Project Mohole

The laconic Bascom was one of the few men I met who would even allow his name to be used in connection with Mohole. Elsewhere I ran into an unorganized conspiracy of silence. The grave dug for the project by Congress in 1966 was still fresh, but not a mention of its demise was to be found in the literature of research institutions. It had vanished without a trace, as if history had been rewritten. In private, scientists dismissed it with a few words, whether they had fought or favored it, and insisted on anonymity. One sensed neither bitterness nor recrimination, only wariness and a state of trauma.

I was quite ready to let Mohole rest in peace, but it refused to stay dead. The project, at its start, involved the drilling of a hole in mid-ocean to the so-called Mohorovicic discontinuity — or Moho — that marks the earth's mantle. Sediments and crustal layers were to be sampled at this site and others. To the seagoing geologist, it was an opportunity to look directly into sediments whose nature he had only been able to study from pinpricks on their surface. To the geophysicist, it meant direct observation of the processes beneath the earth's crust instead of inferences based on similar pinpricks or indirect methods. To the layman like myself, I am sure that it would have appeared as the boldest of scientific adventures, an exploration of the nature and origins of the earth at a moment when the exploration of the solar system had begun. I suspected I was being romantic in this attitude, but I found it shared even by scientists. When I told a French oceanographer, who spends too much time at sea to keep up with political life in his own country or in the United States, about the death of Project Mohole, he was crestfallen. "When I was studying geology at the Sorbonne many years ago, my professor used to tell us: 'Gentlemen, someday I hope to have a piece of the earth's mantle on this desk so that I can show it to you.' The poor old man, he must be spinning in his tomb."

Mohole stood out as an integrator in the infinite variety of oceanographic pursuits. It brought together not only the geologist and the geophysicist but also the physical oceanographer, whose help was needed to cope with deep currents affecting drilling operations and who could expect to gain from the use of a stable platform remaining in the same place for several years. Even the biologist was likely to derive some benefits, for the deep sediments contain the buried record of biological processes in the oceans of the past. When Bascom set out in his book to describe the scope and objectives of the Mohole project, he was forced to write one of the best popularizations of oceanography as a whole that I have come across.

Aside from all these reasons, I must admit that I will summarize the story of Mohole here because, at least in its happy beginnings, it is the kind of story one likes to tell. Bascom's book, from which I have taken most of my information, ended in 1961 just before the completion of the successful first phase of the project that set a long-standing record for drilling in the open ocean. It is particularly revealing as a study in scientific creativity, with serious results coming from what seemed the most frivolous of sources.

Guidance for the Mohole project in its first stage was provided by a body known as the American Miscellaneous Society. It had been created in the summer of 1952 by Dr. Gordon Lill and Dr. Carl Alexis, two geophysicists with the Office of Naval Research in Washington. Lill and Alexis, trying to sort requests for support that had come in from scientists, found that most of the proposals could be grouped only under the heading of miscellaneous. The two men decided that some sort of group was needed to deal with this heading and set up then and there the American Miscellaneous Society, with AMSOC as its acronym. They established five divisions within the society — Etceterology, Phenomenology, Calamitology, Generalogy, and Triviology — and immediately became affiliated with the Committee for Cooperation with Visitors from Outer Space and the Society for Informing Animals of Their Taxonomic Positions. Since the society's rules considered two members as a quorum, it was able to swing into action at once. In the office of one oceanographer, I ran into a communication dating back to December 1952. It read:

"The American Miscellaneous Society wishes to take this opportunity to welcome you into its membership and to apologize for its previous letter of rejection. The membership committee has reversed its requirements so that character references are no longer a prerequisite for joining.

"In addition, we take great pleasure in advising you that you are the recipient of the 1952 award for DYNAMIC INCOMPETENCE. The Award Committee voted unanimously to grant you this honor for your cleverness in getting rid of that taxpayer's nightmare which you so often have referred to as a yacht. Your wilyness in fooling a handful of scientists into removing the old tub to Honolulu under the guise of conducting worthwhile research en route is indeed unsurpassed. The yacht is gone, the scientists are happy, you are relieved of an awkward financial burden, and all was accomplished under the highest principles of Dynamic Incompetence. You are to be congratulated."

The founders of AMSOC had also set up a forum for discussion of matters that could not be handled anywhere else. They gave a serious hearing to John Isaacs's scheme for towing an iceberg up from Antarctica to California and concluded that it was not nearly as impractical as it sounded. AMSOC was willing to look at any ideas, providing they were too farfetched to be considered elsewhere.

So matters went until 1957, when they took a more serious turn. In March of that year, the Earth Sciences review panel of the National Science Foundation in Washington was considering requests for grants in geology and geophysics. It is the National Science Foundation, set up in 1950, that has the responsibility to initiate and support basic science with federal government funds. Walter Munk was one of the members of the earth sciences panel. So was Professor Harry Hess of Princeton, a geologist who had carried out one of the most unusual oceanographic expeditions in history. As a naval lieutenant during World War II, he succeeded in getting a deep-sea echo sounder mounted on an amphibious transport ship and in running it continuously while the vessel operated in the Pacific. In so doing, he had charted a number of isolated volcanic seamounts, some of them with their tops flattened by wave action, though they were far below the surface. Hess's ship not only participated in five major landings but advanced the cause of science as well.

Hess has given an account of the Washington meeting in the spring of 1957. "We had something like sixty projects to review in two days . . . we were rather tired, and Walter Munk mentioned that none of these projects was really fundamental to an understanding of the earth, although many of them were very good. We should have projects in earth science — geology, geochemistry, geophysics — which would arouse the imagination of the public and which would attract more young men into our science." Drilling down into the earth to take a sample of the mantle would be such a project, Munk suggested, and Hess thought it should be discussed by the American Miscellaneous Society.

The society held its next meeting the following month at Munk's home in La Jolla. The meeting, Bascom wrote in the *Scientific American* of April 1959, was a "wine breakfast," whatever that could have been (no treatise on oenology advises on what to serve with cornflakes). I have seen later comments on Mohole that sneered at it as a "wine-breakfast inspiration." If so, I would really like to know what Munk had served. By the time the morning was over, the Committee on Deep Drilling of the American Miscellaneous Society was set up with Lill, AMSOC's co-founder, as its chairman, and with five members. One of them was Roger Revelle, director of Scripps at the time.

Anyone accustomed to the glacier-like pace of ordinary committees can hardly believe the rate at which AMSOC moved. But the dates are on record. In September 1957, the august International Union of Geodesy and Geophysics met in Toronto and adopted a resolution urging a study of the feasibility and cost of drilling to the mantle. Such a study, the I.U.G.G. was told by a Soviet scientist, had already begun in the Soviet Union.

Two members of AMSOC, Hess and Revelle, had pushed through the resolution in Toronto with the help of Dr. Tom Gaskell, a British geophysicist. AMSOC's strength lay in the fact that its members were more powerful as individuals than as a whole. Of the drilling committee that had grown to nine members, five were also members of the National Academy of Sciences, created by Lincoln in 1863 as a private organization to honor scientific distinction and to advise the federal government on scientific matters. Hess was chairman of the Academy's Earth Sciences Division, and in December 1957, he asked the governing board of the Academy to take over the deep-drilling committee. It did, converting it into the AMSOC committee of the National Academy of Sciences. With its new respectability, the committee also acquired an enthusiastic executive secretary in the person of Bascom, who had been employed by the Academy since 1954. AMSOC was now ready to implement its conviction, as expressed by one of its members, that "the ocean's bottom is as important to us as the moon's behind."

It might be well at this point to halt for a few moments to look at the committee's ultimate objective: to drill down to the earth's mantle. How would it know when it got there? The mantle was "discovered" about sixty years ago by Professor Andrija Mohorovicic at the University of Zagreb in what is now Yugoslavia. Studying the seismograms of a major earthquake that had occurred in 1909, he noted that observatories a few hundred miles away from the scene had registered two distinct sets of seismic waves, as if there had been two separate shocks. Since this was not the case, he deduced that compression waves generated by the earthquake and traveling at the speed of sound had used two different paths under the earth's surface to reach the observatories. The late arrivals had not taken a longer route, but were moving through materials in the upper layer of the earth's crust that slowed their speed. The first waves received by distant observatories had traveled through deeper and denser rocks, where the speed of sound is higher. The difference between the two rates of movement was so sharp that Mohorovicic decided it could be explained only by a sudden change in the composition of the earth several miles down. The level where this change takes place is known as the Mohorovicic discontinuity — Moho for short and for the sake of pronunciation.

What seismologists believe to be a cross section of the earth is based on variations in the speed and paths of seismic waves. It shows first a solid inner core about 780 miles in radius and next a liquid outer core, composed perhaps of molten iron and nickel, about 1,380 miles thick.

They are wrapped in the earth's mantle, some 1,780 miles thick, under the Moho. Above the mantle are the crustal layers. Revelle, testifying in 1961 before the subcommittee on oceanography of the House Committee on Merchant Marine and Fisheries, described the earth "as a golf ball that has a liquid core surrounded by a very elastic and quite heavy mantle that, in turn, is surrounded by a crust of slag, like the paint on the surface of the golf ball." It was in a fit of inspiration that Bascom, in his *Scientific American* article of 1959, decided to call a hole through the Moho and into the mantle a Mohole, a label that he tended to regret at the time I saw him. He had given an easy target to congressmen who, seven years later, were able to refer to "Project Rathole" or to proclaim: "Let us not pour any more of the taxpayer's money down the Mohole."

Why drill in the middle of the ocean? Data supplied by seismologists show that the depth to the Moho and the mantle is much shallower under the sea than under the continents. This checks with measurements of variations in the earth's gravity. Bascom relates in his book how Pierre Bouguer, a French mathematician and surveyor, took gravity-measuring instruments (he used pendulums; today a highly accurate version of the spring scale is also used) to the Andes in 1740. To his surprise, he found that the pull of gravity was less on the mountains than at sea level. He then reasoned that the mountains were composed of relatively light rock rooted far below sea level. This has led to a conception of continental land masses as thick masses of "light" granite, extending in depth like icebergs. The crust of the earth is about twenty miles thick under the continents. Under the ocean basins, however, the crust is not granite but denser basalt of volcanic origin and much thinner, only six or seven miles thick. Therefore the force of gravity over the ocean basins is greater than over the continents. This was first shown more than forty years ago by a Dutch scientist, F. A. Vening-Meinesz, who took his sensitive pendulums down in a submarine where they would not be disturbed by the uneasy surface of the sea. His findings corroborated the seismologists' assumption that the dense rocks of the mantle are a great deal closer to the sea bottom than to the surface of the continents. A drill rig on a ship floating over 20,000 feet of water, for example, might have to penetrate only 30,000 feet of rock to reach the Moho. On land, it would have to go through about 100,000 feet, and drillers could have a nasty heat barrier on their hands. At that depth, the earth's temperature is 1,000 degrees C., almost three times the melting point of lead. At the site that would be chosen for the Mohole, Bascom expected a temperature of only 150 degrees C.

Munk and Hess were right in their assumption that this was a project that could appeal to the earth sciences. The mantle might be composed of the same material as the stony meteorites that arrive from space. It might be rocks similar to those found near active volcanoes or deep faults and suspected of having originated in the mantle. (The suspicions are based on the great density of these rocks, the high speed at which they transmit sound and their crystal structures.) Drilling to the Moho, making measurements on the way and sampling the mantle could teach the geophysicist much more about how the earth was made and about its dynamic processes. He already knows a great deal from his deductions based on seismic waves, gravity and measurements of magnetic variations. But going down with a drill to the mantle would have taken much of the guesswork, no matter how educated, out of his explanations.

The beauty of the American Miscellaneous Society in its informal early days was that it brought geophysicists and geologists together under a single flag. The geologists were interested principally in the upper part of the crust under the sea. They had been able to sample it only with corers, long tubes dropped overside on the end of a cable and driven home by their weight into the bottom. A great deal of ingenuity has gone into corers, but they seldom penetrate more than sixty feet into the bottom and usually much less. Consequently, they do not go very far back into time. They are limited to "recent" periods, only a few million years old, unless the geologist is fortunate enough to strike an outcropping of an older layer. Even so, the oldest sediments cored from the deep ocean go back no more than roughly 120 million years. The sea has been around for an estimated two billion years, and this leaves quite a gap to fill. Undisturbed by wind and weather, the sediments on the sea floor should form an ideal history book that could be read with cores brought up by a deep-drilling project.

But the book is too short. The rate of accumulation of sediment on the sea floor varies, but one can say for simplicity's sake, as Revelle did in his scientific lecture to congressmen, that it is about an inch every thousand years. After 100 million years, there should be sediments piled nearly a mile high on the ocean bottom. Instead, as probes with artificial explosion-induced earthquakes show, the soft sediments average no more than 1,500 feet thick. What happened to the earlier pages in the book?

Were they torn out by vast horizontal movements of the sea floor that ground off the sediments on the edges of continents? Or were they transformed into consolidated sediments that show up as harder rocks on seismic records? Or are they really there but simply masked by a layer of volcanic basalt on top of them? All these hypotheses were being argued at the time of the birth of the Mohole project and they are still a fertile ground for controversy. The only way to settle the argument is to take a drill bit down and look in a number of places.

Mohole, therefore, was to satisfy the curiosity of scientists from the top of the sea floor down to the mantle of the earth. Bascom wrote in the *Scientific American:* "Since the drill will pass through the time and place of the first life on earth, there is a chance of finding evidence of this life. As it proceeds backwards through time, the hole will enter the age when the first atmosphere and water caused the first erosion and sedimentation on the newly solidified face of the earth . . . A group of holes through the oceanic rocks to the mantle will not answer all our questions about the earth. On the contrary, they can be expected to pose new and more difficult ones that will tax our ingenuity even more."

The atmosphere was one of high hopes and great expectations. The AMSOC Committee was given $115,000 by the National Science Foundation to make a feasibility study of the project. Lill, the committee chairman, estimated in 1959 that the Mohole could be reached at a cost of $5 million. Even that humble sum prompted the Washington Geological Society to bill the 1960 version of its annual Pick and Hammer musical show as "Mo-Ho-Ho and a Barrel of Funds," with a hero named Bunkum. It was all good clean fun and no feelings were hurt.

Studies went ahead. Bascom and his staff worked out the problems of drilling 10,000 feet down with no visible means of support for their drill pipe other than a shifting mass of salt water. The trickiest problem of all was to keep a ship over the hole that it was drilling. Oil companies, already drilling in 300 feet of water, were using a complicated system of anchors, but this would not do in the deep ocean. The AMSOC Committee's staff decided to try what Bascom called "dynamic positioning," a way of holding their ship in place without anchoring it. According to their calculations, this could be done by mounting four giant outboard motors on the corners of a ship, their propellers steerable in any direction. The engines would be linked to an electronic control system feeding into a simple joy stick on the bridge. There, the pilot had only to shove the joy stick in the direction he wanted to head — backwards, forwards, sideways, any angle — and the propellers would be lined up correctly. To give the pilot his heading, Bascom decided to surround the drill hole with a ring of sonar buoys. The buoys, floating underwater at the end of a taut line limiting their movements, could send a sound signal to a receiver on the bottom of the ship, indicating to the pilot exactly where he was. He would also be helped by radar signals bounced off reflectors on surface buoys.

These proposals were submitted to the National Science Foundation in 1960 and the foundation agreed to meet their cost, an estimated $1.5 million. A vessel had already been selected for the experiment, the *Cuss I*, owned by the Global Marine Exploration Company in Los Angeles. Its name came from the initials of the four oil companies — Continental, Union, Shell and Superior — that had launched it in 1957. It was a surplus Navy freight barge 260 feet long that had been converted for drilling work with the addition of a derrick 100 feet high boring into the sea through a center well cut out of the bottom of the ship. *Cuss I* did its oil company jobs at anchor, and it had to be modified for the experimental Mohole by the addition of four big diesel outboard engines.

In March 1961, *Cuss I* was towed out of San Diego to a site eighteen miles off La Jolla for a test run. Five holes were drilled there in water 3,100 feet deep, the longest going 1,047 feet into the bottom. Everything worked, even though there was a tense moment when the drilling barge came out into the Pacific and caught a swell broadside, heeling over 24 degrees and snapping a guy wire supporting its derrick. At the end of March, *Cuss I* started a journey in tow to the site that had been chosen for the first experiment. It was 250 miles south of San Diego and 40 miles east of Guadalupe Island off the Mexican coast of Baja California. The site had been selected because it offered about 12,000 feet of water over a thin layer of sediments estimated from seismic studies to be only 600 feet thick. Here was a chance to see what lay under the sediments of the deep sea.

The ship took four days to make the 250-mile trip behind a tug, for a zigzag course had to be followed to keep her bow to the waves and prevent her from rolling. *Cuss I* arrived at the site on March 27 and began to drill the next day in winds of thirty miles an hour and waves fourteen feet high. The first hole penetrated only 230 feet into the bottom. On the 31st of March at sundown, another attempt was made. The drill bit, turning at forty revolutions per minute, encountered little resistance in the soft sediments. Cores brought up through the hollow drill pipe were opened on the deck of the ship and identified as grayish-green Miocene ooze, deposited no more than 30 million years ago. At four in the afternoon on April 1, the drill bit's downward journey slowed. It had entered a harder rock 553 feet below the bottom. A core was taken and it came up only five inches long. It was described as "two pieces of dark gray basalt, one of them with a glassy surface." This was the so-called second layer of the ocean's crust, previously identified only by the fact that it transmitted sound two or three times as fast as the sediments above it. *Cuss I* was far from the Moho, but this was the first time that the second layer had ever been seen. The drillers now ran into heavy going, their bit making two feet an hour. Twenty-one hours later, they had gone only another 42 feet and the bit was sticking. At a depth of 595 feet, they had to remove their drill pipe. Their final cores brought up a mixture of basalt and hardened sediment. Three more holes were drilled off Guadalupe Island and then the first phase of Project Mohole came to an end. *Cuss I* was returned to its owners to go back to its routine drilling for oil.

The happy ending to this part of the story came in Washington in May 1961 at the hearing of the House subcommittee on oceanography. Bascom reported on the experiment and Revelle appeared with a polished piece of the basalt that had been brought up from the Pacific floor less than two months previously. Scientists and congressmen got along swimmingly, with one of the latter remarking: "At least we beat the Russians to something." Revelle estimated that the mantle could be reached in three years with a big drilling ship at a cost of $20 to $25 million, but cautiously added: "I am always wrong about costs and everything always costs more than you think it is going to. Here you are venturing into the complete unknown and you would have no idea what problems you are going to run into." The hearing concluded on a gallant note as Revelle declared: "I would like to introduce the most beautiful member of the staff — Mrs. Bascom." The subcommittee chairman stated: "She should have been introduced earlier."

It was at this time that the AMSOC Committee recommended that responsibility for the operation of the project be taken out of its hands and turned over to a "prime contractor," to be selected by the National Science Foundation. The project was obviously going to cost far more than the $1.7 million that the National Science Foundation had spent on the first phase of drilling. *Cuss I* could not do the final job. A ship had to be built that could drill at sea for a year or more in the worst weather that the ocean could offer. New problems of drilling technology had to be solved. A way had to be found to remove the drill pipe from the hole, replace a worn-out bit and find the hole again 20,000 feet down. And there was little resemblance between punching a hole a few hundred feet through soft sediment and boring into miles of dense rock. At the time, the AMSOC Committee's decision looked like a wise one. This was a job not for scientists busy with their own lines of research but for big industry and practical engineers. The AMSOC Committee simply expressed the wish that it should keep overall scientific responsibility for the project.

The first crack in the Mohole edifice seems to have appeared at this time. Because of its flexibility, the AMSOC Committee had provided a home to scientists whose aims were not necessarily concordant. Geophysicists aiming at the deep rocks and the mantle needed a big stable vessel. Geologists concerned with the sedimentary upper layer would have been satisfied with an improvement on *Cuss I*. Within the AMSOC Committee, they had thought of an intermediate ship that could have cored sediments while testing equipment for the final Mohole effort. But the intermediate ship was apparently lost in the shuffle when the AMSOC Committee gave up the management of Mohole.

After asking for bids, the National Science Foundation chose Brown & Root, a large engineering construction firm in Houston, Texas, as the prime contractor for the project, whose cost in 1962 was estimated at $47 million. Politics inevitably intruded into a picture as big as this. There is no need here to awaken acrimony slumbering in the *Congressional Record*. Suffice it to say, the Mohole contractor had to be located somewhere and it was not extraordinary that he should attract prejudiced attention from the duly elected representatives of elsewhere. This would have occurred no matter which bidder had been chosen, though probably to a lesser degree. Crusaders for economy had a field day against money spent in Texas to drill a hole in the sea.

Parliamentarians love a good fight, but this was a tragic one for science. It pitted scientists against scientists on issues that could not be settled by mathematical proofs or indisputable data. To make matters worse, they were under a glare of publicity. Though Bascom had severed all connections with the project in 1962, he still must have shuddered when he saw the press referring to it a year later as "Project Nohole" or "Project Slowhole." In May 1963, *Fortune* ran an article entitled "How NSF [the National Science Foundation] Got Lost in Mohole." In January 1964, *Science* published three articles by Daniel S. Greenberg under the heading of "Mohole — The Project that Went Awry," calling it an administrative fiasco, "a classic case of how not to run a big research program."

It must be said that Brown & Root was more than generous in giving ammunition to its critics. The firm had run into serious management problems on the project, which was without an effective spokesman when one was badly needed in Congress. Its design for a drilling ship was a far cry from the modest solutions using surplus Navy hulls that had been previously proposed. It consisted of a vast platform, measuring 234 by 250 feet, supported by six huge columns on two lower hulls that would be submerged while drilling, for greater stability. A computer-controlled dynamic positioning system would operate propellers, located in the monumental columns, to hold it on station. Critics derided it as a "Texas acre." There seems to have been a clash between two basic approaches to working at sea: that of the oceanographer who cuts corners to get as much as he can out of a meager budget, and that of big industry accustomed to working with figures of the size current in the oil business or national defense.

In any case, scientific support for Mohole was further frittered away when plans for the platform were displayed. Brown & Root's giant had nothing in common with the intermediate ship that had been sought for shallow sediment drilling. Several of the original members of the AMSOC Committee formed a project of their own to take sediment cores. Only a handful of the committee stuck to Mohole until the end.

It came on August 18, 1966, when the House of Representatives, by a vote of 108 to 59, refused to appropriate $19.7 million to enable the National Science Foundation to continue the project. The estimated cost of Mohole by then had risen to $127 million, with $55 million already appropriated, but according to the magazine *Business Week*, only $20 million had been spent. Science was now quite remote from the consideration of the project. One of the main issues discussed on the floor of the House that day was a political contribution of $23,000 by relatives of the president of Brown & Root. Mohole was scored because it had no military applications. Even those congressmen who defended it shied away from its primary justification, the exploration of the inner earth. They brought in practical benefits. The Mohole platform could be used to recover objects from the sea floor, they said, in the event of a repetition of the *Thresher* disaster or the loss of a hydrogen bomb. Such arguments were shredded by opponents who questioned the suitability of a platform plodding along at six knots and unable to use the Panama Canal for such emergency operations. Basic research remained on the sidelines.

In my travels, I did find a scientist who admitted to having been a Moholer, although he too asked me not to use his name. When I assured him of anonymity, he talked freely.

"It was expensive, true, but not unwarrantedly so for what we wanted to do. People just couldn't imagine the magnitude of the job. You must build an awful lot of reliability into equipment if you want it to stay at sea three or four years. We were trying to do new things and some of them, like dynamic positioning, have already been picked up by the oil industry. I would say the project has already paid off in terms of gross national product.

"By killing Mohole, Congress reduced the budget of the National Science Foundation for 1967 from $499,699,000 to $479,999,000. Mohole was accused of taking too big a proportion of the foundation's budget. The trouble is, when you take a piece out of a pie, the whole pie gets smaller. The money saved was not put into other projects. Mohole was the kind of thing that expands science as a whole.

"It was really the victim of a combination of circumstances. Scientists were not unanimous about it and they split badly over the issue of an intermediate ship. This was an honest difference of opinion, but I can't help thinking of the space program. If you want to go to the moon, you can't shoot halfway. To go to the mantle, we had to build a ship that could drill down to it. That was what ran the expense up.

"Then, too, scientists got in the way of feuds between congressmen and between branches of government. Congressmen are lawyers; they build a fence around you without your knowing it. When a scientist comes out of his laboratory and walks into this, he gets shot down. I remember one witness who was asked about the added benefits that could be derived from the project. He suggested that a platform at sea would be a good way to measure precipitation over a long period. The next question was: 'You mean, you want to spend $100 million just to see if it's raining?'

"Mohole left great scars within the scientific community and in the relations of scientists with Congress. The people who thought up the project do not relish the prospect of going through this all over again. My guess is that in about a decade or so, it will all be forgotten. Then someone will look into it and there will be a Mohole project, probably under another name. Today, whenever it comes up in a conversation, I never say anything."

12. The Drifters and the Spreaders

The Mohole crisis may have been symptomatic of the state of modern marine geology. Of all the sciences in oceanography, this is the one where the tempo is quickest. In talking to many marine geologists, I entered a bewildering world where continents barge all over the map and the bottom of the ocean seems to be coming apart at the seams. They may or may not have agreed with these ideas, but they kept them in mind. Some of these men drove themselves like Captain Ahab over the oceans from the equator to the polar ice packs in search of a coherent explanation of how the earth took on its present shape. They drove themselves all the harder because the explanation is tantalizingly within reach.

Marine geology is not relaxing. Competition among schools of thought is intense and controversies are fought out in those muted tones of science where strong language consists of saying in public that the other man's conclusions are "not unambiguous." Marine geologists impressed me as enjoying it all hugely. They live in what Revelle, that eloquent spokesman of oceanography, calls one of the greatest eras of exploration in history. Within the lifetime of a person scarcely old enough to vote, they have found the most massive features of their planet. It was only in 1959 that three scientists — Dr. Maurice Ewing, Dr. Bruce Heezen and Marie Tharp, all from the Lamont Geological Observatory — put their names to a paper identifying a mid-ocean ridge 40,000 miles long, several hundred miles wide, 10,000 to 15,000 feet high and continuous under the world ocean. Hardly a month goes by without a scientific journal reporting on the discovery of another section of this submarine cordillera or an explanation of how it got there. It is the focal point for theoreticians who see it as the source of processes that are forming the sea floor and shouldering the continents aside.

Theories are best built on facts. I have heard the marine geologist's shipmates remark in envy that he has the advantage of studying the floor of the sea that stays still while he looks at it, unlike the uneasy waters or the life drifting and swimming within them. He benefits from a whole orchestra of instruments, most of them recently developed. The echo sounder, the magnetometer, the gravimeter, the underwater camera, the heat probe, the sediment corer and various acoustic methods of taking a subbottom sound picture have been as essential to this age of exploration as the compass, sextant and chronometer were to the last one. When Victorians were complaining at the end of the nineteenth century that there was nothing left to discover on earth, knowledge of the ocean basins was limited to what could be learned by lowering weights on ropes or wires from drifting ships. It was only in 1866 that the laying of the first transatlantic cable demonstrated in a spin-off that the middle of the Atlantic was not its deepest part (what geologists now call the Mid-Atlantic Ridge was first known as Telegraph Plateau).

Most discoveries are not made Columbus-fashion at sea but on drawing boards of research institutions where data must be plotted on maps. The Russians are the world's recognized masters of this painstaking work and their multicolored charts, labeled in Cyrillic characters, could be seen on the walls of all the institutions that I visited. The job can be done by computers, yet there will always be room for human serendipity. One of the most interesting features associated with ocean ridges are great faults that seem to break them into sections offset by many miles. Such faults in the East Pacific Rise, off western North America, run for nearly two thousand miles. They are probably the straightest lines in nature and they were discovered almost by chance. Dr. Henry W. Menard and his co-workers at Scripps first suspected their existence in 1949 when they saw striking depth differences on old charts of the Pacific off northern California. Each time a Scripps ship crossed the area bound for a long expedition, more soundings were taken until the first fault began to appear as a cliff more than a mile high. In 1952, a ship was due to sail to Eniwetok for hydrogen bomb tests and Menard was told that two days would be available for a zigzag survey over a fault zone. "We had only four crossings over that fault zone then," he told me, "and I tried to find the best places to fill the gaps in the shortest amount of ship time. So I got out a great-circle sailing chart and plotted the four crossings. They turned out to be in a perfectly straight line. I guess I was lucky. There was really no reason for a geologist to look at a great-circle sailing chart." Menard summed up the views of a number of members of his profession about sailing when he wrote: "Frankly, the ocean is little more than a nuisance to a marine geologist. It provides a convenient medium for transporting equipment, although it is regrettably unstable. Otherwise it seems to be an unnecessary filter which obscures every bit of information that one manages to collect." Another geologist is reputed to have suggested emptying the water from the ocean so that it would be possible to drive a car over the bottom. Believers in the theory of a hollow earth warned the sponsors of Project Mohole that this is exactly what would happen if they drilled a drain.

Not very many years ago, charts of the ocean bottom were considered no more reliable than the land maps of the mid-eighteenth century. Then the gaps began to be filled in by expeditions and the errors corrected by more precise navigation, now brought to its highest refinement with the use of artificial satellites. Knowledge led to theories. A respected marine geologist, Sir Edward Bullard of Cambridge, has said: "Speculations about the history of the ocean and about the mechanisms and the driving forces of geological change . . . are essential. If we have no theories, we have no means of deciding what to investigate next and are reduced to random sampling of all aspects of the oceans, an expensive and not very rewarding task. The main use of a geological theory is not, as in physics, to predict what will happen next but to suggest what observations are particularly significant and may refute the theory or distinguish between two versions of it. For this purpose, an incorrect theory may be very effective and may suggest experiments or new observations that lead to a theory nearer the truth."

Continental drift meets these qualifications perfectly. There have always been two main arguments in favor of it. One is biological: similar fossils are found on continents now separated by great ocean expanses, particularly South America and Africa. This similarity, which appears to have ended about 130 million years ago, was first explained by a land bridge or even a continent that had sunk into the South Atlantic. The other argument refers to the present outlines of the continents themselves. It takes no great stretch of the imagination to see how the knee of South America fits into the groin of Africa, a description I owe to Dr. Robert S. Dietz of the Environmental Science Services Administration in Washington. Dietz has written well and extensively on the fitting of continents. Unlike those who maintain that everything started from a single land mass known as Pangeaa, he is in the camp of the advocates of two supercontinents, Laurasia in the north and Gondwanaland in the south, that allegedly (the reader will forgive my use of the newspaperman's disclaimer, but drifting continents are dangerous ground) began to split up some 200 million years ago. Laurasia was allegedly composed of Europe, Asia, North America and Greenland, while Gondwanaland consisted of Africa, India, Australia, New Zealand, Antarctica and South America. The existence of a mid-ocean ridge outlining Africa as a "ghost" contour has led some to believe that it was the heart of Gondwanaland before the other continents moved away from it.

The two supercontinents each measured 32 million square miles before they split up, Dietz has calculated. India made the journey north from Gondwanaland to Laurasia, breaking away from Australia's western coast and crashing into Asia with an impact sufficient to raise the Himalaya Mountains like a crumpled fender. At the collision point, Dietz says, the earth's crust is two continents thick, with the Tibetan Plateau resting on what had been the northern edge of a peripatetic India.

There is nothing new in the idea, first suggested by Francis Bacon, that continents have moved around. Its most vigorous supporter was Alfred Wegener, a German meteorologist and Arctic explorer, who published his book on *The Origins of Continents and Oceans* in 1915, revising it three times before his death in 1930 on an expedition to Greenland. Wegener's circumstantial evidence for drift, based mainly on the arguments already mentioned, was impressive, but he lent himself to criticism when he tried to bolster his case with questionable geodetic measurements to prove that North America and Europe had actually traveled many yards away from each other in a few years. He also came up against the problem of how to move the light granitic masses of the continents through the heavy basalt crust of the ocean floor. The "pole-fleeing force" and the "westward drift" that he suggested were dismissed by geophysicists as far too puny.

After Wegener's death, the idea of continental drift fell into disgrace. Mere mention of it was enough to cause a general lifting of eyebrows. Land geologists, among whose ranks are still to be found the most determined antidrifters, tended to think more in terms of vertical rather than horizontal movements. "It may be because they started out by looking at their feet," one oceanographer gently said to me.

Then came the golden age of marine geology after the Second World War. Evidence was being amassed that had to be either explained or explained away. The verticalists' traditional view of the ocean basins as sunken continents took a severe blow when no signs of the wrecks could be found. Geologists trying to follow certain older geological formations on land noticed that they seemed to have been chopped off at the steep slope where the continental shelf dives into the deep sea and the boundaries of the true ocean can be said to begin. Then there was that matter of the sediments, in layers apparently too thin to justify their eternal presence on the bottom. The sea floor was not simply land with water over it.

The mid-ocean ridges drew more and more attention. In many sections, they were split along their crest by a median valley, a rift that might be an open seam. The plotting of earthquake epicenters indicated great seismic activity under the ridges. Heat probes were dropped into their flanks on the ends of cables. Heat flow up from the mantle there was several times higher than normal for the ocean floor, another hint that something unusual could be going on. These observations were just starting to come in. Knowledge had reached the proper stage for the formulation of theories, when large rules can be laid down and all the exceptions have not yet appeared.

If the Fifties saw the first major exploration of the ocean floor, the Sixties have been a decade of explanation. Continental drift has been rescued from its limbo by geologists like Dr. J. Tuzo Wilson of Canada

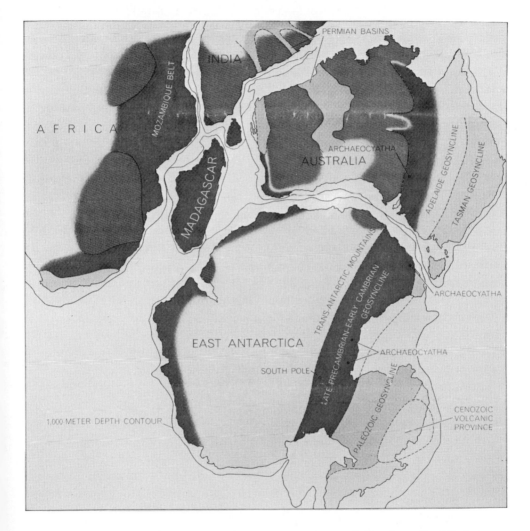

This might have been the southern supercontinent of Gondwanaland before it was split by the spreading sea floor.

who are convinced that no understanding of land geology, geophysics or evolution is possible until the issue is settled. A number of theoreticians have found a way to move continents and to time their speed. They believe the driving force comes from the sea floor spreading out from both sides of the mid-oceanic ridge. It is hard to say exactly who led the way into this trend of thinking, but most marine geologists I met referred me to the work of the same Harry Hess of Princeton who had surveyed the seamounts of the central Pacific from a wartime landing ship.

In 1962, Hess published what he called an "essay in geopoetry." He began his epic with the formation of our planet something like 4.5 billion years ago. At that time, he assumed, the earth contained a high proportion of short-lived radioactive elements. They heated it to the point where a "great catastrophe" occurred, a convection that "segregated an iron core" and "produced the primordial continent."

Convection is a word that one often hears from marine geologists. They explain it with the analogy of a long, deep pan of oatmeal on the stove. Heat from a burner in the middle will send a column of oatmeal up to the surface, where it spreads out and then descends at the edges of the pan to form rotating "convection cells."

Hess ventured that 50 percent of the land mass of the continents was formed during this single great catastrophe. The other half has been produced since then by smaller convection cells, under the mid-ocean ridges, that send molten material up from the mantle. Water too has been coming up from the mantle to fill the ocean basins. From the rift valleys along the ridges, mantle material emerges and spreads out on either side, at the rate of about one centimeter (a centimeter is four-tenths of an inch) a year. That makes a total spread of two centimeters a year away from the ridge. Hess applied this calculation to the mid-oceanic ridge in the South Atlantic and multiplied it by 200 million years. His answer was 4,000 kilometers, the distance that separates South America from Africa. Perhaps they had once been a single land mass, riven by rising mantle. Hess thought this was a better explanation for continental drift: "Continents ride passively in convecting mantle instead of having to plow through ocean crust."

He saw other clues. The seamounts he had found and called guyots in honor of a Princeton geology professor, were not nearly as numerous as they should have been on the ocean floor. He suggested that guyots began as volcanoes atop a mid-ocean ridge. Then they were edged away from it at a rate of a centimeter a year, traveling down the flanks of the ridge to the deep sea floor where he had found them. They rode this conveyor belt of moving mantle until they reached the "jaw crusher" of the descending column of the convection cell, where they were "metamorphosed and eventually probably welded onto continents." Such could also be the fate of the ocean's sediments. They might journey along the belt and disappear before they had time to accumulate to any great thickness. In short, Hess theorized, "the whole ocean is virtually swept clean every 300 to 400 million years." As for the continents, they ride the belt, but when they reach the descending side of the convection cell, they cannot be forced down. Their density is too low; they float. So the "leading edge" of the continent is strongly deformed, as in the case of the west coast of North America on the Pacific. The Atlantic, Indian and Arctic Oceans are "surrounded by the trailing edges of continents moving away from them."

Dietz reached about the same conclusions and gave them a name, "the spreading sea floor theory," that has subsequently stuck. He saw the deep ocean trenches as a way of completing the conveyor belt. Material comes up from the mantle through fissures in a ridge and moves along the ocean floor until it reaches a deep trench, where it descends again to the mantle. He favored this explanation because it enabled sea floor spreading to exist without an expansion of the earth to twice or even twenty times its original size, as other writers had implied.

All this was highly conjectural, but it is hard to stop anything as big as the floor of the ocean once it has been put into motion. The next major piece to be fitted into the case for continental drift came from researchers of a different bent who had been looking closely at the earth's magnetic field. Work with paleomagnetism, pioneered by Dr. Stanley K. Runcorn in England and by others, had already indicated that land masses might have moved. The dip of "frozen compasses" — rock particles magnetized in the past — did not correspond to their present geographical position. Then the problem was looked at from a different slant. Scientists had two factors to go by. It had long been known that lava is magnetized as it emerges on the surface. When it cools below the Curie point of about 500 degrees C., it retains this magnetism permanently. Recently, strong evidence has been found for periodic reversals of the earth's magnetic field about every 400,000 to 500,000 years. Prior to the present magnetic era, which began 700,000 years ago, a compass needle would have pointed south. And lava emerging at that time appears today as reversely magnetized.

This has been called a natural tape recorder by writers who force me to shift my analogies. Instead of oatmeal coming out of the ridge, they ask me to visualize a magnetic tape. As it unrolls, it registers the earth's magnetic field as normal or reversed. It lies on the sea floor, waiting to be played back into a magnetometer towed over it. If the tape has really been unrolling — that is, if the sea floor has been spreading — the magnetometer should register a striped pattern of crust, on which reversed and normal magnetic directions alternate.

In 1963, the tape recorder was found and its testimony taken as a witness to sea floor spreading by F. J. Vine, now at Princeton, and Dr. D. H. Matthews of Cambridge. They had looked at magnetic surveys of the Mid-Atlantic Ridge, and a detailed survey of the Carlsberg Ridge (named in honor of the Danish brewery's financial contributions to oceanic research) in the northwest Indian Ocean that had been made in 1962 by a British vessel, H.M.S. *Owen*, during the International Indian Ocean Expedition. Study of the results led them to suggest that "50 percent of oceanic crust might be reversely magnetized" in the area of the Carlsberg Ridge, and that "if spreading of the ocean floor occurs, blocks of alternately normal and reversely magnetized material would drift away from the center of the ridge and parallel to the crest of it."

Three years later, Vine was able to take another look at the evidence. In the meantime, many more surveys had been made, particularly over ridges in the North and South Atlantic, the eastern Pacific and the Red Sea. A pattern of reversals of the earth's magnetic field for the past four million years had been worked out. Vine could now hold a stopwatch over the sea floor and clock its speed, interpreting the stripes in the magnetic record. A narrow stripe during a magnetic era of known duration meant a slow rate of spreading, a broad stripe during the same period indicated faster spreading. He suggested that the sea floor was moving away from the East Pacific Rise in the southern hemisphere at a rate of 4.4 centimeters a year, nearly five times higher than in the Atlantic and Indian Oceans. Magnetic chronology also enabled him to determine how long the ridges had been active. He estimated the age of the main part of the Mid-Atlantic Ridge to be between 150 and 200 million years, and that of the northwest Indian Ocean Ridge between 80 to 100 million years. Rates of spreading calculated from available magnetic profiles "are in exact agreement with those needed to account for continental drift."

As research at sea intensifies, theories are often modified by the type of geologist who believes only what he has seen for himself. The theories themselves are skeletons that must be fleshed in. There are some bothersome aspects. Gravity measurements do not always fit conveniently into the concept of a mantle upwelling through cracks in the mid-ocean ridge. Opponents of convection like to point out that the deep trenches that are said to engulf the moving sea floor are found in the North Pacific 7,000 miles away from the nearest ridge. The whole idea of continental drift is discarded by a leading Soviet geophysicist, Professor Vladimir V. Beloussov, who maintains that the continents have never moved at all on a horizontal plane. Changes in their shape have been brought about by vertical movements, and the bottom of the Atlantic Ocean itself may be a continent that sank and was transformed into oceanic crust in the process.

Even the variations in the layers of sediments do not make an airtight case for steady spreading. According to theory, they should be thin over the ridges and thicken gradually on the flanks and the plains. The sea floor unrolling from the ridge should be clean at first, then grow slowly dustier towards the edges. It is true that seismic studies of the Mid-Atlantic Ridge show its crest to be free of sediments for 50 to 75 miles on either side. Beyond this distance, the dust does not thicken gently. Instead, there is a sudden increase in the depth of the sediments. This has led Maurice and John Ewing at the Lamont Geological Observatory to suggest that sea floor spreading has occurred in fits and starts. The clean areas over the ridge might have been produced during the last 10 million years during an active period, while the thick layer farther out shows a previous era, lasting from 30 to 40 million years, when the ridge was quiet and sediments fell onto a stationary carpet. If this timetable is correct, then estimates of continental drift rates may have to be revised.

Some geologists have reminded me that it would be very abnormal indeed if mid-oceanic ridges were covered with thick sediments. On this jagged terrain, falling sediment, like snow, should not be asked to stick to the steep sides of bare mountains, even if the mountains are standing still. Others have made very close studies of small selected areas of the Mid-Atlantic Ridge that lead them to remark that "ocean-wide concepts are not necessarily present in a small area." Under the magnifying glass of such a study, for example, the smooth stripe of normal magnetization over the center of the ridge can break down into bits and pieces of varying magnetic strength that must be explained. The theoretician in marine geology bears the burden of proof. I met one leading geophysicist whose measurements do not jibe with the concept of material rising from the mantle. When I asked him if he could produce another theory to explain how the sea floor has been created, he said relievedly: "I can't — but just because I'm stupid, it doesn't mean that I'm wrong."

A way to get at the problem is to study an ocean before it has grown to an unmanageable size. There should be some places on the planet where the process can be seen at its start. One might be the Gulf of Aden on the northwestern corner of the Indian Ocean, separating Somalia on the Horn of Africa from the southern edge of the Arabian peninsula. To the east, the Gulf of Aden faces the open ocean; to the west, it ends in the bottleneck of the straits of Bab el Mandeb leading to the Red Sea. In recent years it has been scrutinized by Dr. Anthony S. Laughton of the National Institute of Oceanography in Great Britain.

Laughton is a product of the seedbed of marine geology and geophysics that was nurtured at Cambridge during the 1950's by the late Maurice Hill, and he spent a year at Lamont, a hotbed, in 1955. At his laboratory in Surrey, where he was working up data harvested by the International Indian Ocean Expedition, Laughton expressed a view held by many of his contemporaries: "Our outstanding problem is to demonstrate the existence of a mechanism for continental drift. Even if we are convinced that it happens, we must decide how it happens."

The Gulf of Aden, only 150 nautical miles wide, lends itself to such a purpose. Laughton has remarked that it is one of the few places on earth where the mid-ocean ridges are linked to a continental ridge system. The Great Rift Valley of Africa, starting in Mozambique 1200 miles south of the equator, gouges its way north on the map of Africa to Ethiopia, where it splits, one branch striking north through the Red Sea and the other bending east into the Gulf of Aden. Researchers from Cambridge were able to connect it up to the Carlsberg Ridge in the Indian Ocean when they found the link lying on the sea floor in three separate sections displaced by fracture zones.

Laughton believes that we are witnessing the birth of an ocean in the Gulf of Aden. As early as 1935, soundings showed a rough spine of ridges and high valleys running through the middle of the gulf. Since

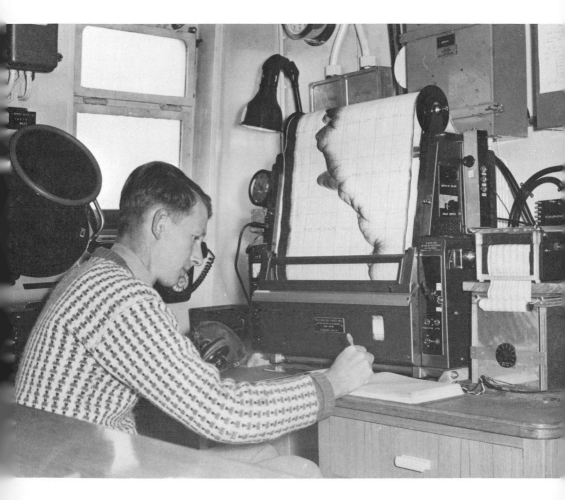

Anthony Laughton logs a precision echo sounder as it brings in the edge of a volcanic island structure.

this miniature ocean lies on a route often used by survey ships, it is now covered by sounding tracks less than ten miles apart. A detailed cross section of its topography can be drawn, looking like that of a full-sized ocean: a steep continental margin, a flat trough, and a rough central zone from Africa out to mid-gulf; then the same picture in reverse from the center to the Arabian coast.

To qualify as an ocean, the Gulf of Aden must also pass seismic tests. It was first suggested in 1958 by scientists from Lamont that continental crust ended here only twenty miles at sea. In the spring of 1967, Laughton made a thorough seismic survey. It revealed the crust under the gulf to be only six miles thick, as under an adult ocean. Magnetic and heat flow measurements showed the mountainous center to be behaving like a mid-oceanic ridge.

Consequently, Laughton is ready to assume that the gulf represents not a dropped continental block as once was thought but a horizontal split, with Arabia moving away from Africa on a northeasterly course at the rate of two centimeters a year. This means that the two shores were joined 20 million years ago. Land geological features formed prior to the schism should match on both sides of the gulf. Laughton believes they do and he has made some convincing fits, particularly of river canyons now separated by 210 miles of salt water.

Much of this is speculation, Laughton admits, and he would like more data. A key point about which little is known is the junction in the Afar depression of Ethiopia where the Great Rift Valley starts to split into the Red Sea and the Gulf of Aden, cradling Arabia. Here, there should be signs of oceanic crust on dry land, formed when Arabia was first torn loose. Unfortunately, information about this area is sparse because, as Laughton writes, it is "extremely inaccessible, uncomfortably hot and peopled by unwelcoming primitive tribes." The lot of the land geologist is not always an enviable one.

Laughton foresees the day, not too far off, when geodesists using laser techniques will be able to set up stations on two continents and lay down a figurative tape measure to see if they are actually separating, even at less than an inch a year. Until that day, marine geology will continue to flourish in productive controversy as one side tries to determine whether the continents are drifting, and the other, reduced to a stalwart handful, argues about whether they are drifting at all.

13. Project More-holes . . . .

As these lines are being read — but, embarrassingly, not while they are being written — a team of twenty scientists and technicians aboard a ship the size of a small ocean liner should be on an expedition drilling into the sediments of the Atlantic and the Pacific. For once it is the writer who hangs from the cliff, while the reader already knows the next episode. I can only report on how it all came about.

The idea of sampling a wide area of the ocean with a number of shallow holes took shape, as I have noted, at about the same time as the Mohole project itself. It led to the establishment in May 1964 of a Joint Oceanographic Institutions Deep Earth Sampling program. Involved in JOIDES were Scripps, Woods Hole, Lamont and the Institute of Marine Science at the University of Miami. Support came from the National Science Foundation, first for experimental drilling off the coast of Florida in 1965, and then for the much bigger phase that is now going on. The NSF earmarked $12.6 million to equip a drilling ship and take it to sea for the present operation, a comparatively modest sum. JOIDES's more-holers have been able to take advantage of the extraordinary progress made by the oil industry in offshore drilling. The necessary techniques are now available without expensive research and development, thanks in part to research already performed for Mohole. As the jargon goes, they have been able to get these techniques more or less off the shelf.

Though the project is not intended to come within miles of the Moho discontinuity and the earth's mantle, it is still putting down holes in 20,000 feet of water, the greatest ocean depths ever to be explored by drilling, and it is going farther than ever before into deep-sea sediments. More important than these incidental drilling records, it aims to supply marine geologists with the kind of evidence that they have always envied their dry-shod colleagues. The oil drillers have been restricted to the continental shelf. In the deep sea, geologists have had to rely on their gravity-driven corers that really never get beyond the preface to the story of the seabeds. The JOIDES drill can go through all the oldest sedimentary chapters and into the first rocks beyond them. The slender cores, which are hauled up by a wire inside the drill stem, can then be read not only by the institutions originally involved in JOIDES but by qualified researchers throughout the United States and abroad. What the drillers are bringing up is a lending library of best sellers.

Unlike poor Mohole, JOIDES has a home. The National Science Foundation in 1966 gave Scripps overall responsibility for the management of the deep-sea drilling program that is now in progress. At La Jolla, I talked to several of the men who have been involved in the project. They all emphasized that Scripps is only putting a roof over it. The Scripps press office leans over backwards to the point that it does not even use the term JOIDES anymore so as not to create the erroneous impression that the precious cores might be reserved for the project's four founding institutions. Scripps's representative on the JOIDES Planning Committee has been Dr. Tjeerd Van Andel, an ex-Dutchman who told me very precisely: "What we are operating here is a facility for the community of scientists. Scripps's direct responsibility ends with the initial descriptions of the cores as they come up — a visual description and preliminary estimates of age." Then he became less official. "Of course, even the initial core descriptions will be getting close to people's flesh. If, for example, they show sediments definitely getting older as the ship moves away from the crest of a ridge, the preliminary results will be published . . . anonymously. All that we want to do is to produce a Sears catalog that scientists will be able to use to order samples."

Van Andel gave me charts and documents setting out the purposes of the program and how they are to be achieved. Basically, it wants to learn the age of the ocean basins and the processes that have made them what they are today. The ship is spending eighteen months at sea, nine in the Pacific and nine in the Atlantic, from the end of 1968 through 1970. The longest haul between ports will be two months, more than enough time to spend aboard a drilling ship (scientists on the experimental Mohole project reported that sleeping was highly problematical with nineteen diesel engines running at once). Cruise tracks in both oceans have been carefully worked out by the JOIDES Planning Committee to cover as many question marks as possible in the time available (which has led to irreverent remarks about Joyous Days in committee meetings). The tracks run from the Philippine Sea to the South Atlantic. About seventy holes have been plotted, with top priority assigned to forty of them.

Drilling in the Atlantic should produce more results more quickly. Since their ocean is half the size of the Pacific and much better explored, the members of the JOIDES Atlantic Advisory Panel were able to narrow the scope of their search. The panel felt that "conclusive evidence necessary to establish the age and origin of the ocean basin may lie within reach of the drill," and set up a program accordingly. On the chart, the expedition route starts in the Gulf of Mexico, loops around the Florida cape to New York, then slashes diagonally to Dakar on the hump of Africa. From there, it drops nearly 3,000 miles due south, zigzags east to Rio de Janeiro and finishes in the Gulf of Mexico once more after skirting South America.

The route was laid out with two principal areas in mind: the Mid-Atlantic Ridge, where the ocean bottom is supposed to be the youngest, and the very edges of the deep basin near the boundary of the continental slope, where it should be the oldest. It is hoped to pierce the ridge with six holes in the North Atlantic and four in the South Atlantic. Between New York and Dakar, the drillers will scale the ridge with three holes on its western flank, then move down from the crest with three more holes to the east. A distinctive striped pattern of normal and reversed magnetism has been found here and geologists are eager to get into the rocks below the sediments to see what causes it.

Van Andel told me the ship may not be able to work over the bare crest of the ridge itself because at least 100 feet of sediments are needed to stabilize the drill before it can start chewing into rock. He also warned me against great hopes that the drill will bring up all the answers. "Those large-scale magnetic patterns were found by ships using surface magnetometers. But they might never have been discovered if there had been no water in the ocean. Deep water acts as a filter to get rid of small variations. When we tow a magnetometer close to the bottom, we don't get such broad stripes. Instead, the record shows small ups and downs very close to each other. True, the overall trends correspond to what is seen on the surface. But when we drill, what we find will depend largely on which of these variations we penetrate. We will get more evidence, but we may be sorry for it at first."

The deepest water over any Atlantic site is 18,000 feet in the neighborhood of the Puerto Rico Trench. The deepest planned penetration into the bottom is 6,000 feet in the area of the Sigsbee Knolls, a puzzling belt of submarine hills in the middle of the Gulf of Mexico. They are thought to be salt domes, the type of structure the petroleum geologist seeks as a trap for oil and gas deposits. If they are, the Sigsbee Knolls still will only be of scientific interest. They lie 11,000 feet down, and there is no way at present to work an oil field at such a depth.

A large number of the Atlantic sites have been chosen because seismic exploration has shown thick sediments that may yield an undisturbed historical record. Microscopic fossils in these sediments tell of changes in climate, the life in the past oceans and the position of their major currents. This work can lead to some interesting comparisons between the Atlantic and the Pacific. "Both oceans are open at both ends to polar water," Van Andel said. "Naturally, this governs their circulation. But what if sediments had been deposited in the Atlantic at the time when Europe and North America are supposed to have split like a pair of dividers with its hinge north of Iceland? If they did, the sediments may show a more stagnant circulation at that time, something closer to what is now found in the Black Sea sediments. I doubt if this will be seen in the Pacific. The evidence in the sediments there should be that of a normal open ocean at all times, even when the Atlantic was only a puddle."

Tracking the Equatorial Current through time is one of the project's main objectives in the Pacific. JOIDES's Pacific Advisory Panel has drawn a north-south line on the globe about 900 miles west of San Francisco. Eleven holes will be bored along this line, which runs for 4,500 miles. When life borne by the Equatorial Current dies, it leaves a swath of microfossils on the bottom, like bones along a trail. If the current had been further north or south in the past, then fossils should be present in buried sediments under its old path. There is the possibility that more than just water masses shifted. If the earth itself had been spinning on a different axis in the past, then its poles and its equator would not have been where they are today. The old sediments could indicate a current that had flowed along a paleo-equator.

It is particularly in the Pacific that the drilling project will blaze a trail for future expeditions. The advisory panel has laid out a reconnaissance of island formations, seamounts, little-known basins, and sites suspected of being the ocean's oldest. Over one of these basins, the drill is going down in 19,800 feet of water, the greatest depth in the whole program. Signs of sea floor spreading will also be sought in a series of holes across the East Pacific Rise.

I was able to glimpse some aspects of the problems in the Pacific when I talked to William Riedel, Van Andel's alternate as the Scripps representative on the JOIDES Planning Committee. Riedel is a big friendly Australian who proved an excellent source of information. He keeps up with everything his colleagues are doing, a necessity in his work as curator of Scripps's collection of 3,000 cores plucked from the ocean bottom. Riedel was senior scientist on *Cuss I* when the experimental Moholes were drilled off the Mexican coast in 1961, and he is a paleontologist of the first order. Most of the time, I would interrupt him with questions while he was peering through a microscope at one of the 46,000 slides in his office, particularly at radiolarians.

The ocean's sediments consist of many things — material brought down from land, volcanic ash, meteorite particles from outer space, grains of quartz blown from the deserts over the sea, and the remains of marine life. Paleontologists are interested mainly in the microscopic shells that once housed single-celled plants and animals leading a planktonic existence near the surface. When they die, their homes settle to form thick beds of ooze. Riedel patiently explained to me that ooze comes in two main varieties. Most prevalent are the calcium shells of foraminifera (animals) and coccoliths (plants), an ooze blanketing a third of the ocean floor. A tenth of the bottom ooze is formed by the silica shells of radiolarians (animals) and diatoms (plants). But the radiolarians and the diatoms have exclusive rights to the deep ocean. Pressure at depths greater than 12,000 feet dissolves the calcium carbonate in the shells of the foraminifera and the coccoliths. Below this depth, the story of the past is best read in the radiolarians.

Riedel easily becomes enthusiastic about his subject. After he had helped me adjust his microscope, I had to agree radiolarians are a pretty sight. They are named after the radiating structure of their shells, and the earliest, found in marine sediments on land, go back nearly half a billion years. Families disappeared or took on new characteristics with the passing of time. "The first radiolarians had spherical shells, with spines coming right out from their center," Riedel told me. "In more recent ones, the spines end at the innermost sphere, not in the center." He regaled me with slides and drawings of his little beasts, whose size is measured in thousandths of a millimeter. Some were conical spongy masses of latticework, others resembled a tooth with a three-pronged root. One species looked to me like a cup with ribs coming down from it. "It's called *Ceratoikiscum avimexpectans*," Riedel said, writing in my notebook. "It means 'stony house waiting for a bird.'" The name was a great deal bigger than the object it described.

Once he has magnified them a few hundred times, Riedel can assign dates to his radiolarians. It may have taken 10 million years for something called *Hexaspyris papilio* to lose four little spikes under its shell and acquire a bigger one above it, appearing in a later incarnation as *Dipodospyris forcipata*. A "young" version, only 25 million years old, is a pair of ice tongs with a few spines on its edges and still another name.

Riedel has gone as far back as samples taken by the *Challenger* in 1875 to try to show where radiolarians have been living in the Pacific during various epochs. The work has been rewarding. At the time I met him, he was giving up his days to introduce me to hexaspyrids, and spending his nights on a paper for *Science* to report on what the radiolarians have to say about the spreading of the sea floor. He had taken a 1,200-mile section of the East Pacific Rise from the equator to the point where it runs aground on the Mexican coast, then he had studied the radiolarians found in sediments seaward of the rise almost as far west as Hawaii. He had to rely on fortuitous finds of old microfossils in places where they had worked their way up or where recent sediments were thin enough to

William Riedel and Phyllis Helms inspect a fragment of sea bottom in Scripps's chilly core locker.

allow the corer to get into older layers. From this information, he plotted the zones where radiolarians identifying past epochs had been discovered in the greatest numbers. A clearly defined parade away from the East Pacific Rise could be seen on his charts. Microfossils 60 million years old were found as far as 2,700 miles to the west of the rise, but none at all near its crest. To explain their presence there, Riedel calculated that they had traveled away from the rise at a rate of eight centimeters (3.15 inches) a year, twice as fast as the East Pacific Rise is thought to be spreading in the South Pacific.

Riedel will be much happier as soon as something resembling a verdict can be brought in on the theory of a spreading sea floor. His own experience on the early Mohole drilling test showed that the top layer of the sediments conceals more than it reveals. When the usual short cores a few yards long are taken on that site off the Mexican coast, they come up devoid of fossils and there are only a few organisms living in the water above it now. But the deep drill penetrated hundreds of feet of ooze rich in tiny shells that had once sheltered organisms. "The area is now covered with a desert water mass because the productive California Current hugs the coast further inshore," Riedel said. "Yet it was no desert during the Miocene epoch about 20 million years ago. The drilling cores show that the California Current existed in those days and that it was further offshore. Or else, I'm afraid, the current might have stayed in one place while the sea floor moved out from under it. That's the impasse we're facing. Before the spreading sea floor theory, we could always say that something had changed in the water above the floor. But now we can't. We either have to disprove sea floor spreading or understand it completely. On the deep-sea drilling ship, you can be sure that pieces of a core will be going under a microscope ten minutes after it hits the deck."

I had never seen a core, short or long. Riedel took care of that at once. He turned me over to his assistant curator, Phyllis Helms, and she led me down to the Scripps core laboratory. When a ship comes in from a cruise, the cores are brought here, split open, photographed and then placed in a refrigerated room where they are kept at 42 degrees F. to preserve their moisture. Half of the split core goes into the archives, the other half is used for sampling. Cores are cut up in sections and stored in shallow plastic troughs about five feet long and two and a half inches wide. The corer, I could see, really doesn't bring up much more than a

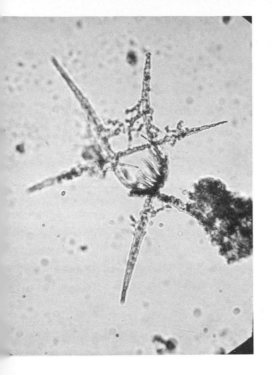
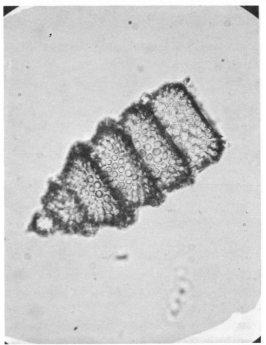

*"Stony house waiting for a bird" (upper left)
and other radiolarians, all magnified 280 times,
from deep Pacific sediments.*

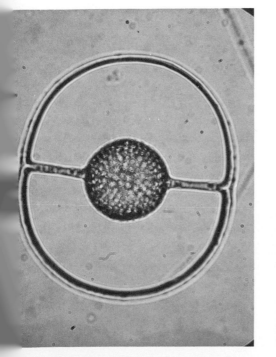
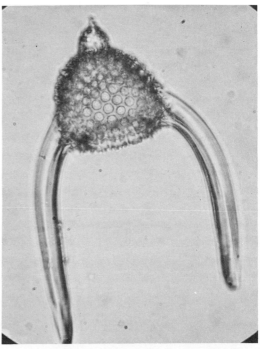

thin vertical sliver when its tube slams into the bottom. Drilling cores are much longer but no wider, since they have to pass through the drill pipe.

The storage troughs were sealed with masking tape. Miss Helms obligingly opened one for me. My first view of the ocean bottom. Just mud. She looked at me scornfully. "That's not mud, it's brown radiolarian ooze. Feel it. It's more like sugar than sand." I did. It was. "Each of these little grains you feel — they're much smaller than a grain of sand — is a radiolarian." She showed me mottled zones inside the cores that she always avoids when she scoops out samples for researchers. "They're probably worm burrows. The worms can move material all around." The biggest samples, as much as half a core at a time, go to people interested in soil mechanics. They are tested to see how much weight the bottom can be expected to support. The Navy, she said, has a steady demand for such samples. "I don't know what they're putting down there, but I guess they don't want it to sink out of sight." Miss Helms unwrapped one of her prize exhibits, the experimental Mohole core taken when the drill got through the calcareous ooze of the sediments for the first time and began to gnaw into basalt. She pointed to the ooze, then a dried grayish-tan chalky rock, then a chunk of dark basalt. Several sections of the core were missing and replaced with the names of the persons who were working on them. It has been one of Scripps's most popular cores.

Despite ventilation pipes, there was a rich pungent smell inside the core locker. It was cold, too. Miss Helms must be one of the few people in Southern California who wears a fleece-lined Windbreaker much of the time at her work. I began to shiver and she took mercy on me. We finished the visit in a warmer room, used for storing manganese nodules of all shapes and sizes, from the dimensions of a marble to a big slab that had come up entangled in a steel line put down by a ship for an entirely different purpose. There were rocks, too, hundreds of them broken off by dredge hauls. "I think we could throw out most of these rocks and no one would miss them," Miss Helms said. "But not the manganese nodules. They're always in demand." Which ones in particular? "The ones that the other fellow has just published on. We never give out more than half a nodule."

Then she showed me the equipment that was to be used to photograph the cores aboard the deep-sea drilling ship. The cores would be shot in color as they were cut open, in a continuous operation that could go on for thirty-six hours if necessary. Getting a clear picture on a vibrating ship seemed the main problem that had to be overcome. What bothered Miss Helms a great deal more was space. Miles of cores were to be brought up by the drilling ship and she needed a new building to handle the ones that would be stored at Scripps.

After I had thawed out, Miss Helms delivered me to Riedel, who suggested that I learn something about the production side of the drilling project now that I had been given a preview of the product. The manager of the project at the time was Dr. William W. Rand, who had drilled the first hole in the sea floor.

Rand's office was in the comfortable frame house that had been the home of Scripps's directors during earlier days. The old house, scheduled for demolition, had been given a reprieve to serve as headquarters for the project. It was slightly to one side of the rest of the institution, and so was Rand. In my album of encounters around the ocean, he has a page all to himself. He turned out to be a businessman and a humanist, a driller and a scholar. During the few hours that I spent with him, he told me a story of offshore oil prospecting that began with a man hammering a pipe into tidal flats and ended with a fleet of drilling vessels under such proud names as *Exploit, Decatur, La Busca* or *La Ciencia.* He had sold out his drilling interests for a sum more than enough to allow him to live exceedingly well in his home at Santa Barbara and to travel wherever he pleased, indulging in his weakness for puddle-jumping airlines in Australia or South America. Now he was back in harness on a drilling job where the profits can be only scientific.

Well into his sixties, Rand was a hale man with steady blue eyes beneath black eyebrows. His coat was off, but he was wearing a necktie with his white short-sleeved shirt. I mentioned that I had not seen such formality very often at Scripps. "I'm still used to the unsubsidized world," Rand said. "And I'm not yet accustomed to not having competition." He has had it nearly all his life and has thrived on it. He now enjoys an independent fortune and an independent mind that he speaks freely.

The son of a cattle rancher, Rand was born in Utah but came to California with his family in 1904. As a young man studying at Berkeley, he got his first whiff of the oil business while pumping gasoline in his spare time at a filling station. "I started out in engineering, but my math wasn't very good," Rand said. "Since I didn't have enough brains to be an electrical engineer, I went into geology." The Shell Oil Company must have had a higher opinion of him because they hired him in 1926 and he stayed with them until 1945, except for occasional relapses back into university life. He took leave from Shell on one occasion for two years, returned to Berkeley and then taught at Sacramento Junior College ("I was their whole geology department at the time"). Rand began in geological exploration for oil, but he was managing the distillation plant in Shell's Martinez refinery in 1933 when he was awarded his doctorate from Berkeley. By 1945, he had looked for oil on the continent of the United States from California through the coast of the Gulf of Mexico to Florida. He switched to the management side. "You might say I was office boy to the vice-president in Houston. My job was to evaluate fieldwork in geology and geophysics, to get the play together for executive action."

It was becoming routine, and Rand looked out to sea. Not very far, just to the Channel Islands off Santa Barbara. He had written his Ph.D. thesis on one of them, Santa Cruz, and he convinced the Union Oil Company of California that it might be worth going offshore. The geology of the coast and of the islands was known. Something worthwhile could lie in between. Rand probably had some salt water in his blood, too. A Bostonian grandfather had been lost at sea as the captain of a clipper ship, the *Ceylon*, whose name Rand later bestowed on an oceanographic vessel in his drilling fleet.

"We got prints of the original Coast Guard soundings, we added sea floor elevation contours, then we started seismic work in 1947. Seismic exploration shows only folds, not the geologic age of the formations. Besides the structural picture obtained from seismic surveys, one must also know the ages of the folded beds. We decided to get samples near shore to demonstrate to a somewhat skeptical management that undisturbed core samples containing diagnostic fossils for age determination could be recovered at sea. We took a two and a half inch pipe, inserted a slightly smaller pipe that was longitudinally split, and tried it. I drove it in with a sledgehammer at low tide, and dug it out with a geologist's pick as the tide came in, getting thoroughly soaked in the process. Then I showed the sample to the Union people. It was an undisturbed core two feet long. The conservatives had said it couldn't be done just by punching a tube. A conservative is someone who believes that nothing should be done for the first time."

As a next step, Rand made a longer tube and took it seven miles south of Santa Barbara to Carpenteria Reef in a skiff with a friend. "When we were in twelve feet of water, we threw out an anchor. He held the pipe with his hand while I stood on the gunwales and hit it with a sledge. The second day, he turned up with a pair of wooden pliers two feet long."

From the skiff, Rand graduated to a converted minesweeper equipped with a winch for dropping dart corers into the bottom and hauling them out. "The winch operator lowers a dart corer until he feels bottom, then he raises it and lets it fall freely. We call it a cookie puncher. It was good in areas where there wasn't too much overburden — sand, for example — above the shale we wanted to look at. If you bury a dart corer in fifteen feet of sand, you can lay a small ship over trying to get it out in some areas where the bottom is covered with quicksand."

There were places where 200 or 300 feet of overburden covered the layers that Rand wanted to examine. To get at them, he devised a corer with a high-pressure hose clamped to its wire. The hose cleared a path down to hard shale for the heavy tubelike coring tool. "We couldn't pull too hard on those, either, when we wanted to bring them up or else the hose would separate from the wire. We've got several core tools permanently planted out there."

By 1951, Rand decided that he had reached the point of diminishing returns in coring. Drilling was the next logical move. He built his first rig, mounted it on steel beams over the side of the *Submarex*, a 173-foot converted naval patrol craft, and drilled the first hole in the bottom of the Pacific Ocean. The following year, he was already drilling more than a thousand feet down and operating a fleet of drilling vessels for Union Oil and other major oil companies. Rand also happened to drill the first hole in the Atlantic. In 1956, the rig on the *Submarex* was shipped east, mounted on a Navy tug and taken to sea 90 miles east of New York, where it drilled 300 feet down in 300 feet of water to test foundations for a Texas tower.

Offshore oil drilling was a rapidly growing business. To keep up with it, Rand took a 200-foot lumber carrier, an ex-Navy landing ship, and converted it into a drilling vessel, the first to have a rig mounted over a central well or "moon pool." Other pioneers did the same, and in 1957, oil was found a mile out to sea between Santa Barbara and Ventura. The rush was on. Rand set up four different corporations and drilled "thousands of holes" between Canada and Mexico before he sold his stock and assets in 1966. "It was about the time I was selling that I got a call from Scripps. In June 1966, I was in business and drilling for sulphur over salt domes in the Gulf of Mexico. On the first of July, I was an employee of the University of California. Now, I'm spending the taxpayer's money. I'm not sure I've justified it yet, but I'm trying."

I asked Rand how big his business was at the time he sold it. "I was operating a fleet of eight drilling and sampling vessels, and I had 300 employees. This year, I've paid Uncle Sam over $75,000 and I'll pay another like amount next year. I figure that I could work about ten years and my taxes will more than repay all my present salary."

Then I wondered what had attracted him in the first place to the scientific drilling job. "It's not nearly as matter-of-fact as it sounds," he answered. "Nobody has ever hung 20,000 feet of pipe from a ship with no lateral support except water. A drill string that size is worth $225,000. If you drop it, you'll never see it again. The difficulties are much greater than they were in moving from the *Submarex* to bigger ships. Safety is vital. An engineer can design for 50-foot waves and 110-knot winds, but no one knows the maximum storm conditions at sea nor in what condition the vessel may be when they are encountered. A 100-mile-an-hour gust can hit a ship just when she is at her maximum angle of roll. The crown block on a drilling rig weighs several tons. Let's say it's on top of a 142-foot mast and the ship is rolling 30 degrees single amplitude, with a 10-second roll period. That crown block will accelerate from zero to 35 miles per hour, and then go back to zero, all in five seconds. The job is inherently and unavoidably hazardous. I've watched a drilling ship operated by another contractor go down in a storm. But we've never had any fatalities or serious injuries, and we have never lost a ship. It's like crossing a busy street. If you know it's dangerous, then you really watch out."

The technical problems can be formidable. Rand reminded me that drilling with 20,000 feet of pipe, five inches in diameter, is the equivalent of trying to bore a hole with a strand of baling wire 300 feet long. Materials will be put to their utmost test. A computerized system has been worked out by General Motors on a 500-foot Navy tanker to keep the

Above, William W. Rand aboard SUBMAREX *in 1952, with equipment used to drill the first hole in the Pacific. Below,* GLOMAR CHALLENGER *performs scientific exploratory drilling in 20,000 feet of water.*

ship in position. The computer pilot, changing the speed and direction of propellers mounted fore and aft, can hold the vessel within a horizontal radius of 600 feet of the hole in the sea floor. The drill pipe, Rand said, is designed to take that much movement without serious damage.

Deeper holes have already been drilled on land. An oil company has gone down to 25,000 feet, an expensive record that commercial firms will probably soon break. The Soviets should be a great deal farther down than that in their own deep-hole exploration on the Kola peninsula east of Finland, where they are shooting for a depth of nine miles. The JOIDES holes, however, are the deepest that anyone has tried to drill using only salt water for circulation. Rand explained to me that drillers usually pump mud down into their hole to prevent it from caving in and to bring up the cuttings from the drill bit. On the scientific drilling ship, salt water is pumped down through the drill pipe to the bit to keep it from clogging and to remove the cuttings. Rand was concerned about the possibility of holes collapsing with this technique, but it was the best available for such unprecedentedly deep work at sea. He was also worried — no doubt for the first time in his life — about the possibility of finding oil. "All sorts of territorial questions are still unanswered, and the ship is not equipped to handle blowouts. If it struck oil or gas, it would be a disaster."

Rand has thought about the broader consequences of the march of science into the sea. He showed me a copy of a talk he had given in Los Angeles to the Harvard Business School Club of Southern California. In it he described the objectives of the deep-sea drilling program and the interest it had stirred in the business world. Then he ended on the challenge of social rather than technical problems:

"Let us suppose that a hostile power should use submarines to place a number of nuclear devices in reasonably deep water off our coasts, which could be simultaneously detonated by remotely controlled or delay mechanisms. The explosions could generate waves of great height, traveling at some 400 miles per hour, which could sweep rapidly inland and depopulate our coastal cities — thus, in effect, presenting them to an invader without the nuclear contamination of an air-burst nuclear explosion.

"Here we have an event that is not technically impossible. Neither is its prevention technically impossible. But it may be far easier to prevent such a happening by solving social problems connected with its possibility than by developing technical means to prevent such a disastrous chain of events from being set in motion.

"The ways in which we choose to employ our tremendous and increasing capability for changing our environment will determine whether or not mankind will at last be successful on the earth and in the universe."

When he took over the management of the deep-sea drilling project, Rand thought that he would be most useful in the preparatory stages. He showed no signs of age or weariness when I talked to him, but he did feel that he should step aside at the proper moment to make room at the top. "I'm cheating a young man out of a job," he said to me.

Rand later retired and he was succeeded by Kenneth Brunot from the following generation of oil geologists and drillers. The project moved forward. Scripps announced that, under its mandate from the National Science Foundation, it had selected Global Marine Inc. of Los Angeles as the drilling contractor. Their vessel, the *Glomar Challenger*, has a displacement of 10,500 tons, and an overall length of 400 feet. It was to go to sea with its crew of seamen, drillers and scientists just about the time that this story is going to the printers. From my already-buried stratum in time, I can only wish them bon voyage and refer the reader to his newspaper. Here, as in many other stages of my race to keep up with oceanography, I am in the same predicament as the meteorologists who tried to make long-range forecasts in the precomputer days. They had the data and they could set up equations to see what would happen. But by the time they solved the equations, it had already happened.

14. On Torrey Cliff

Strictly speaking, the first JOIDES holes were drilled long ago. In 1965, just a year after the four institutions got together on their deep-earth sampling program, the holes were put down in a modest way off northern Florida by a small ship bound from California to Newfoundland to explore for oil on the Grand Banks. An oil company generously allowed a team of scientists to take over the ship on one leg of the voyage and the National Science Foundation paid the cost of a month of scientific drilling.

Six holes were bored, starting from the Florida coast and then going off the continental shelf onto Blake Plateau, under 3,500 feet of water. Two of the holes went into sediments laid down 70 million years ago. The result was a clear profile showing how land sediments gradually thinned as they sloped away from the coast. As a bonus, the ship struck fresh water twenty-two miles at sea when the drill pierced an aquifer. Perfectly good drinking water spurted through the drill pipe with enough pressure to send it thirty feet above sea level.

The Lamont Geological Observatory of Columbia University was in charge of operations on these first JOIDES holes. Lamont is accustomed to firsts. I have already mentioned that the mid-ocean ridge as a world-wide mountain range was discovered by its geologists. So was the thin crust that distinguishes the ocean's floor from the continents. Lamont has put a date on the beginning of the Ice Ages and advanced an explanation of their cause. It has drawn relief maps that show the grandiose land-scapes of the ocean basins for the first time. Lamont's scientists believe they have found submarine avalanches, where sediments race down the continental slope at sixty miles an hour to carve out submarine canyons. As reported here in another connection, they put the first seismograph on the bottom of the deep ocean. Sooner or later, they will put the first one on the moon.

Lamont is first an observatory, then a think tank. It has collected more information about the solid earth under the sea than any other scientific institution in the world. It goes on collecting it, gradually shrinking the blank spaces on its maps. It runs its ships harder and keeps them longer at sea than any other institution I know. It is not a restful place. After a few days there, one feels that this is what the atmosphere will be like when a manned observatory is finally set up on another planet to explore it and learn its origins. Time will be short, facilities will be expensive. Such an observatory will be tense and seething . . . like Lamont. Time on Planet Earth is not unlimited, either.

Few theories come out of Lamont which are based largely on bril-liant armchair speculation. Scientists there are as brilliant as anywhere else, but they do not have much time to spend in armchairs. Most of them are on a ship two months a year in an environment that does not encourage speculation. Given a questionable theory, their immediate tendency is not to argue but to take it to sea to see if it holds water. They gather mountains of evidence and do not hesitate to announce that they have proven themselves wrong. When a Lamont researcher does produce a controversial hypothesis of his own, it is not so easy for his colleagues elsewhere to put it to the same test. Lamont usually has most of the available information.

Since a layer of seawater separates Lamont from geological truths, it is an oceanographic institution more by necessity than choice. It does work in marine biology and physical oceanography, but these are acces-sory goals. While it is far from the biggest oceanographic institution in the United States, it is the most intensely purposeful. More than any of the others, it is the emanation of a single man. Lamont was founded and forged by the only director it has ever had, Dr. Maurice Ewing.

I had found Lamont and Ewing by following a trail of remarkable scientific papers. At the International Oceanographic Congress in Moscow in 1966, a geologist from Lamont reported on the end of the world, after having described its beginnings. At a symposium in Zurich on the world rift system, fifty papers were presented by scientists from thirteen countries. Nine of them were from Lamont, a typical proportion at affairs of this nature. The trail finally led me on a scenic drive from New York over the George Washington Bridge and then up along the cliffs of the Hudson Valley to Palisades, New York, just above the New Jersey line and on the edges of the city's overspill. A barely discernible sign on Route 9-W indicated Lamont Geological Observatory and what looked like a sharp turn into a forest. I followed a winding road past small buildings planted among the trees until I reached a broad lawn. A massive bronze plow-horse was grazing on the lawn, with a bronze Abraham Lincoln sitting in its saddle and reading a book. The lawn ran up to Lamont Hall, a sandstone and clapboard house, long and low, only two stories high, manorial but not overwhelming. It looked as if it had been there forever.

I first met Ewing indirectly through his wife, Harriett, who worked for him as his assistant before their marriage and still does. Mrs. Ewing is a pleasant, attractive woman, petite and blonde, who speaks of her husband with insight and reverence. Her minute frame is the only barrier between him and the world outside. None of the oceanographic institutions I saw were top-heavy with administrators, but Lamont had the clearest decks of all. Mrs. Ewing answers the director's phone there, and if she happens to be out, the director answers it himself except during the two or three months of the year when he is at sea.

The house was newer than it looked, Mrs. Ewing told me in her office upstairs. The site of the geological observatory had been a rocky cliff above Sneden's Landing on the west side of the Hudson, a little more than a hundred years ago, when it attracted the attention of John Torrey, one of America's greatest botanists. Torrey found a plant paradise there, and bought some land for a botanical garden and a summer house. After his death, Torrey Cliff slumbered until it was purchased in 1928 by Thomas W. Lamont, a partner of J. P. Morgan & Company and later chairman of its board. Lamont built the stone house I had admired, and improved his 125 acres on a scale befitting his position. His covered swimming pool merely had to be boarded over to serve as the present staff cafeteria. His tennis courts were ample enough to accommodate the geophysics building subsequently built over them. The world's biggest collection of deep-sea cores was housed until only recently in his garage. Lamont died in 1945 and his widow gave the property to Columbia University four years later, keeping only a small part of it that is still set aside as a bird sanctuary.

Ewing at the time was a professor of geology at Columbia and the university offered him the site for an observatory. He came to Torrey Cliff in 1949, taking his seismographs from the basement of Schermerhorn Hall in uptown Manhattan and installing them in the Lamonts' root cellar. The cellar measured thirty by fifty feet, and according to a local rumor reported nationally by *Time*, it had once been stocked with enough provisions by the Lamonts to ride out the revolution they expected during the depression. When the invasion did come, it was carried off peacefully but completely. On the Lamont estate, there is now a staff of 500, minus two shiploads of scientists who are always at sea.

Ewing brings the curse of hard work into once-leisurely surroundings. In 1953, Columbia University acquired the observatory's first ship, the *Vema*. She had been built in Denmark in 1923 as a 734-ton yacht, a lovely three-masted schooner for the Hutton family. She later passed into the hands of the Norwegian shipowner, G. Unger Vetlesen, who renamed her *Vema* after his wife, Maude Vetlesen. In 1932, Mrs. Ewing told me, *Vema* set an unofficial record for an ocean crossing under sail, running from Montauk Point to Bishop's Rock in a shade under eleven days. She was a magnificently appointed vessel, with a Louis Seize boudoir and French period furniture throughout. All of this remains only in albums. Her sky-raking topmasts were not used when she became a research vessel, although she did carry a press of sail during her early years with Lamont to steady her. The sails went with the introduction of stabilizing tanks, and now the masts have gone, too, in a major reconversion. She has been shorn of her wooden figurehead, a screaming eagle painted white and gold, after corrosion was found in the hull beneath it. The eagle was moved to the parking lot outside Lamont's oceanography building, where it now stands like a totem. What apparently lasts forever, Mrs. Ewing said, is *Vema*'s 202-foot iron hull. At twice the retirement age of most ships, the ex-schooner still takes a 300-day trip around the world every year. In 1963, she was joined by Lamont's second vessel, the new 1,320-ton *Robert D. Conrad*, which also goes around the world every year. The two ships, it has been said, circle the earth as faithfully as a pair of satellites.

By now they have nearly a million miles of cruise tracks behind them, seldom over the same point except when they necessarily funnel through the Panama Canal. The ships have covered all the oceans and all latitudes from Decepcion Island off Antarctica to the Greenland Sea. They continuously map the sediments on the sea floor by seismic reflection. The *Vema* used to do it with half-pound charges of TNT, firing nearly 130,000 of them during a trip. An airgun is now used instead and the ships no longer sail with sixty tons of explosives aboard. Once a day, each ship stops to take a core. The Lamont corer goes down with a camera, a 50-gallon water sampler, and probes to take the temperature of the sediment. Winching it up sounds like a daily miracle. Lamont takes sixty-foot cores, their length limited by the deck space available for handling the coring tube. It is fortunate that drilling in the deep is now feasible or Ewing might have looked enviously at the *Queen Mary*.

Ewing was born in 1906 in Lockney, Texas, and studied physics at Rice Institute. He published his first paper in *Science* when he was only twenty. Entitled "Dewbows by Moonlight," it was based on his observations of rainbows formed on the dewy grass of the campus under a bright moon. It was romantic, but seismology proved more interesting. In 1931, he received his Ph.D. at Rice with a thesis on the calculation of paths which seismic waves follow within the earth. He kept at this subject all through his early career as a physics instructor, first at Pittsburgh and then at Lehigh. Oil companies were already using explosions to generate their own seismic waves, and by recording the travel time of the waves through different strata, they could learn the structure of the earth below. In 1934, Ewing was asked by Professor Richard Field of Princeton and William Bowie of the U.S. Coast and Geodetic Survey if he would be interested in doing such seismic work at sea. No one had ever done it, but he leaped at the chance. He later told a reporter: "I was so desperate for a chance to do research that if they had said the moon instead of the ocean, I would have tackled it."

Ewing and two other men, A. P. Crary and H. M. Rutherford, began shooting explosions on land along the coastal plain of Virginia. When they reached Cape Henry, they kept going right out to sea, using nitro-

Maurice Ewing and VEMA

gelatin as an explosive and a whaleboat as a shooting ship. Their explosions were picked up by a seismograph lowered to the bottom. The result was a profile showing that the structure of the coastal plain continued out beyond the water's edge. Ewing did not stay in shallow water very long. Shortly before World War II, he, J. Lamar Worzel, and Allyn Vine of Woods Hole devised their deep-sea camera to take photographs of the ocean bottom, another way to get through the seawater barrier between the marine geologist and his subject. During the war, Ewing turned to underwater sound and took leave from Lehigh to work at Woods Hole, where he remained until he joined Columbia's geology department in 1944. Five years later, he had carried his seismic work at sea to the point where he was able to prove that the crust of the earth was thinner under the ocean.

I learned all this from Mrs. Ewing and the library in Lamont Hall. Ewing himself does not have time for reminiscing. At Lamont, I had come across a bulletin board notice he had signed. It gave instructions to ships' masters and chief scientists for reporting by radio on the results of stations taken at sea. He had devised a code to get the most information into a message at the lowest cost in transmission charges. The notice made it clear that Ewing is not willing to wait more than a few hours to learn if an unusually old core has been taken in the sediments. The reason why he is in such a hurry, so I was told, is that he wants to be able to alter the ship's operations and get the extra data needed to capitalize on an important discovery. On the other hand, he did not want anyone wasting words and money to report measurements unlikely to warrant a change in plans.

Ewing was recording a station when I entered his office, the breakfast room of the Lamont family. I had called his wife for an appointment and it was he who answered the phone and told me to come over. An old globe stood in the middle of the room, charts rolled under it and a tape measure draped over the Pacific Ocean. "I was looking at the station of the *Conrad* when you phoned up," Ewing said. "Something went wrong with the corer." I asked him why he was doing this himself. "Everyone else gives a damn only about his own work," he said. "The chance to do science is my pay. The other junk I have to do." The director of the Lamont Geological Observatory continued to set down on a chart what had happened at Conrad Station 150 at 1000 h. on the 26th of June just north of New Guinea. He had once called science "a million tedious little jobs about as humdrum as drilling a hole in a piece of brass."

Ewing is a heavyset man with determined features and strikingly white hair who kept a cigar going as he spoke. He was not a bland talker. He tended to let his eagerness get the better of him whenever he mentioned his aims. Though he is Higgins Professor of Geology at Columbia, his manner is more Texan than professorial. We were interrupted only once by the telephone. When he answered it, he put his feet up on the windowsill and thrashed out the problem of getting *Conrad* into a dry dock to repair a leaking fuel tank. His mind was never far from his ships.

"I started trying to work at sea in 1935," he said. "Then, the great problem was just to get on a ship. We grew up under the rule that nothing is more precious than the ship's time. If you get time, you want to use it. When I started at Columbia in 1949, a few of us got together and drew lines on a chart from New York to Bermuda and 200 miles beyond. We thought if we could cover that area with seismic measurements in a lifetime, we could consider it a rich life. But we've kept going."

Ewing has not forgotten the lean and hungry days of oceanography. "We put down every damn track as though it's the last time we'll ever get to sea. A monkey wrench hasn't been flung into the works yet, but you never know. The most expensive factor is ship's time. But it's not the cost that worries me, it's that I'm going to live just so many years more." His gnawing impatience has always led him to build his own instruments instead of waiting for them to be developed, and he still has a bench and a toolbox set aside for him in the Lamont workshop. With his younger brother John, he put together a device to enable a ship to take a seismic reflection profile while under way, literally photographing hundreds of thousands of miles of sediments below the bottom. "It was about 1960 that we got our continuous profiler working. We sent *Vema* down to the Argentine Basin. She dropped bombs every two minutes — every two minutes day and night, Sundays and holidays. If you've spent twenty years trying to measure a few spots and then you get something that can measure at 10 knots, well, that's a red-letter day."

Ewing always races time. "I had my own training in physics. I used to feel the great heroic days had passed, the period between 1898 and the 1920's that saw the discovery of radioactivity, relativity and quantum theory. When papers came out in quantum mechanics, we were taught them a few weeks later by our professors. Earth science is now where physics was then. I missed that heroic period, but I won't miss this one. Geology used to be a great big debating society. Now it's becoming like physics. We're getting to be able to describe processes. Who has ever had so many wonderfully big questions so close together?"

He is in the thick of all of them. Ewing had been dubious about sea floor spreading until he and his brother John wrote their paper stating a case for intermittent spreading. "A theory cannot violate what we see," he told me. "The sediments look undisturbed to us in the deep-sea trenches, yet this is where they should be mashed up against the continents. But when we look at our crossings of the ridge system, we see evidence of a recent burst of spreading following a quiescent period with heavy sedimentation. We think there has been ten million years of intense spreading . . . if there has been spreading at all." Ewing did not sound very satisfied with his explanation. His search for a fuller answer is still going on. On half of the deep-sea floor, he has remarked, there is less than 300 feet of sediment. In other places, there is as much as 3,000 feet, and in the Argentine Basin of the South Atlantic, sediments are piled two miles thick. He told another interviewer a few years ago: "Is there a pattern? When will I see it? I feel every night when I go to sleep that surely I'll see it when I wake up."

The Argentine Basin has led Ewing into a completely different question. In 1961, *Vema* discovered a thick layer of clay there that was not linked to the continent, its most obvious source. How did it get there? How are the sediments formed? Ewing is now photographing the waters of the ocean from the surface to the bottom. He and a colleague have devised a nephelometer, a camera that is lowered by Lamont's ships when they stop to take a coring station. On the way down, it keeps taking pictures to register the cloudiness of the water (its name comes from the Greek word for cloud, *nephos*). Ewing calls it the underwater equivalent of a fog-indicating device.

"The purpose of this study is to see how clay particles get out from the continent onto the ocean floor. There was the classical idea of sediments in the open ocean raining down on the just and the unjust, but the bottom doesn't look that way. Nor does the water. Our nephelometer profiles may show a cloudy surface, cloudiness near the bottom and clear water in between. We have speculated about this for years. We thought the water might have looked cloudy off the bottom because we were getting bad pictures. Perhaps the camera wasn't in focus or there was a thumbprint on the lens. So now we put down barrels with the camera. We collect the water and we centrifuge it on the ship. Not all our pictures are good, but *some* of that water has clay particles in it."

Lamont's cameras have found cloudy layers rising hundreds and even thousands of feet off the bottom. Analysis of certain water samples show they contain enough suspended clay particles to maintain a downhill flow. What Ewing suspects is that this is a gravity-powered system shaping the ocean floor. Clouds of suspended clay particles might roll gently down from the continental rise and hundreds of miles out to sea, leaving behind them a blanket that smooths over rough rocky features, fills depressions and produces the flat abyssal plains.

A short talk with Ewing can be exhausting for anyone trying to keep up with his flow of ideas. Ewing admitted that he had trouble keeping up with them himself. "It's a problem of time. If something gets 90 percent finished, I can't touch it anymore. If I had to start over again, I think I'd work two years on a newspaper to learn to meet deadlines. More and more things deflect me. My desk never gets clear before I go to sea." Mrs. Ewing told me she had managed to clear it only three or four times in all the years she had been working with him.

It is true that Ewing is one of the few men in his bracket of oceanography who still go to sea. "I love it," he said. "Going to sea is a little like dying. You go whether you're ready or not." At one point, he nearly combined the two. He did not tell me the story, but I came across it in a scrapbook in the Lamont library. In January 1954, just a year after *Vema* had started to work for Columbia, she was five days out of New York when she ran into a bad storm. The two Ewing brothers and the first and second mates were out on deck trying to lash down some shifting oil drums. A wave swept all four men into the sea. The *Vema*'s captain climbed the masthead, giving instructions to his helmsman as he tried to spot them. *Vema* put about and crossed the area again. On her first pass, she picked up John Ewing. On the second try, she missed the men in the water. Then on the third pass, the ship's crew recovered the second mate and the elder Ewing, temporarily paralyzed and suffering from a brain concussion. The first mate was never found.

John Ewing is eighteen years younger than his brother. He has the same features, but they are cut more softly and he talks in a mild Texas drawl. On his desk, he had a paperweight, the end of a corer that buckled when it hit the basalt of the Mid-Atlantic Ridge. He told me of his attempts to find a sound source that could penetrate the bottom more conveniently and safely than TNT, which requires the geologist to double as a *dinamitero*. His airgun fires a blast of air, compressed to 2,000 pounds per square inch, every five seconds. The profiles it makes slice the layers of the sediments as neatly as a club sandwich. He let me look at a few. The loud noise had bared the roots of mountains half-buried by sediments. Layers were clearly defined and Ewing identified them for me: sand, silt, and coarser pebbles that had been rafted over the ocean by icebergs during an ice age and dropped there.

Lamont now has a quarter of a million miles of such profiles, and it shares them with other institutions. Geologists have come to Palisades from as far as the Soviet Union to study the technique. Oil companies come there, too, to look at the profiles which can reveal promising structures. Mrs. Ewing remarked to me: "Back before the war, Maurice Ewing told the oil companies there was oil on the continental shelf. They didn't believe him. Now he tells them there is oil much farther out. They believe him." Lamont not only runs its seismic reflection profiler, but it still takes seismic refraction measurements that go much deeper. These require two ships: one to shoot and the other to listen. It also leads to a high degree of cooperation with the nations that supply ships to work with Lamont's vessels. Programs have been carried out with Argentina, Australia, Chile, Japan, South Africa, Spain and Turkey.

There are no other Ewings at Lamont, but the associate director, Dr. J. Lamar Worzel, studied under Maurice Ewing at Lehigh in 1937 and he has been with him since then. Though Worzel comes from New York and not Texas, he has the same energetic determination. He has made his name as an authority on gravity measurements at sea. Seismic shooting and gravity work complement each other very well: one shows the profile of the rocks, the other their density. Dr. Dennis Hayes, who works with Worzel, explained to me that instruments used on Lamont's ships measure variations down to one-millionth of the earth's average gravity field. Results are useful in geophysics and astrophysics. Hayes contours deviations from the norm on maps, of equal interest to research geologists and oilmen. Such deviations are also valuable in accurately determining the orbits of artificial satellites, which bend and bow in response to the pull that the earth is exerting. Gravity measurements are a delicate

An airgun sub-bottom profile

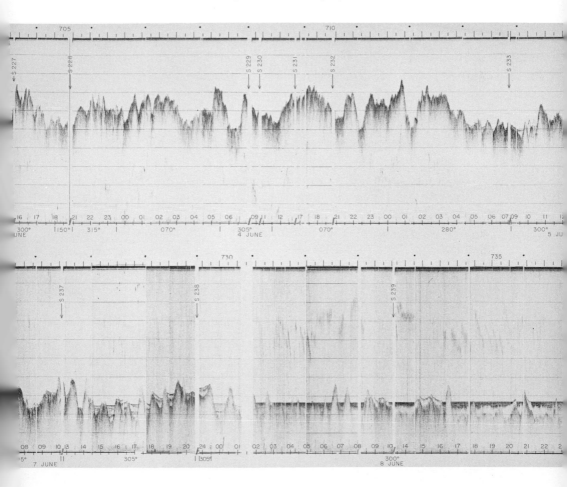

business. Even though the shipboard instrument sits on a stabilized platform, it still moves 100,000 times as much as the changes it is measuring, This can be filtered out by a computer, but Hayes told me sadly: "Gravity measurements are not completely unambiguous. That's life."

His chief, Worzel, was responsible for two-thirds of the 4,000 gravity measurements taken at sea from submarines. Worzel's submarining days are over; he ended them himself in 1957 when he devised a system for accurate measurement of gravity on board a surface ship. Before that, he had organized twenty-five research cruises by American and British submarines, going on six of them himself. These measurements still serve as base points to check the accuracy of readings taken from surface ships. Submarine commanders, Worzel recalled, had mixed feelings about the work. "They were enraptured at first by the training their crews got, diving five times a day for science. But later they viewed gravity measurements with alarm. They couldn't participate in exercises to track surface ships. Gravity was a hiatus in their careers."

Worzel's desk, like Ewing's, was coated with a mixture of science and administration. "We know it cuts into our professional lives, but we have not allowed administrative control to pass out of our hands." He gave me some housekeeping details about Lamont: 70 scientists on the total staff of 500; 86 graduate students; two large ships at sea; a geophysical field station on Bermuda with a smaller vessel, the *Sir Horace Lamb*, working mainly in the Caribbean. Lamont's overall annual budget is about $12 million, with $4 million going specifically to oceanography. The budget has gone up 10 percent a year for the past ten years, but there is no excess fat in it. This is a point very close to Worzel's heart. "We deliberately avoid recreational facilities on our ships. There are no movies aboard, we try to discourage pleasure reading, and we have not gone out of our way to make the quarters lavish. When at sea, we want to work at every possible moment. I lose lots of weight, and it's not because I eat less. I lose huge quantities of sleep, too. The opportunities are so costly that we can't let them slip by." *Vema* goes to sea with a Nova Scotian crew and a captain, Henry Kohler, of the same stamp as Ewing and Worzel. There is mutual respect between those who do the science and those who do the work. The same spirit prevails in Lamont on shore.

"We don't want sea lawyers, we want dedicated people," Worzel said. "We don't try to outbid other institutions. If we did, we would get people coming here for money, not for science. Those people kill you. Our whole goal is science. All the rest is peripheral."

Worzel does not speak much of his theoretical work, and he likes to dismiss sea floor spreading as "cookbookery." But he talks with enthusiastic faith about the economic potential of the sea. "Ocean drilling is the most fundamental thing we can do. There are vast amounts of oil under the deep sea. All oil is manufactured down there and it migrates to shallow layers. The deep-sea drilling program is going to look at the real factory. And oil isn't the only resource. I think that the dredging of building sand from the continental shelves will become as big a business as offshore oil. Unlike oil, there aren't so many other places on land where we can still get it."

Sand is the kind of humble resource in great quantities that Worzel sees in the ocean. Fresh water is another, whether from above or below. He reminded me of the pocket of fresh water tapped by the scientific drillers off Florida in 1965 and speculated that other such layers should exist along the coast. Then there is all the water in the damp winds that blow over thirsty ocean islands. Worzel and Robert Gerard, a physical oceanographer on Lamont's staff, think there is a way to get it. "We can mine the moisture out of the air," Worzel told me. "The ocean is the world's best icebox. Then why not use it as a cold source? We could put a pipe down into a deep canyon near shore and bring up cold water into a condenser, a heat exchanger 600 yards long. We could condense a fresh-water supply out of hot damp trade winds and turn them into cool dry air. Then we could air-condition a whole resort downwind from the condenser."

Gerard had already looked at the possibility of giving New York a fresh-water supply by damming Long Island Sound and turning it into a reservoir. (The worst problem, he found, would be to clean up the rivers draining into the sound so that it would not become a storage tank for polluted water). Then he joined forces with Worzel to see how they could get drinking water from the air and they put their idea down on paper, taking St. Croix in the Virgin Islands as an example.

They estimated that 300 million gallons of fresh water a day, locked up as vapor in the trade winds, are delivered over every mile of the windward shoreline of St. Croix, where some inhabitants must pay $14 for a thousand gallons delivered by truck. A mile offshore and 2,700 feet down, there is that icebox with seawater at 40 degrees F. A pipe a mile long and three feet in diameter, they calculated, could bring up 30 million gallons of cold seawater a day, which would condense a million gallons of fresh water from the atmosphere.

The more they looked at their idea, the more appealing it became. The same trade winds carrying in moisture could generate the electricity needed to run the system's pumps. There is plenty of wind for that purpose, as attested by the ruins of seventeenth-century windmills that once extracted juice from sugarcane on the island. As for the seawater, it can be kept busy after it has done its work in the condenser. Like other oceanographers I had met, Gerard and Worzel are attracted to the possibilities of artificial upwelling. The nutrients that came up with their deep water could be used to fertilize the surface, thereby increasing the catches of sports fishermen already attracted to an air-cooled resort. Or else, they note in reference to an idea expressed by Gifford B. Pinchot, the deep water could be sent into a circular lagoon to raise captive whales for food in a "coral corral."

One advantage they claim for their system is that it provides fresh water without harming the environment. As we've seen, desalinization plants running on nuclear energy not only dump heat back into the sea but also pour out huge quantities of brine that can be another source of pollution. Worzel saw no reason why the method had to be confined to ocean islands. Once it had been tested by a pilot plant on the scale that he and Gerard had described, it could be put to work during the tropical summer months in the New York area. A pipe going down into the Hudson submarine canyon could bring the blessings of fresh water and cool air to a place like Atlantic City.

Worzel's excursion with Gerard into the problems of resort towns tended to belie the early impression he had given me of Lamont as a single-minded institution. It really isn't. "Ewing is a strong leader," one of his staff told me. "He's right most of the time, not all the time." A large amount of work goes on under his active encouragement to prove him wrong. He was a reluctant latecomer to the ranks of the sea floor spreaders and his associate director, Worzel, has not even got there. Yet Lamont has done as much, if not more, than any other institution to put a firm foundation of data under the theory.

Dr. J. R. Heirtzler had just come back from two months aboard the *Conrad* working on a cooperative program with Australian oceanogra-

phers when I spoke to him. He was the senior man on a Lamont team
studying the magnetic striping of the sea floor. His approach to the problem was typical of Lamont: he overwhelmed it. Along with magnetic
data taken by *Vema* and *Conrad*, he had a survey of the South Pacific
and Antarctic by the *Eltanin*, a ship operated by the National Science
Foundation, and an airborne magnetic survey of the Reyjkanes Ridge
southeast of Iceland by the U.S. Naval Oceanographic Office and Lamont. He has put as many as four computers working on these findings
to reduce them to what he called a "well-organized chaos." From the
chaos has come order. Heirtzler and the four other researchers on the
team have sorted out a series of thirty-two distinct stripes laid down into
the rocks of the sea floor by normal and reversed magnetic periods.
Stripes on one side of the mid-ocean ridges match those on the other
side in almost perfect symmetry to form a mirror image. Heirtzler and
his co-workers have been able to correlate magnetic patterns from one
ocean to another and to estimate total spreading rates. They run from a
centimeter a year on either side of the Reyjkanes Ridge in the Atlantic
to five centimeters a year in the South Pacific. In one of a series of papers
devoted to the Atlantic, Pacific and Indian Oceans, Heirtzler and his
colleagues explain this difference in speed: "The distribution of relative
ocean floor spreading rates suggests that the oceanic crust which is raft-
ing or pushing a continental block has the slower spreading rate." This is
the case of the Atlantic floor that is driving North America into the
Pacific, which in fact seems to be surrounded by oncoming continents.
They have also been able to plot the breakup of Gondwanaland, the
single continent of the southern hemisphere, from its beginnings a quarter of a billion years ago. The magnetic chronology they have established points to a period of active movement for nearly 100 million years
that created the ocean basins between Argentina and South Africa. Then
followed a calm that lasted until 80 million years ago when South America began to move farther from Africa and India started to split away
from Australia, beginning its "rapid" journey north only 50 million
years ago and crashing into Asia 10 million years later.

Heirtzler had been working on these papers at the time I saw him.
After I received them, I could fully appreciate a remark he had made to
me during our little talk: "The history of the earth? We know it."

15. Chronicle of the Ice Ages

Recent as well as ancient history of the earth is studied at Lamont. The top layer of the sea floor constitutes the archives of what happened yesterday and the day before, in terms of the geologist's time scale. Lamont has been prying into this layer and its immediate predecessors since 1953, when *Vema* first put to sea.

On Torrey Cliff, there is now a collection of more than 5,000 deep-sea cores, by far the world's largest. They represent twenty-five miles of ocean bottom that have been squeezed into a coring tube, hauled to the surface, and shipped to a core laboratory to be photographed, classified and dissected. Six hundred of these cores go back beyond the beginning of the Pleistocene epoch, over a million years ago. Every year, 600 more cores are taken. At eleven yards per core, that makes nearly four more miles of history to be processed annually. The core collection has burst out of the Lamont family's old garage and now occupies a new building with space to store the results of another five years of work at sea.

These figures were given me by Dr. James D. Hays, a youthful-looking man in his thirties with a flaming red beard. He is the head of the core laboratory, a function that automatically keeps him informed about all the uses to which it is being put. Hays got his Ph.D. from Columbia but he started at Ohio State, where he worked on Antarctic glaciation. When he wondered about the causes of glaciation and why it fluctuates, he came to Lamont to see what answers he could find in deep-sea cores. He got so far into the cores that he is now responsible for them.

I spent some time with Hays in his office, in his laboratory and in a diner three miles from the observatory, where we fled for lunch on a couple of occasions. I was curious about glaciation, but I also wanted to see how a young scientist bore up under the regime Worzel had described to me. Surprisingly well, I had to conclude. Neither Hays nor any of his colleagues whom I saw bore marks of the lash. Lamont is no scientific sweatshop. The air is just as sweet on Torrey Cliff as it was when one of the wealthiest men in the world chose it for his home. The birds chorus just as heartily outside the core laboratory as they did under the windows of the Lamont family. Yet Hays and others I met had a sense of urgency. Perhaps they had caught it from Ewing as they too compared the eons they were exploring to the length of their own limited lifespans.

Hays explained that he did double duty at Lamont. As head of the core lab, he regarded his job as one of maintaining the proper atmosphere for what he called a "factory setup." The cores winched up by *Vema* and *Conrad* must go through routine handling, and Hays showed me his operation. He began with a model of the piston corer that Lamont uses. It worked as neatly as a guillotine. A small weight hit the bottom, in this case the floor of the core laboratory, and tripped a long tube. The piston sucks sediments into the tube, getting a much longer sample than an ordinary gravity corer. Lamont's core room was bigger than the one at Scripps and smelled less. It was not refrigerated and the cores were drier. I did not feel qualified to discuss the merits of keeping cores at room temperature, and Hays assured me that it did them no great harm. I imagine that the advantages of cooling a collection of this size, covering 10,500 square feet of floor space, would be outweighed by the cost.

The cores are like witnesses. They suffer from lapses of memory, their tales can be jumbled and disjointed, but some kind of meaning can be found in their testimony if it is constantly correlated and cross-checked. Lamont has ways of making cores talk. Paleontologists like

Hays go over them for fossil life. This is oral history. Hays is like the anthropologist who listens to the tales of the past told by a tribe that has no calendar. He can put things in order, but he can only date them approximately on the basis of some known event. Written history must be read in a core with other techniques based on the known chronology of reversals of the earth's magnetic field or on the decay of radioactive isotopes. As dating methods become more precise, more events can be connected by researchers in different fields. Lamont is a small institution and isolated enough on its cliff so that any two people thinking about the same problem are bound to meet and put their heads together on it. They barge into each other's offices, never very far apart, they chew things over with their food (wholesome, but certainly not distracting) in the cafeteria, or Hays himself makes sure that they do not run on parallel tracks without crossing over. All this increases the number of references listed as "personal communication" in scientific papers.

I decided to follow in time and space a major line of research here. One such line has been the dating of the ice ages and the explanation of their causes. It is as exciting a subject as sea floor spreading and more immediate in its implications. The most recent glacial period ended only 11,000 years ago and we may be retarding or accelerating the advent of the next one. Some scientists have proposed sprinkling the Arctic ice cap with carbon black so that it will absorb rather than reflect heat and warm the frozen North (or freeze it more deeply, warn other scientists). Before we start trying to change the climate, it does seem wise to learn how nature does the job.

Changes in climate are represented in the sediments by the fossil shells of radiolarians and foraminiferans. Some species of these minute animals live only in cold water, others appear as the climate heats up. When they die, they drop into the bottom ooze as recording thermometers that are picked up by the coring tube. Cores are plotted until, step by step, the boundaries of ancient climates can be drawn. A change at the same relative level in a number of cores indicates that something of widespread importance occurred, perhaps the onset of the ice ages. The cores tell not only what lived in the sea but also what grew on the land. Pollen blown far out over the ocean falls into the sediments and finds its way into the core laboratory and under the microscope. All these investigations can be fitted into a narrative of the ice ages.

It was begun at Lamont by Dr. David B. Ericson and Goesta Wollin, who have spent much of their professional lives on it. I met them in their office in the old core laboratory, where they have been collaborating since 1950. Ericson is a quiet gray-bearded man with a warm manner and appealing modesty. He had roamed as a geologist for oil companies in prewar days before he went to sea, first for Woods Hole and then for Lamont. Wollin, who was born in Sweden, is the younger of the team and acts as its spokesman. They have always published together and Wollin has the final job of getting words down on a paper, a job that naturally falls to him because he worked as a journalist and wrote two novels before he began to interview cores with Ericson. They have written a book, *The Deep and the Past,* that tells how they dated the start of the Pleistocene ice ages in the northern hemisphere. It relates the trials of working at sea and the toil that follows on land.

They started with only a hint. From 1925 to 1927, the German research vessel *Meteor* had surveyed the Atlantic, south and north, in an expedition based on a strange dream. The German government had hopes of paying off its war debt by extracting gold from seawater, and it sent the *Meteor* to sea in search of promising fields of wet ore. Nowhere did the scientists aboard the *Meteor* find water containing even a tenth of the gold needed to make the process practical. On the other hand, they took this opportunity to study the Atlantic more thoroughly than it had ever been studied before (or since, I have heard it said). They also looked at the bottom of the ocean with a corer that penetrated only four feet. Yet this was enough to get through sediments deposited during the present postglacial climate. Wolfgang Schott was studying some of these cores from the equatorial Atlantic when he noticed that they were layered. The top ten inches of the sediments contained shells of the same species of foraminiferans that live in these tropical waters at present. Below this level, however, the shells were of species that are now found much farther to the north. He concluded that the shells must have been deposited during the last ice age, which at the time, was thought to have ended 20,000 years ago.

When Ericson and Wollin took up where Schott had left off, they had a number of advantages their predecessor never enjoyed. Cores from the bottom of the Atlantic were no longer as scarce as gold from its waters and they were nearly 20 times as long. Estimates of the age of specimens did not have to be based solely on how deeply they had been buried by sediments. In 1955, the radiocarbon method was devised. Based on the known rate at which this substance loses its radioactivity, it measures the amount of radioactive carbon remaining in a fossil organism. It quickly enabled scientists to determine that the ice ages ended only 11,000 years ago.

But it is not an absolute tool. In a paper they wrote for *Science*, Ericson and Wollin, along with Maurice Ewing, described its flaws. It could only be considered reliable for specimens no more than 35,000 years old. They had to use it as a clock to time sedimentation rates during this period, then extrapolate these rates to the older sections of the core.

Then came the matter of reaching back a million years or more with a coring tube. A million years meant 27 yards of sediments, at the rate of accumulation that Ericson and Wollin had worked out. No corer could penetrate that far. It was like trying to bridge a chasm with a plank that is too short. The only way to do it is to put a few planks together, paying great attention to the places where they overlap. That was precisely how the two scientists crossed their chasm in time. They looked at the thousands of cores stored at Lamont and picked twenty-six in an area running from Florida through the equator and well into the South Atlantic. Some of these cores were taken purposely on steep slopes where recent deposits had slid away ("slumped" is the proper word) to bare older material to the corer. The cores were correlated so that segments of time missing from one could be seen in another. Finally, there was a composite record.

First, it enabled the two scientists to conclude that the change in climate marking the end of the Pliocene and the beginning of the cold Pleistocene was an abrupt one. It could be read in a layer of sediment only four to six inches thick, laid down in less than 6,000 years. One species of foraminiferans disappeared in that time, another appeared in abundance. *Globorotalia menardii* registered the sudden chill by coiling its shell to the left instead of the right. Discoasters, which the authors describe as minute star-shaped shells of calcium carbonate, vanished and were never seen again, though they had flourished for nearly 75 million years. Reconstructing these events was like reading a book engraved on the head of a pin. Discoasters must be magnified a thousand diameters before they appear as a field of stars under the lens of the microscope.

From such lumps of dried mud (vertical sections of the sea floor taken by corer), Goesta Wollin and David B. Ericson (right) pieced together the story of the Ice Ages.

Foraminiferans are bigger, but they must still be magnified twenty diameters to be studied and identified. Their chambered shells are little white blobs, not nearly as attractive as the discoasters.

The two researchers were now certain of what had happened at the start of the Pleistocene ice ages. They had to answer the next question: when had it happened? The available planks did not quite reach across the chasm. But a new one was found, a core taken with a device using water pressure to drive a tube into the bottom. The device had been tried only once and not very successfully. It had used the pressure supplied by 14,000 feet of water so well that it almost wrecked itself. The core from the experiment looked disturbed and was relegated to oblivion in the collection. Almost in despair, Ericson and Wollin got it out. They found an undisturbed section over 60 feet long and going deeper than any other core they had. It filled the last blank in their chronology of the ice ages. In *The Deep and the Past*, they wrote: "We now had before us a complete record of the Pleistocene, the epoch of earth history in which occurred that momentous step in organic evolution which led to the emergence of man. The record indicated that the Pleistocene spanned a period of about 1,500,000 years." Here, they brought their study into its true perspective. They had long been convinced that earlier estimates of the age of the Pleistocene, running as low as 300,000 years, did not allow time for the accelerated evolution brought about by the conditions of the ice ages and, above all, for *homo sapiens* to appear. They subsequently extended the age of the Pleistocene to more than two million years.

When I saw them at Lamont, they were still looking at cores, but they had moved from the Atlantic to the Pacific in an attempt to find the same Pleistocene boundary there. They were grappling with a different sort of puzzle. The microfossils seemed to be saying that the Pacific had turned cold at a time when the Atlantic had warmed up. "It may be that the Pacific responds to direct causes such as a change in solar energy, while the Atlantic responds to secondary effects," Wollin said. He and his colleague were once again in the state of uncertainty that had sent them groping for the dawn of the ice ages in the Atlantic.

As for Hays, he is stalking the Pleistocene boundary in the Antarctic. He began by counting 35,000 radiolarians to the north and south of the Antarctic Convergence to see what conditions are like today. He found fewer species but a much bigger population in cold Antarctic waters, which are stirred by freezing and are consequently much more productive. One general indicator, almost as handy as the little foram that starts coiling to the left when it is cold, is the thickness of the radiolarians' shells. They wear overcoats in the Antarctic; that is, their shells are heavier, perhaps because there is more silicate (the raw material for the shells) in the water. Hays then went deeper into cores taken by *Vema* and other vessels, mainly between Cape Horn and the northernmost tip of the Antarctic continent. He found nineteen that contained species not living today. It was the same sort of layered effect that had been seen forty years before in the Atlantic. He worked out four zones tagged by distinctive species of radiolarians, and drew a line between the two bottom floors that seemed to indicate a major climatic event. At this boundary level, too, in his cores, he ran into a change from the red clay deposited beneath nearly barren waters to an ooze rich in fossil shells. This also pointed to higher productivity and colder waters.

Five of the cores that Hays had scanned for radiolarians were reexamined by Dr. John R. Conolly and Maurice Ewing, who were looking for something else: sand, pebbles and other material that could have gotten out from land into the deep ocean only if transported by icebergs. As the Antarctic glacier spreads to the sea, it grinds off material from the surface of the continent. Then, when the bergs are calved, they go to sea with a cargo of land rocks which they unload as they melt. In certain cores taken in waters that are now cold, this material was present all the way down to a depth of nearly thirty feet, but then disappeared. Conolly and Ewing suggested that this point represented the start of ice-rafting and, consequently, of Pleistocene glaciation in the Antarctic. In cores from the Argentine Basin further north, they found peaks and lows in the amount of ice-rafted material all along the core. Such fluctuations could represent glacial and interglacial periods, an assumption that looked all the better when it was matched against a parallel study of changes in pollen deposits on the sea floor.

Ewing had told me that he regretted not having worked as a newspaperman. As a geologist, he asks the same questions as a reporter: what, when, why, where and how. Perhaps who, too . . . As soon as they saw effects of the ice ages in cores, he and his fellow scientists at Lamont started to look for causes. Talking to people at Lamont and reading papers in the library, I came across at least three different explanations. I later learned there are a good sixty more extant in the scientific world, with new ones appearing all the time. They speak of cosmic dust clouds masking the sun, changes in the orbit of the earth or sharp tilting of its axis. The most oceanic of all has been advanced by Ewing and Dr. William L. Donn, a senior research scientist at Lamont and professor of geology at City College of New York. I read up on it while taking a break from the core factory.

Donn and Ewing have looked to the oceans rather than the heavens as the cause of glaciation. Through most of its history, the earth has been free of ice. The oceans act as a heating system, moving warmth from the furnace at the equator to the sun-starved poles. When the system works, the polar regions are not cold enough to freeze. They would not be frozen today if the North Pole were not in the middle of the landlocked Arctic Ocean and the South Pole on the Antarctic continent. While the earth does wobble on its axis, Donn discounts any tilt great enough to explain extensive polar wandering. The poles may have remained right where they were while the continents drifted around and under them. The presence of coal beds on Antarctica, for example, seems to show that it once benefited from a warmer location. Paleomagnetic studies say that at one time the Pacific covered the North Pole and the South Atlantic the South Pole. I could follow this reasoning because I had long shed my old ideas about the immovable rocks of the ages.

So continental drift changed the plumbing of the ocean. Instead of worldwide warm-water heating, the earth went over to its present English type of system, with a hot ground floor at the equator, sniffles in the bedrooms and chilblains in the attic. Scientists prefer to say "a zoned climate." Antarctica, completely isolating the South Pole from the ocean, froze over three million years ago and has never thawed since. The North Pole is a more complex case. Donn and Ewing think that glaciation started — and will start again — in the northern hemisphere with an ice-free Arctic Ocean. The open Arctic evaporated moisture into the cold air, manufacturing the precipitation needed to start the forming of glaciers. Once the glaciers had grown into an extensive ice sheet, they drove the temperature down even further, creating their own climate. The Arctic froze over and the glaciers advanced into North America and Europe, picking up a new supply of moisture from the North Atlantic. The Siberian ice sheet, however, never got very far from the edges of the Arctic Ocean because it had a desert to the south.

Once Donn and Ewing had started the ice ages, they had to propose a way to stop them. The two scientists again found their answer in the ocean. Once the glaciers have cooled it to the point where it no longer evaporates sufficient moisture to supply them with snow, they shrink. In the wake of their retreat, temperatures rise on land. But the ocean stores cold longer than the continents. It took the surface of the Atlantic 5,000 years to warm up at the end of the last glacial stage. By that time, the ice sheets were too far gone to benefit from increased precipitation. The climate had become what it is today.

Will it stay that way? Probably not, because of a combination of factors. During the Pleistocene, according to cores taken by Lamont, the level of the Atlantic along the shores of North and South America was between 450 and 600 feet lower than it is today. As the ice sheets melt, perhaps with the help of a small increase in solar radiation, the sea level rises slightly. The oceanic heating system displays faint signs of life, sending more warm Atlantic water into the Arctic. The ice pack melts until once more the Arctic is open water. At this point, the two scientists have calculated, it will absorb 90 percent of the sunlight it receives, instead of reflecting 60 to 65 percent as it does at present. Evaporation may begin all over again to start another glacial stage. And this will go on as long as the poles of the earth remain isolated from the full benefits of the heating system. I read Donn's conclusion gloomily: "The ice age now in progress is only a couple of million years old, whereas the ice ages of earlier geologic eras persisted for tens of millions of years. By analogy, it is certainly not unreasonable to expect a continuation of the present basically cold climate of temperate and polar latitudes for a long time to come."

Such tidings drove me out of the Lamont library and back to Hays's office in search of warmth and cheer. He was not much of a help. When Lamont gets its teeth into a subject, it does not let go all that easily. Hays next suggested that I look into paleomagnetic studies that had put some dates onto the start of the long, long winter in the Antarctic. It appears to have begun some three million years ago, he told me. Events such as the extinction of warm-water radiolarians and the appearance of ice-rafted pebbles could be identified almost as if contemporary newspapers had been laid down with the sediments. With paleomagnetic dating, the core laboratory could begin to write a chronicle. Hays advised me to make a point of seeing Dr. Neil Opdyke, who would tell me a great deal more about the method.

Opdyke was a straightforward man of Hays's age. (Nearly all of Lamont's top researchers that I met were not far out of their twenties.) He is a native of New Jersey who has traveled around a good deal of the world, learning and practicing his somewhat rare profession. His Ph.D. came from the University of Newcastle in Britain; he had studied in Australia and conducted research in Rhodesia. He came to Lamont only in 1964, and he gave Columbia due credit for hiring him. "Paleomagnetism was an *infra dig* subject in those days," he said. "It was too radical. The geological establishment didn't like it. We were called 'paleomagneticians.' "

I had already learned a little about magnetic reversals from my dealings with Heirtzler at Lamont and from what I had read about the striped sea floor. Opdyke had a different slant. Instead of hauling a magnetometer over the bottom to register horizontal variations in the magnetism of volcanic rocks, he was looking at vertical sections of the sediments in cores. He and his assistant, John Foster, had written an article about their work, and it spared him an afternoon of explaining it to me.

What I did not understand, until I read the article and talked it over with Opdyke, was how sediments could record the magnetic field. I had digested the idea of volcanic lava being cooked down in the mantle and then being permanently magnetized as it rose to the surface and cooled. But the sediments were never cooked at all. How could they, too, act as a tape recorder? In fact, such a possibility was only raised in 1964. Two British guest scientists at Scripps, Dr. Christopher Harrison and Brian Funnell, found reversals in a core from the central Pacific. The explanation, no doubt, was so simple that no one had ever thought of it before. As magnetic particles settle in seawater, they are lined up in the direction of the earth's magnetic field just like a compass needle in its bowl of alcohol. When the particles reach the bottom, they keep pointing in the same direction until they are awakened from their long slumber by an oceanographer's coring tube. Particles deposited during a magnetic reversal point the other way. That is all there is to it. Opdyke and his staff take a core nearly eleven yards long and scoop little cubes of mud out of it every four inches. They run the cubes through a spinner magnetometer, which gives them the direction of their entombed compasses.

Reversals in sediment cores would be just so many hieroglyphics if a Rosetta Stone did not exist. It was discovered by American and Australian scientists working with lava flows on land. They had recorded the same striped pattern of normal and reversed polarity found over the sea bottom, but it was easier for them to time the changes. They drilled into the rocks just on the edge of a stripe and dated their specimens, using the potassium-argon method, which is restricted to material of volcanic origin but accurate over periods of millions of years. From their work, they were able to say that we are now living in a normal epoch (magnetically normal, if nothing else) that has lasted 700,000 years. Before that, the magnetic field was reversed for 1,800,000 years, except for two short flashes back to normal, each lasting 50,000 years or so. Reversals can be traced back much farther than that, and a magnetic time scale extending over four million years has been worked out. Since a magnetic reversal happened everywhere on earth at the same time, the scale derived from lava flows on land can be applied to sediments in the ocean. Geologists have finally found a worldwide time clock. "It's the most precise way of dating anything between zero and four million years old," Opdyke said. The method works both ways. If an archaeologist knows the date of an artifact, he can turn it over to a scientist like Opdyke, who can then determine the exact strength of the earth's magnetic field at the time the object was produced. This holds true for kiln-fired bricks and ceramics in which iron particles become permanently magnetized when they cool. "We have a unique record," Opdyke went on. "We know that the intensity of the magnetic field has dropped from .8 to .5 gauss over the last 2,500 years in western Europe. In Japan, it was .7 gauss in A.D. 300 and it is now .55 gauss. We also know that reversals of the magnetic field are not random. Its behavior is cyclical, it goes through zero and comes out the other side. Intensity drops before reversals. They occur on an average of every half a million years."

Then aren't we about 200,000 years overdue for another one? "Reversals have been as far apart as a million years and as close together as 50,000 or 60,000 years. What does seem likely is that if the intensity of the field keeps dropping at the present rate, the ionosphere will collapse and that will make hash of radio reception."

More than radio reception might become hash. The magnetic field acts as a barrier to protect the earth against cosmic rays. Without it, radiation from outer space would go up and so would mutation rates. At least this was the assumption made in the early 1960's by a Canadian geophysicist, Professor Robert J. Uffen, then at the University of Western Ontario and now chairman of Canada's Defense Research Board. Some animals might even be wiped out. What did Opdyke think of that? He referred me to what he and Foster had written in their article: "The subject is very tantalizing, but must be left open to further investigation."

It became tantalizing at Lamont when he and Hays compared their notes on Antarctic cores. Some of the extinctions of radiolarians coincided with magnetic reversals. Hays had joked about it at the time: "I told Neil the rads are changing the magnetic field." What bothered Hays about the extinctions is that the radiolarians live under a hundred feet of water, the equivalent of the whole atmosphere as a shield against cosmic ray bombardment. He suspects that the shells of some radiolarians may contain more iron, rendering them more vulnerable to magnetic reversals.

The collaboration of Hays and Opdyke has dated Antarctic ice age events. With two other Lamont scientists, Foster and Billy Glass, they concluded from paleomagnetic data that icebergs began to raft material from the Antarctic continent 2,500,000 years ago and that the less hardy radiolarians were wiped out half a million years later.

16. This Is the Way the World Ends

At this point, Lamont had left me with the impression of a Hobson's choice for mankind: congelation in the next ice age or irradiation in the next magnetic reversal. And I had not yet seen Dr. Bruce Heezen, one of its most outspoken prophets of doom.

I had heard Heezen at the International Oceanographic Congress in Moscow, where he had described the work Lamont had done on the extinction and mutation of radiolarians when the magnetic field folds up and the cosmic rays come charging in. "Of current interest is the fact that the magnetic field is now decreasing," Heezen had said in Moscow. "If this drop continues for 2,000 years, it will be zero. I don't want to sound like an alarmist, but we may be next." Reporters, including myself, behaved in predictable fashion. No one really cared what happened to one-celled beasts 700,000 years ago, but here was a bit of news that affected the only animal with which man is really concerned: himself. The reporters took it all down, while most scientists in the audience harrumphed at the idea. For a change, the reporters may have been right. Lamont's findings were later corroborated by two researchers at Florida State University who independently found the same correlation between radiolarian changes and magnetic reversals in nine cores from the South Pacific. The reputable *New Scientist* magazine in London ran the story under the headline "Death as the Compass Swings."

Heezen has an enclave for himself and his students in Lamont's oceanography building, guarded by the wooden eagle that had once glared at the sea from the bow of *Vema*. While the rest of the institution seethes, the enclave never even cools to the boiling point. I had written Heezen that I wanted to learn more about his group's latest work, particularly on the extinction of radiolarians by cosmic forces. He must have thought I was Rip van Winkle. When I arrived at his office, his secretary had instructions to bring me up to date. She ushered me into the office of Billy Glass, one of Heezen's graduate students. Within five minutes, I was careering on a wild ride through time, ducking my head every few hundred thousand years beneath a hail of extraterrestrial shrapnel while the earth shuddered under my chair, and my eyes dimmed as they tried to follow the flipping of the compass needle.

I have only my imagination to blame for my cosmos-sickness. Glass told me the story much more calmly. He is a soft-spoken, slenderly built young man from Oak Ridge, Tennessee, the youngest of all the scientists I had met at Lamont. He was born in 1941, and only twenty-six years later he was busily shaking the earth with the help and approval of Heezen, an old hand at the game.

In March 1966, Billy Glass (his first name is his legal name and a refreshing change in scientific references) was mapping cores from the Scotia Sea, between South America and Antarctica. He had trouble concentrating. "I was working next to the paleomagnetic lab and I kept hearing a machine," he said. "I asked John Foster what was making all that noise. He showed me the spinner magnetometer he had developed to test sediment samples and he told me about magnetic reversals. I asked John how long it took him to spin a specimen. Just a few minutes, he said. So I thought I'd try. We got a core from the Antarctic and found a reversal in it. At the time, I was interested in the boundary of the Pleistocene ice ages and I thought I could get some help with paleomagnetic dating."

Glass was seeking the characteristic giveaway: a change of coiling in foraminiferans as the water cools. He started to look for it in cores taken south of Australia. "In the first core that I examined for forams, glassy spherules kept getting in the way. I didn't know what they were — they were no more than a millimeter long — and I called them 'cosmic spherules' in my notes. Then I talked to Dave Folger, another of Dr. Heezen's students. We had taken a course on meteorites with Professor Brian Mason at Columbia and we had written a term paper on tektites. It was Dave who suggested the spherules might be tektites."

That was but a hunch. Tektites had previously been found only on land and in much larger sizes. Glass explained to me that they are small meteorites. When they reach the earth's atmosphere on their journey from outer space, they are heated to the melting point and shaped as teardrops or other aerodynamic forms. On land, where they run from half an inch to four inches in size, tektites have fallen in four known fields: in the Far East, from China south through Australia to Tasmania; in Czechoslovakia; in the Ivory Coast in Africa; in Texas, Georgia, and on Cape Cod, in the United States.

The objects that Glass had seen in his microscope were similarly shaped but much smaller. He called them microtektites and went on from there. Chemical analysis showed that some were of the same composition as the tektites found on land. If, despite their microscopic size, they were tektites, Glass realized that they must have arrived on earth in a farflung shower. He and Folger remembered what they had written in their term paper about the tektite field in the Far East and Australia. The tektites on land had been dated as 700,000 years old, the time of the last magnetic reversal. It seemed only reasonable that the sea had received some of the glassy meteorites. The two graduate students started to examine cores from the Indian Ocean to the south and southwest of Australia. Microtektites were found in five of them. More turned up in a sixth core from the south of Sumatra, in a seventh from south of Japan and in two from southeast of Madagascar. All the microtektites were in a layer of sediment that had also been dated as 700,000 years old. The cosmic rain had fallen on land and sea at the same time.

"It looked as though something had exploded off the tip of Africa while it was traveling northeast," Glass went on. "It seems to me that a cosmic body entered the atmosphere and blew up. What it was or where it came from, I don't know. We do know that in 1908 a fireball was seen streaking through the sky in Siberia. Astronomers thought it was a small comet. It must have exploded, for it set the sky aglow, but the Russians never found the crater. Trees were blown down over a thirty-mile radius in the forest of the Tunguska Valley. Then, after a diligent search, small glassy spheres were found and the Russians assumed that a small comet had exploded in the atmosphere."

Fearsome though it may have looked to man, the Siberian explosion was puny compared to what had occurred 700,000 years ago. When Glass mapped the locations of his ocean cores and tied them up with the land tektite field in Australia and the Far East, he had a fan-shaped swath. It opened from the tip of Africa off Madagascar and spread northeast, the upper edge running beyond Japan, the lower past Australia. It spread over an area 4,000 by 6,000 miles.

After he had measured the size of the swath, he decided to weigh it. "Here we had to make some assumptions," Glass warned, giving me time to take cover against what was coming next. On the basis of what he had counted in the nine cores examined under his microscope, Glass estimated that fifty microtektites had fallen over every square centimeter of the swath. He assured me it was a conservative estimate. Even so, they represented a total weight of 300 million tons.

He and his professor, Heezen, concluded that a body at least this size of cosmic origin had reached the earth at the time of the last magnetic reversal 700,000 years ago. It appeared to be much more than a coincidence. The old joke about the radiolarians changing the earth's magnetic field could not be applied here. An impact of 300 million tons was nothing to joke about. Glass and Heezen speculated that such a blow might have sent the compass reeling. They proposed the idea in a paper they submitted to an American scientific journal, but it came back with a rejection slip from the journal's referees.

It was finally published in Britain by *Nature*, and three months later the *Scientific American* ran a less arid version under their double by-line. In the latter, they stated: "It seems entirely possible that the tektites of the Far East resulted from the fall of a cosmic body, and that the body fell at the time of the last reversal of the earth's dipole magnetic field. If it can be assumed that the reversal of 700,000 years ago took place during a cosmic encounter, the encounter may have somehow disturbed the earth's magnetohydrodynamic dynamo."

With this remark, Heezen and Glass were leading with their chins and they knew it. I found no geomagnetists who agreed with them. One, whose name I will not mention because he mentioned no names, told me: "There are some who are computing what would happen if a ball three miles in diameter hit the earth. Let them do it. It would not have enough energy to cause a reversal. I think the origin of the magnetic field is within the earth's iron core and so is the origin of its disturbances." However, Glass and Heezen made a point of reminding him in their article that "there is no generally accepted theory that explains why the earth's magnetic polarity should be unstable at all."

Having taken on the geomagnetists, they next turned to the biologists. In *Nature*, the two authors said: "An encounter of a cosmic body with the earth would have obvious direct biological effects at least in the area of impact. It has already been suggested that the temporary reduction in the earth's field attendant with the polarity reversal would effect organic evolution through the increased bombardment of the earth by cosmic rays." In the *Scientific American*, they climbed much farther out on an important limb of the tree of evolution: "The remains of Java man, now known as *Homo erectus* and considered the direct precursor of *Homo sapiens* . . . are found mixed with nut-sized tektites in sediments deposited in Java 700,000 years ago." The story was well told by John Lear in the *Saturday Review* under the title "Were Comets the Midwives at the Birth of Man?" He put it this way: "The two-footed mammals who lived around Peking and on Java 700,000 years ago were unquestionably among the ancestors of modern man; their descendants would have felt the genetic consequences of a magnetic field collapse that had occurred then, and they may have been physically scourged by the glass hailstones."

Billy Glass then became the victim of a rewrite man. *Nature* does not get around to newspaper editors looking for a local angle, but the *Saturday Review* does. Evolution, of course, is always a local story in Tennessee. Glass told me that his hometown paper credited him with a new theory, headlining the story "Did Man Evolve from a Comet?" This prompted his father, an electronics engineer, to write a letter to the *Oak Ridger* "to remove any doubts its readers may have concerning the sanity of my son, of whom I am justly proud."

Under the guidance of Heezen, who never thinks a scientific argument is over until he has won it, Glass is going on with his work. He is trying to map the limits of the Far Eastern field more accurately by straining more and more cores for bits of cosmic glass, some no bigger than a speck of dust. He would also like to show that the magnetic flip 700,000 years ago was no fluke. This has sent him looking for other reversals in cores the world over to see if they can be associated with microtektites. In particular, he has his eye on the land tektite field in the Ivory Coast, which has been dated as a million years old. A short magnetic reversal is known to have occurred at about that time.

"Everything started just because I happened to ask what that stupid noise was in the paleomagnetism lab," Glass told me. "If I hadn't, I might have written my thesis on the Scotia Sea. That's what is so exciting here, there is so much new to be discovered." I hastily apologized for taking up his time, thanked him for the interview and moved out of range of whatever he might discover next. He thrived on the competition and excitement at Lamont, but it was getting the better of my nerves. When I would drive back to my base camp in New York after a day there, the streets of Manhattan seemed a haven of quietude, almost a vacation community. Yet I fervently wished Glass the best of luck in his search for an explanation of cosmic airbursts before any more occur . . . particularly over Siberia or Texas.

Just as Glass had been drawn to the din of the spinner magnetometer, the man in the next office had dropped by to see the source of the noise I was making. He was Dr. Dragoslav Ninkovich, a young geologist of Yugoslav origin who had earned his degree at the Sorbonne before he came to Lamont in 1963. Ninkovich and I gossiped for a few moments about life on the Boul' Mich', a welcome breather after Glass and his catastrophes. Then I asked him what he was working on at the time.

"I hope to estimate the energy in the volcanic explosion of 1400 B.C. at Santorini in the Aegean Sea," he said. "We think it must have been around a thousand megatons. It was at least ten times as powerful as Krakatau in 1883, the biggest known eruption in history."

Eyewitnesses of the Santorini explosion of 1400 B.C. must have thought that history had ended once and for all. I gathered this from a paper that Ninkovich and Heezen had done in 1965 on the event. Since then, the Santorini eruption has been almost as widely publicized as if it had happened this morning. If the reader is familiar with the books and articles published on the subject, he is advised to skip the following few pages. If he is not, he can bear with me. The story is worth retelling.

Once more, it begins with those unfortunate cores. Strained for tektites, scanned for radiolarians, squeezed for soil strength tests, spun for magnetism, they still know no peace. In his turn, Ninkovich puts them on the rack and wheel to hear what their layers of volcanic ash can tell about catastrophic eruptions. The thicker the layer that had settled into the ocean sediments, the greater the eruption. By charting the cores, he can see how far the ash was blown from the volcano, another clue to the size of the explosion.

Ninkovich and Heezen became involved with Santorini when they were reviewing studies of cores taken in the eastern Mediterranean by the Swedish Deep-sea Expedition of 1947–48. An ash layer in these cores had been attributed to the explosion of the Santorini volcano, whose shattered crater now appears above the surface of the Aegean, seventy miles north of Crete, as a few small islands. Thera, the largest of the islands (but only 30 square miles in area) can be clearly seen as the eastern half of the crater's rim. When the top blew off the volcano, it left a caldera, a bay covering what had been the center of the island.

Some ten years after the Swedes, the tireless *Vema* moved into the eastern Mediterranean on her latter-day odyssey, and came back with her usual full load of bottom cores. Ninkovich and Heezen examined them to see if they could find more traces of the layer of ash that had been previously reported. They did in five cores. On the map, the ash layer could be seen to extend 400 miles southeast of Santorini, covering an area of 80,000 square miles.

Next, the layer had to be dated. Radiocarbon techniques were put to work on fossil shells in the ash layer. It was estimated as "no more than 5,000 years old," close in geology but no cigar in archaeology. The inquiry into the cores became an inquisition. "Samples of the ash were boiled in a 20% solution of hydrogen peroxide and sieved," the scientists reported in their paper. As a result, the refractivity of the volcanic glass in the ash could be calculated. Then it was compared to the refractivity of volcanic glass in the 100 feet of ash that now lie on the island of Thera. The figures agreed: the ash in the sea and on Thera had come from the same Santorini eruption. Greek scientists, using the radiocarbon method on a piece of wood found beneath the ash layer on land, had dated the eruption as 1400 B.C.

What were its effects? Ninkovich and Heezen knew it was a far more violent explosion than the one that had torn the top off Krakatau (or Krakatoa) in 1883. The eruption at Krakatau occurred in what is now western Indonesia, on an island on the Sunda Strait between Java and

Sumatra. It left a caldera 9 square miles in area. At Santorini, the caldera measures 32 square miles. Another comparison was easily made: ash is piled 100 feet high on the islands around Santorini and is only one foot thick on the surviving half of Krakatau. Yet Krakatau was awesome, according to accounts that the two scientists found. When the eruption reached its peak, a cloud of dust and vapors reeking of sulphuric acid rolled over much of Java and Sumatra, blacking out the sun for two days. Then the northern half of the island collapsed into the sea, creating a tsunami (a seismic sea wave, erroneously called a tidal wave) that rose to a height of 360 feet before it crashed onto the coasts of Java and Sumatra, drowning nearly 36,000 people and wiping out 295 towns. The authors related in their paper: "In a short period of time, tsunamis were recorded on the coasts of almost all oceans. The aerial vibrations produced tremendous roars or destructive vibrations, depending on the length of the waves. The area where the roar was heard is about one-thirteenth of the surface of the globe. The aerial vibrations broke windows at a distance of 90 miles, and in some cases, old houses were damaged at a distance of 500 miles from Krakatau. As lamps were used because of the total darkness, they were quenched by aerial vibrations, causing fires . . . It has been estimated that the energy liberated by the eruption of Krakatau was far greater than that of any volcanic eruption in historical time."

Yet it was insignificant compared to the Santorini explosion of 1400 B.C. in Minoan times, which had split a large volcanic island known as Stronghyli (round) into its present fragments. The collapse of Stronghyli, too, must have raised a seismic sea wave. In 1961, Greek geologists reported a trace of it. They had found an ash layer sixteen feet thick lying 810 feet above sea level at the head of a valley on Anaphi Island, fifteen miles east of Santorini. They suggested that the layer had floated away from the exploding volcano, then had been washed up to this fantastic height by the ensuing tsunami.

Knowing the depth of the Aegean, Ninkovich and Heezen were able to estimate that the great wave had moved away from Santorini at a speed of 215 miles per hour. "The whole northern coast of Crete must have been inundated twenty or thirty minutes after the collapse of Stronghyli Island. The Minoan tsunami may also have been destructive beyond the Aegean Sea. The most vulnerable areas were the coasts of Tunisia and the low delta lands of the Nile. The coast from Tunisia to

Syria must have been inundated no more than three hours after the collapse of Stronghyli Island. If the Minoan eruption of Santorini was only equal in power . . . to Krakatau, the roar of the explosion should have been heard as far as Gibraltar, Scandinavia, the Arabian Sea and Central Africa. It may be assumed that . . . the tephra [ash], gas and vapors covered the southern Aegean Sea and the eastern Mediterranean with total darkness."

That certainly could not have gone unnoticed. To seek the effects of this apocalypse, Heezen and Ninkovich moved from tsunamis and marine geology to archaeology and mythology. Professor Spyridon Marinatos, now Greek inspector general of antiquities, had suggested as early as 1939 that the Santorini eruption was linked to the destruction of the Minoan palaces on Crete. It must have brought starvation as well. Studies of the immediate effects of volcanic eruptions on agriculture in Iceland over the past eight centuries show that land was deserted wherever the ashfall was more than four inches thick. The farmers returned only after the ash had been removed by rain or had decomposed. Such a layer covered central and eastern Crete after Santorini erupted. In the dry Aegean area, it could have ruined farms for as long as a century. Refugees from Crete streamed onto the mainland of Greece, bringing their advanced culture with them. Heezen and Ninkovich wrote: "Contrary to the opinion of historians that the destruction and decline of Minoan civilization was caused by an invasion of the Achaeans from the mainland, we might infer, on the basis of the geological and archaeological data, that the important move forward of the Late Helladic III civilizations, usually called Mycenaean, after the eruption of Santorini in 1400 B.C., was influenced by the presence of Cretan refugees who introduced the traditions of Minoan art and alphabet to the mainland of Greece."

Then the two Lamont geologists followed the noxious clouds and surging seas to Egypt to see what archaeologists had found. A papyrus spoke of days of violence and tempests, plagues and blood. A historian, writing in the present tense, wailed: "The sun is veiled and shines not in the sight of men." And oil to embalm rulers no longer came from Keftiu (the Egyptian name for Crete). In 1963, it was suggested for the first time that the plagues of Egypt related in the Bible could have followed the Santorini eruption. Professor Angelos Galanopoulos, a Greek seismologist, agreed with this interpretation and carried it further. He wrote Ninkovich and Heezen that he believed Santorini erupted in the summer, when its ashes could have been carried over Egypt by prevailing northwest winds at high altitudes.

What did the Bible have to say? The geologists knew that the biblical name for Crete was Caphtor and that the Cretans were called Philistines. They claim that "three biblical chapters refer to the destruction of Minoan Crete, of which one (Amos) shows that the Exodus was contemporaneous with this destruction." This reference (Amos 9:7) reads: "Have I not brought up Israel from out of the land of Egypt, and the Philistines from Caphtor, and the Syrians from Kir?" Zephaniah (1.15 and 2:5) spoke of the ash clouds: "That day is a day of wrath, a day of trouble and distress, a day of darkness and gloominess, a day of clouds and thick darkness . . . Woe unto the inhabitants of the seacoast . . . the land of the Philistines. I will even destroy thee, that there shall be no inhabitant." And Jeremiah (47: 2, 4) described the tsunami: "Behold, waters rise up out of the north, and shall be an overflowing flood, and shall overflow the land . . . Because of the day that cometh to spoil all the Philistines . . . for the Lord will spoil the Philistines, the remnant of the country of Caphtor."

From the Bible, Ninkovich and Heezen turned to Greek mythology and the research that Galanopoulos, the seismologist whose interests ranged as wide as theirs, had undertaken. He had already correlated the Santorini tsunami with the great legendary flood that Zeus in his anger had sent over the earth. Its sole survivors were Deucalion and his wife, Pyrrhas, who landed in an ark on top of Mount Parnassus, where their son, Hellen, founded the Hellenic race. Having explained this myth, Galanopoulos went into another: the lost continent of Atlantis. He was convinced that Atlantis and the site of Santorini were one and the same.

The legend of Atlantis had been brought to Greece by Solon, the Athenian statesman and historian, who heard it in Egypt in 590 B.C. Two hundred years later, Plato reported the tale in *Timaeus and Critias* and he too figures among the references in this Lamont paper on marine geology. Plato related what Solon had been told by Egyptian priests: "You do not know that there dwelt in your land the fairest and noblest race of men which ever lived; of whom you and your whole city are but a seed or remnant . . . But afterwards there occurred violent earthquakes and floods, and in a single day and night of rain all your warlike men in a body sank into the earth, and the island of Atlantis in like manner disappeared beneath the sea . . . The consequence is that, in comparison of what then was, there are remaining in small islets only the bones of the wasted body, all the richer and softer parts of the soil having fallen away and the mere skeleton of the country being left." The event, according to Solon, had occurred 9,000 years before. He had also given the measurements of the island, and Plato concluded that it must have existed beyond the Gates of Hercules. It was far too large to have fitted into the Mediterranean that he knew.

Galanopoulos suspected Solon's figures and his capacity for reading Egyptian hieroglyphics. By lopping a zero off each of them, Galanopoulos fitted Atlantis into the island of Stronghyli that the Santorini eruption had destroyed 900 years before Solon's time, and not 9,000. Here, Ninkovich and Heezen ended their tale that had begun with a description of volcanic ash collected by the coring tube 1400 fathoms down.

For readers who have not kept up with subsequent developments, it should be added that the caldera of Santorini was later surveyed by the *Chain* of the Woods Hole Oceanographic Institution. With the remaining islands above the surface, it was found to fit perfectly into the dimensions of Atlantis as given by Plato and corrected by Galanopoulos. The final answer to the question should lie under the 100 feet of volcanic ash on the island of Thera, where excavations are being pursued.

When Heezen invited me to dinner with another of his collaborators, I fully expected it to be cooked on brimstone at the bottom of a crater. The three of us arrived instead at the peaceful home of Marie Tharp, on the edge of the Hudson. Miss Tharp does her work there, drawing maps of the ocean floor. She had left her upstairs drawing board to prepare a civilized Italian meal for us. The food was fine, the Hudson was calm except for a ripple of cars crossing the Tappan Zee Bridge in the distance, and the conversation was excellent. It was a shame that I had to break up the evening by asking questions.

Heezen in private is not the same as Heezen in public. He always had something to say when I heard him in scientific congresses, but it was hard to catch the drift of it. He reads his text in a mumble, as if he were trying to get it out of the way, then he sits down to await the fallout from the bomb that he seldom fails to explode. In his mid-forties, he has remained boyish in many ways. He easily becomes enthusiastic or resentful, never hiding behind a facade. As a Columbia professor of geology, he has a dozen graduate students under his guidance, yet he refuses to limit himself to the role of team leader. "I avoid administration fiercely," he said. "I went into science because I didn't want to go into business. Administration would be the same thing."

Nothing seems to have predestined Heezen for marine geology. He was born in Vinton, Iowa, about as far from the sea as one can get on the American continent. His father, a county agent, sent him to the University of Iowa, where he studied micropaleontology. It was there that a human tsunami reached Heezen and swept him out to sea.

"I was sitting in a lecture hall in 1947 at Iowa when Maurice Ewing gave a talk on his geophysical work in the western Atlantic. It was a good lecture, instructive and stimulating, but no one was interested enough in the subject to ask any questions. I did, though. Afterwards, I spoke to him and he asked me if I wanted to work at sea that summer.

"It was an astonishing suggestion. My summer work was all planned, but I was getting tired of Paleozoic fossils. I went to Woods Hole. The first thing I had to do was to go to the Harvard library and look up what they had on the Mid-Atlantic Ridge. Then Ewing made an even more astonishing suggestion. He asked me to go out on an expedition off the continental shelf of New England to take pictures and cores of the bottom.

"At Woods Hole, I was given a couple of cases of TNT and a stopwatch. That was how we took our soundings. One guy would lie on his bunk with his ear against the side of the ship and clock the time it took for the explosion to echo off the bottom. We took 200 cores and 200 pictures, from the continental slope down to a depth of 10,000 feet. I took the pictures back to Iowa and, with another geologist, I wrote up the results. They showed that erosion was occurring on the continental slope."

The county agent's son had found his sea legs. The next summer, he went out on an expedition over the Mid-Atlantic Ridge. Ewing didn't have the equipment he needed to do his seismic work, so his scientists built it themselves on the ship. "We used empty beer cans as floats for the TNT charges. But first, we had to empty the cans by drinking the beer through a hole the size of a matchstick. The system worked as long as the beer drinking kept up with the seismic shooting." Heezen caught the spirit of the game. When explosives were shipped by freight car to a port of embarkation, he would take the detonators down by Pullman train in a suitcase.

In 1949, Heezen got into his first major scientific controversy. He was the same age as Billy Glass when he sailed with Ewing that spring. Their ship crossed the Hudson Canyon. "The Coast and Geodetic Survey had already surveyed the canyon to a depth of 1,500 fathoms. I asked Ewing if we could zig on it. We zigged two and a half days with our echo sounder. We extended the known length of the canyon 250 miles and its known depth from 1,500 to 2,600 fathoms. We took cores that showed erosion had occurred in the canyon within the last 10,000 years."

Heezen was now on a terrain as unsteady as the eroding canyon floor. Submarine canyons were (and still are, in many quarters) believed to be old river canyons formed on dry land during the ice ages, then drowned by the rising sea level that turned the land into what is now the continental shelf. The depth of the Hudson Canyon seemed to rule this out as a sole cause. "Ewing and I calculated that half the water would have to be removed from the Atlantic Ocean to explain the presence of a river canyon 1,500 fathoms down. We thought of doing a key paper on what would happen if half the water were pumped out of the Pacific and the Atlantic. Luckily, we didn't publish it."

Then Ewing's student thought of turbidity currents, a downhill flow of muddy water through clear water. Not much was known about them. In the late nineteenth century, a Swiss said that they might explain how river mud from the Rhone was carried out in suspension over the bottom of Lake Geneva. A slow-moving turbidity current had been generated by a Dutch scientist, Philip Kuenen, using a small tilted tank in his laboratory. On a bigger scale, another was seen by engineers at Lake Mead behind Hoover Dam on the Colorado River when they watched their reservoir silted by a slow flow of mud along the bottom. In 1936, the possible role of the turbidity current as a mechanism for digging out submarine canyons was suggested by Reginald Daly, a respected Harvard geologist whose name lent credibility to the idea. It looked tempting to the two marine geologists as a way of explaining all the sand and silt that kept appearing in ocean cores taken far from any possible source on land. A force great enough to move sand that far could also carve a canyon out of the sea floor.

How could its existence be proved? Ewing and Heezen reasoned that these underwater avalanches, if they existed, must have played havoc with submarine cables. "I'm a great book collector," Heezen said. "I had bought a secondhand copy of some old proceedings of the American Geophysical Union. I was thumbing through it when I came across a report of an earthquake in November 1929 on the Grand Banks south of Newfoundland. It was one of the greatest days in my life. I had an idea that became my master's thesis at Columbia."

From the companies' records of the exact time when their lines went dead, Heezen and Ewing saw that cables within sixty miles of the earthquake's epicenter were instantly snapped. For the next thirteen hours, they kept breaking downhill from the epicenter. The last one was severed 300 miles away. The turbidity current had timed itself by cutting cables the way a runner snaps a tape. Heezen calculated it had moved at nearly sixty miles an hour down the steep continental slope, then slowed to fifteen miles an hour on the flat abyssal plains. A core taken over the site showed that a three-foot layer of sediment had been instantly deposited on the plains over an area of 40,000 square miles.

An almost equal volume of turbid words began to flow on all sides as soon as Heezen and Ewing published their paper, and it has yet to settle. Heezen sticks by his figures, and he can show similar avalanches that wrecked cables in the Mediterranean and off the Magdalena River in Colombia. Such evidence must always be circumstantial. "No one will ever see a turbidity current and survive," he told me. I remembered talking to a diver in California who had the job of planting a nine-foot bar into the narrow head of Scripps Canyon to moor current meters there. My diver was glad when the job was over. He believed in turbidity currents and he wanted neither to see nor be in one.

Even at this early stage in his career, Heezen was sounding dire notes. He wrote in an article of the possibility that "an offshore atomic blast might trigger a turbidity current which would spread radioactive debris throughout an entire ocean basin." This is another of his ideas that I hope will never be proven right during my own lifetime.

Heezen spends as much time building up the ocean bottom as he does tearing it down. He and Dr. Charles Hollister, the third of Miss Tharp's dinner guests, believe that rivers flow along the sea floor. Like rivers on land, they pick up particles of sediment when they move at high speed (less than a mile an hour, in their case) and then deposit them when their flow becomes sluggish. Hollister and Heezen think that these rivers are planetary bottom currents, their "beds" formed by the contours of topographical features.

Not so many years ago, such an idea made the classical oceanographer shudder. He was convinced that nothing ever happened in the deep ocean basins. Then in 1933, Dr. George Wüst, a great German student of the ocean, advanced the revolutionary idea that bottom currents existed in the South Atlantic. Proof of their existence had to await the development of the deep-sea camera. When it came, it showed that Wüst was right. Photographs revealed sediments corrugated by ripple marks, or rocky outcrops scoured free of mud. Hollister and Heezen are now looking at thousands of photographs for such signs of submarine riverbeds, correlating the pictures with current measurements. This work incidentally brought Heezen into zoology. Animal tracks and burrows often appear on the photographs, and the most puzzling have been isolated spirals measuring as much as six feet in diameter. In 1965, Heezen and Donald Bourne, a Cambridge zoologist, found a photograph taken three miles down in the Pacific which, they reported, identified the source of the spirals. It was a giant acorn worm. Specimens of these worms had been dredged up as early as 1873 by the *Challenger*, but none had ever been seen in action.

From the photographs, from hundreds of thousands of miles of soundings made by Lamont's vessels and others, from steady reasoning and sudden intuition, Heezen has been mapping the ocean floor with Marie Tharp. They published their first physiographic diagram of the North Atlantic in 1957. The South Atlantic followed in 1961, and three years later, the Indian Ocean. These are bold conceptions that display the ocean bottom as if it had been sketched by an observer flying over it without any water to blur his view. Miss Tharp does them in her house at South Nyack, built, so she told me, of Triassic sandstone. When I went upstairs to wash up for dinner in a bathroom boasting marble basins and a tub sitting on four clawed feet, I dated the plumbing as Pleistocene.

It was Miss Tharp, Heezen told me, who had discovered the rift valley in the Mid-Atlantic Ridge and led him to postulate a theory of an expanding earth as early as 1958. It was illustrated in the Tharp home by a globe, splitting apart along its mid-oceanic ridges. "At the time, everyone told me I was crazy," Heezen said. "I was criticized, I was lambasted. But now it's forgotten. If a paper is more than five and less than twenty years old, it's always ignored."

To cook our dinner, Miss Tharp had taken time out from her biggest project of all, a diagram of the topography of the Pacific Ocean in three parts. She had needed five years to do the North Atlantic, four years for the South Atlantic and two and a half years for the Indian Ocean. For the Pacific, she had the help of a computer to pick out the highest peaks in each area, but it was by far the biggest job of all. "I started it nearly three years ago," she told me. "I don't think I've got more than one-quarter done."

At the same time, she was putting the finishing touches to a second edition of the pictorial conception of the North Atlantic she had published with Heezen. The last stage of the job consisted of finding an appropriate quotation to go with the map. "It's not easy," Miss Tharp complained. "All the good quotes are about the top of the ocean, not the bottom."

I do think she found a good one for the Atlantic. It came from *The Physical Geography of the Sea*, written by Matthew Maury in 1855, and it read:

"Could the waters of the Atlantic be drawn off, so as to expose to view this great sea-gash which separates continents and extends from the Arctic to the Antarctic, it would present a scene the most rugged, grand and imposing. The very ribs of the solid earth with the foundation of the sea would be brought to light and we should have presented to us at one view the empty cradle of the ocean."

17. The Oceanographic

The waters of the ocean have not been drawn off, and I must reluctantly put them back into my story. I hate to leave the marine geologist with his substantial ridges and plains. I am comforted by his assurance when he tells me where India was a hundred million years ago or where Arabia will be a million years from now.

The physical oceanographer, who deals with the part of the ocean that moves by the hour rather than by the epoch, has much less self-assurance. He cannot state with any absolute certainty where the Somali Current was a week ago or where the Gulf Stream will be tomorrow. Communication is much more difficult with him than with the geologist. He likes to say that the water with which he deals is only a very thin layer of the planet: so thin, in fact, that its scale is accurately represented by the coat of varnish covering the blue patches on an ordinary desk globe. He must be right, but I find that I am quickly out of my depth as soon as I venture into his.

At first, he is deceptively simple. He sets his layer of varnish moving horizontally in stately carousels that turn clockwise in the northern hemisphere and counterclockwise in the southern hemisphere. These are the wind-driven "gyres" that form the main systems of surface currents. But next, the movement becomes an intricate three-dimensional dance staged by water spreading from the warm tropics to the vicinity of the cold poles, where it becomes denser, sinks and starts a centuries-long journey through the depths. With density and wind calling the tunes of his water ballet, he brings in another choreographer and that is where I lose him. This is the Coriolis force, named after the French mathematician who discovered it in the nineteenth century and who thereby explained deflections in movement caused by the earth's rotation. Artillerymen correct for it when they aim their guns, and so do launchers of ballistic missiles. The oceanographer asks me to imagine a water particle in an infinitely slippery layer on top of the earth, which is spinning beneath it. To the observer on the "fixed" earth, the particle apparently is moving: it veers to the right north of the equator and to the left in the southern hemisphere. All these forces are put into equations by the physical oceanographer, and at this point, communication with him becomes problematical. One drowns in fluid mechanics.

Yet I found him an appealing figure in my gallery of marine science, an intellectual sea dog. One branch of his ancestry goes back to the great names of mathematics and physics attached to the quest for an understanding of the earth and its environment, the other to the shellbacked windjammer captains who had to observe currents because their livelihoods and their lives depended on them. The physical oceanographer shows marked signs of this dual lineage. His theories can be truly appreciated by only a learned few, but his findings are widely applied. Masters of gigantic tankers look to him for forecasts of waves and currents just as airline pilots turn to the meteorologist for wind conditions, and for the same reason: to save time and money by using the environment instead of fighting it. These forecasts are experimental; the physical oceanographer feels his way cautiously as he moves from a description of the steady climate of the sea to an explanation of its fickle weather. More than the interests of shipping companies are involved here. Upon his research depends the possibility of long-range forecasting — and perhaps control — of weather in the ocean and weather in general. This augurs both good and evil to a number of outstanding scientists who think that one sorcerer's apprentice in the ocean is enough.

I had been advised that one of the most appropriate places for inquiring into such matters is the Woods Hole Oceanographic Institution. The advice came at the right time. Woods Hole is on Cape Cod and I had grown weary of imaginary oceans in institutions either landlocked or beachbound. I needed a sea change. I wanted to awake to the hooting of foghorns, with a breath of salt air to accompany my breakfast. Next to going to sea on a research vessel, where I would only stumble in the way of science as I had during that short excursion at Scripps, I could think of nothing better than going to Cape Cod.

Thoreau had forsaken the ponds of Concord and gone there for the same reason over a century and a quarter ago. He was not disappointed and neither was I. In his walking excursions, Thoreau had concentrated on the then-wild "outer cape" ending in Provincetown, the elbow and beyond of what he called "the bared and bended arm of Massachusetts . . . boxing with northeast storms." Woods Hole, which he overlooked, is tucked under the boxer's shoulder.

Guidebooks make short shrift of Woods Hole. It lies south of Falmouth, an old whaling town where, the guides always mention, a plaque marks the birthplace of Katherine Lee Bates, who wrote *America the Beautiful* without ever having seen the shopping centers on State Highway 28. Woods Hole is of interest as the mainland terminal of the big ferries that serve Martha's Vineyard and Nantucket, and also as the site of an aquarium operated there by the U.S. Fish and Wildlife Service (admission free, admittedly an oddity on the cape). From Falmouth to Woods Hole, Highway 28 shrinks to a two-lane strip of blacktop that winds through five miles of woods interspersed by occasional cottages with a look of year-round occupancy. It reaches the heights overlooking Vineyard Sound, slithers downhill and manages to come to a stop at the foot of Railroad Avenue (the origin of the name seems to be forgotten) on the water's edge where the ferries take over. As the land ends, Woods Hole begins. Water Street is the main artery that serves the Oceanographic Institution, the U.S. Bureau of Commercial Fisheries and the Marine Biological Laboratory. It barely manages to separate Eel Pond, where small craft are moored, from the harbor proper. At certain places, it has railings to prevent pedestrians from falling overboard. The harbor is equally cramped. Dockside space is filled by scientific vessels, some moored gunwale to gunwale, while the big car ferries, hooting angrily, must perform prodigies of seamanship to reach their berths. At the time I visited Woods Hole, a steam pile driver was putting down the foundations for the institution's new $2,000,000 pier, financed by the National Science Foundation, to wrest more space from the only possible source at hand: the sea. The institution's newsletter described this as "an apparently confusing sequence of operations" that was great fun to watch and did wonders for local color. One's ears rang with the deep-chested gasps of the pile driver, the cries of kibitzing gulls, the blasts of the harbor foghorn. One's eye feasted on Water Street, peopled by salty types in yellow sou'westers who all looked like whalers until the eye became discerning enough to spot lunches carried in brown paper bags, the telltale cross borne by the research scientist.

None of this was forced. The institution fits into salty Cape Cod as easily as Scripps into the casualness of California or Lamont into the patrician Hudson Valley. There is an honest old-fashioned tang in the name by which it refers to itself: The Oceanographic. No danger of confusion, there is only one. No mixed salad of letters, no slick acronym. W.H.O.I., pronounced disastrously as "Hooey," is heard only off-cape.

The Oceanographic has made Woods Hole a company town for science. Water Street is dominated by its original building dating back to 1930, a long, narrow red-brick slab, four stories high and as grim as the climate. It could be mistaken for a mill or a reform school if its architect had not indulged in an extravagant folly, a model of a galleon moored to the weather vane above the steeply pitched roof. The galleon never drags its anchor in the local windstorms, which have not changed much since Governor Bradford described one in 1635 in his *History of Plimouth Plantation:* "It caused ye sea to swell up above 20 foote, right up and down, and made many of the Indeans to clime into trees for their saftie."

The buildings erected since the war are anonymous enough not to clash with the old lady wearing the galleon in her hair. It is she who appears on the postmark of every letter that goes out of the Oceanographic, with a big ketch moored in the foreground and "Study of the Seas" written in the sky above the scene. The ketch is the *Atlantis,* the Oceanographic's first vessel, which was sold to Argentina in 1966 upon the condition that she could be repurchased when her career finally ends. Only those who refer to the Oceanographic as "Hooey" call her *Atlantis;* to everyone else, she is "the old A-boat."

The CHAIN (*below foreground*), *and behind her the original building of the* Woods Hole *Oceanographic Institution. The old* ATLANTIS (*above*) *sails forever on the Oceanographic's coat of arms.*

The Oceanographic is everywhere in Woods Hole. The one drugstore in town shares a frame building with a "Deep Submergence Research Group." The one bookshop is as small and quaint as any in Provincetown (excuse me, P-town), but it deals in fluid mechanics and marine biology rather than in psychedelia and posters. The one bank in town cashed a check for me only when an official of the Oceanographic pledged to stand behind it (a better reference than the Chase Manhattan). The one bar is Captain Kidd's, a relaxing saloon that flaunts liferings from most of the world's major research vessels. It is at Captain Kidd's that one hears old-timers speak mournfully of the old A-boat: "The skipper apologized, said he would be a little late on the next station. He has two hands pumping out the bilge."

The sentimentalists at Captain Kidd's have much to mourn. Growth, that most evil of necessities, has overtaken the Oceanographic. A new sixteen-acre campus is being planned well behind the waterfront to accommodate an accelerated intake of students following an agreement between the Oceanographic and Massachusetts Institute of Technology that will lead to their awarding joint doctorates in oceanography. About forty graduate students are now on hand at all times, and it is hoped to increase their number to 200. Farther back in the hills, a 140-acre estate is in the process of being purchased to be kept in reserve. On Water Street itself, it is proposed to build a library (the Oceanographic now shares the library of the Marine Biological Laboratory) and, equally important, a cafeteria to provide food and togetherness. It will mean a mutation for the Oceanographic's individualists who hope that it is not carried too far. "This is one of the few places where people are not regimented," one of them said. "We carry a begging bowl, but we have freedom. We do not wear numbers back and front."

The begging bowl is mostly metaphorical. Under Dr. Paul Fye, who has been its director since 1958, the Oceanographic has expanded to the point where its annual budget is $10 million, nearly 60 percent of which comes from the Office of Naval Research and 30 percent from the National Science Foundation (the rest is supplied by other government agencies and private sources). It has a staff of 600, of whom 150 are scientists, making it Cape Cod's largest year-round private employer and the world's second largest center for marine science, outranked in size (and only in size, according to local consensus) solely by Scripps. It operates four conventional seagoing research vessels, among them the 2,100-ton *Atlantis II*, commissioned in 1962, and the *Chain*, a converted submarine rescue ship of slightly more displacement. Among its less conventional vessels have been the late *Alvin*, the best-known of American research submersibles; a monstrous catamaran that serviced *Alvin*; a four-engined C-54 for meteorology and the upcoming science of oceanography from the air; and a light seaplane for such odd jobs as spotting whales. While I was mainly interested in its long-term study of currents and particularly the Gulf Stream, the Oceanographic makes major contributions in all branches.

The forbidding facade is only an accident of regional architecture. The Oceanographic makes a point of keeping its doors open to industry, civic organizations and ordinary citizens, an attitude explained by the circumstances under which it was founded. In 1927, a committee of the National Academy of Sciences recommended the establishment of a center in the neglected field of oceanic research on the Atlantic Coast. According to the customs of the time, the suggestion was not tossed to another committee but into the lap of private industry. The Carnegie Corporation offered money to purchase land at Woods Hole, chosen because of the research in fisheries and marine biology already being carried out there. A grant of $2,500,000 came from the Rockefeller Foundation for buildings, operating expenses and a ship. In 1930, the Oceanographic came into being as a nonprofit scientific corporation and *Atlantis*, a 142-foot steel ketch built in Copenhagen, was logging the first of half a million miles of scientific cruises. The ship is still the symbol of Woods Hole.

Through its trustees and the membership roll of its corporation, the Oceanographic has been able to put out strong landward roots in the worlds of science and business. For its friends, it produces a dense, competent annual report that has the merit of laconism: from 1931 to the last one I saw, the report had grown from seven to only seventy pages, including tables and illustrations. The report shows the pragmatism that has always characterized the mariners of Cape Cod.

From an old whaler's log:

Sunday, January 9 — Sixtyfore days out of Falmouth Mass & not won single whale have we tuk yit. Our Capting has ordered the man on lookout to come down, says mebbe the Lord is taking his vengints upon us for looking for whales on the Sabbith. Hear after the lookout will not go aloft no more on the Sabbith xcept oncet every our.

From the Oceanographic's annual report:

> While the *Crawford* was in the port of Paarden Bai in the Caribbean her radio operator, Philip Clegg, borrowed the rubber Zodiac boat for a fishing trip just off the harbor entrance. When the motor failed the boat was carried off to the northwest by wind and current. During the evening of the fifth day, Mr. Clegg and the boat were sighted by a tanker. Mr. Clegg was in good physical condition as a result of his resourcefulness in catching fish for food and fluids. The drift of the raft was found to have been much slower than expected and its set had a component across the wind and seas.

Much weightier is an annual "summary of investigations" that tells the specialist exactly what projects are going on at the Oceanographic before results are formally published, a risk that not many research institutions care to run. The corporation wants to inform and attract as many figurative stockholders as possible. In 1952, it created a new category of participants, the "Associates" of the Oceanographic. They now number more than 400 individuals, along with fifty corporations. Membership dues start at $50 a year (tax-deductible) and offer one of the best ways I know for the terrestrian to learn what oceanography is really all about. For his $50, he can attend an open house every year at the Oceanographic, hear talks as I did on "the migration of tuna" or "the use of satellites in oceanography," and participate in a luncheon where conversation takes precedence over food (his money is not wasted on frills). Above all, he has the satisfaction of knowing that his contribution with no strings attached is appreciated all out of proportion to its size. As a token of thanks, he receives a subscription to *Oceanus*, the quarterly that the Oceanographic has been putting out for nearly fifteen years. *Oceanus* takes its name from the river that, so the ancients believed, circled the known world. It is a modest publication, written by literate scientists without a trace of the P.R. man's glibness, and it has fine photos in black and white, also taken by scientists. It catches the flavor of the Oceanographic to perfection. In the same issue, there can be room for an account of exploration on the suspected site of Atlantis in the Aegean, and a couple of pages of reminiscing about the other *Atlantis*, the old A-boat. To *Oceanus*, the investigation of the continental shelf is news and so is the bird-watching of a research vessel's chief engineer.

The Oceanographic tries equally hard to keep its own people, at every level from research scientist to deckhand, aware of what is going on. I had a chance to attend a luncheon of the staff's Peanut Butter Club, where the only membership requirement is a sandwich. One takes pot-luck on the weekly talk, and I think I did very well. It was given by Robert E. Kutzleb, a chunky underwater executive from Ocean Systems, Inc. The company was formed in 1965 to meet a need that had become tragically evident with the loss of the submarine *Thresher* two years previously. It is owned principally by the Union Carbide Corporation, and its guiding light is Edwin A. Link, who invented the Link Trainer for airplane pilots before he turned to the ocean. The company uses divers and specially designed submersibles to look for anything underwater anywhere in the world, from oil to the H-bomb off Palomares in Spain.

In his talk, Kutzleb described the search for the wreckage of a Constellation from Otis Air Force Base at Falmouth that had gone down only two months before in Nantucket Sound. There were seventeen "almost eyewitnesses" to the crash and they helped him select a point of departure. "I can't overemphasize the importance of eyewitnesses," said the speaker, oblivious to the feelings of any sonar experts present. "Oceanography in a hurry" could have been the title of his talk. "In a search, the emphasis is always on haste. You can't study currents or take bottom cores. You must go on the information available." It was the turn of the physical oceanographers to be reminded of what the working-man's life is like underwater. "We have much information about the currents north of Nantucket and very little south of Nantucket. But at least we now know why there are no tourists on the south shore of Nantucket. The prevailing winds are from the south and they average 30 to 40 knots." Nevertheless, Kutzleb and his crew recovered 95 percent of the wreckage of the Constellation, a radar plane, in twenty-seven days. They dragged for it with a chartered New Bedford trawler, whose crew was kept busy shoveling overboard the fish that persisted in getting caught by the trawl net. When the first piece of wreckage was found, the site was buoyed and the divers went down. Visibility in a "sandstorm of microorganisms" was from zero to six inches. "We found objects by swimming into them. I swam into a wing section and it almost knocked my mask off. As soon as we were more than six feet down, we couldn't see another diver unless we stayed right on his flippers." The divers combed a stretch of bottom 200 yards wide and 350 yards long, the area over which the wreckage of the Constellation had been scattered, bringing up small fragments themselves or fixing slings lowered from their trawler to the engines and shattered fuselage sections. "I much prefer hunting manganese nodules or laying oil-well pipe to searching for a tragedy," Kutzleb remarked, and concluded his Peanut Butter talk with a plea to oceanographers for more information about the continental shelf and the waters above it, particularly in Europe and Asia. "We really need to know the temperature of the water column before we plan a search. There are places where we have found 67 degrees on the surface and only 36 degrees at a depth of 80 feet. That's like going into a bucket of ice cubes." Seamanship and a knowledge of currents, temperatures, and bottom topography are the searcher's most valuable stock in trade, Kutzleb expectantly told his audience before he sat down. One cannot always assume that natives will be as observant — and as friendly — as they are on Nantucket.

The Constellation had gone down only thirty miles out to sea from Woods Hole. Some of Kutzleb's listeners may have known the crewmen or their wives. There is almost a kinship between the institution and its setting. Industrial firms that work with the Oceanographic know this. One of them, Geodyne, has a plant in Waltham, Massachusetts, that turns out $2,500,000 worth of instruments a year. But a co-organizer of the firm, Paul Ferris Smith, holds down a one-room office next to a job-printing shop in Woods Hole. When his current meters come in from a tour of duty in the Atlantic, he is at the dock to learn how they work. "Originally, I came here because this village is the hub of oceanography on the East Coast, but later there was another reason: the wives of our electronics engineers didn't want to live in the sticks," he said, "The superhighways have changed that, but I still want to stay in Woods Hole. If I didn't enjoy this business, I wouldn't be in it at all. The environment is rough, the problems are complex and the best direction to go is not yet really known. We have to create fundamental science at the same time that we are creating a business to serve that science. This is why I must be at the dockside when our gear comes in: to provide a link between the cruel sea, as it were, and a modern instrumentation industry." Smith had other reasons for sticking to Woods Hole. He relished telling me how he and his daughter had gone out on a sailboat with a current meter off Martha's Vineyard and gotten better results than a research vessel (not from the Oceanographic) using a different instrument.

Smith seems to be in business for the fun of it and so does Sam Raymond, founder, president and chief engineer of Benthos, at North Falmouth. At the time I saw him, Raymond was still operating in a farmhouse that had been his own home before his business expanded to the point where it drove him out. The walls of his former bedroom were covered with orders, his barn housed the milling machine and the three lathes of his machine shop, his backyard was planted with surplus 16-inch naval shells from the battlewagons of World War II. He converts them into pressure chambers for customers seeking to test devices under deep-sea conditions. The shells can withstand the pressure of the greatest known ocean depths. Raymond turns them into test chambers and sells them with a slogan from the Song of Solomon: "They shall beat their swords into plowshares." One new building on the Raymond homestead shelters the firm's 10,000-gallon test pool, eight feet deep and fourteen feet in diameter, used in underwater accoustic measurements. Divers go into it regularly, and when they do, they swim in a cedar pickle vat. Raymond acquired the vat by bidding $100 for it at an auction. No one else could think of a use for it.

A business the size of Raymond's meshes well with the Oceanographic. They swap ideas freely, he takes over the headaches of design for production and, once he has put the product into marketable form, oceanographers everywhere can benefit from the collaboration. They do not represent what one might call a mass market. Raymond told me about an electronic flash he makes for research submersibles. Mounted outside the vessel with its own batteries, it switches on automatically as the submersible comes to the surface, then sends out a beam that can be seen seven miles away by searching ships. "We've only sold twelve, but I guess that's half the total market," he said.

Most of Raymond's products are the result of his matching wits with deep-sea pressures. Previously, he housed instruments in stainless steel cases, but he now has a more effective and aesthetic solution. Radio beacons, pingers or depth recorders go down inside two glass hemispheres clamped together with a thin coating of grease at their joint. It is a way of working with the sea instead of against it: the greater the pressure, the stronger the jointed glass sphere becomes. Glass has been proved capable of withstanding compressive stresses of as high as 300,000 pounds per square inch. Raymond told me that he once tried to smash one of his glass floats. "We put it under pressure such that the force on the hemispheres was equivalent to a stack of cars as high as the Empire State Building. But we just smashed the smasher."

Benthos is far more widely known than one would estimate from its volume of business, about $300,000 a year. One of its best-liked products is a "boomerang corer" with a flashing light, developed by Raymond and the Oceanographic. Instead of lowering a corer by winch and then hauling it up, a research ship need only drop a boomerang that plummets to the bottom, takes a four-foot core and pops up again. Or else the ship drops seven or eight corers in a line at cruising speed, then turns around to pick them up. Captain Alan Phinney, whom I had talked to at Scripps, found it one of the most pleasant aspects of his job as a master of a research vessel. "It's a lot of fun trying to spot those flashing spheres. You black out the ship, you run along at flank speed and everyone is out on deck to see if the old man is going to flub the next one." Phinney said his batting average was 85 percent recovery. Savings in ship time more than pay for lost corers.

What worries Raymond is that he is beginning to enjoy his work less than his customers do. Benthos too is growing, and he was preparing to move to a new building a half-mile away with 15,000 square feet of floor space. Benthos's founder, president, etc. is a small quiet man just turning forty who lights up like one of his beacons when anyone asks about his work. Then his Cape Cod reserve, assuming that he had any, breaks down and one feels like a member of the family. A graduate of M.I.T., he formed Benthos in 1962. The first bylaw of the corporation seems to be that the president never wears a tie. The second, as far as I could see, forbids the head of the electronics department — a 23-year-old Californian named Clyde Tyndale — to get a haircut. Tyndale, so a company folder explained, builds guitars in his spare time; Raymond plays the clarinet in a jazz band.

"As the company grows, I feel frustrated," Raymond said. "I can't do the creative design work that I used to do. But I hope to get back to it by taking an administrative assistant. Right now, I've got an idea for a one-man glass submarine, but I'm too busy to work on it. In a way, I'm a

Seated on the wharf, Columbus O'Donnell Iselin.

slave to my own business. I was unhappy with jobs I had in the past because I couldn't do just what I wanted. And I still can't."

Columbus O'Donnell Iselin went into oceanography because it was exactly what he wanted to do. He was the first master of the old *Atlantis* and he now holds the Henry Bryant Bigelow Chair in Oceanography (named after the institution's first director and most ardent supporter until his death in 1968) at Woods Hole. Iselin succeeded Bigelow as the director of the Oceanographic in 1940. He is known for his study of the Gulf Stream, improvements in navigation, and refinements in the use of underwater sound that kept German and Japanese submarines at bay during World War II. He is considered one of the founders of present-day American oceanography, yet his name is not a household word. It has been said about him that "he is one of the few people who have enlarged their subject without enlarging themselves as a public figure."

I spoke to Iselin in his office at the Oceanographic where *Atlantis*'s mahogany wheel, removed before she was "sold" to her new owners for $5, hangs on the wall. Iselin is a big man in every sense of the word, though he shows traces of the battering he received during a recent illness. He reminisced and he yarned, casting himself nearly every time as the butt rather than the hero of his stories.

He had come over from his home on Martha's Vineyard aboard the ferry, a change of habit forced on him by his health. For over thirty years, he had commuted in his 36-foot launch, the *Risk*, wearing out three engines in the process. The ferry is a more decorous way, too, of going to work in an Oceanographic that has left its modest beginning far behind.

"The first winter I was at Woods Hole," Iselin said, "I was the only person in the building except the janitor. I came in one morning in a northwest gale. I got off my boat, went into the office and put my pants on the radiator to dry. That was the day that A. Lawrence Lowell, the president of Harvard, walked in for a visit. He found me with my pants down."

Iselin was brought into oceanography by a gift for mathematics and long familiarity with the sea. His family had sailed an America's Cup defender and he had a schooner of his own. "She was a wooden vessel 100 feet long and I called her the *Atlantis*. I had to sell my schooner to get married, but I kept the name." His talent for mathematics, the sub-

Diver checking the Oceanographic's Sea Spider. This aluminum float 120 feet down is tethered to the bottom by three 3,200-foot legs to form a stable mooring for instruments which send data through a surface mast (diagram page 293).

ject in which he majored at Harvard, gave him time to let his curiosity run through meteorology, geology and biology, first in the university library and then in graduate courses. It was at Harvard that he met Bigelow, who fired him with an enthusiasm that has never cooled. Iselin built a 72-foot schooner, the *Chance*, and took her up to Newfoundland to study the Labrador Current with a crew of fellow students. Part of the expedition, he recalled, was spent on land collecting plants and living on Newfoundland hardbread. After it was over, Iselin leaped at an offer from Bigelow to come to Woods Hole, and forgot about the career that had been planned for him in his family's bank on Wall Street. "I took mathematics because I thought it would be helpful in banking, but I was thirty years too early."

Still, he is connected with an Iselin bank, and thereby hangs one of the many tales he told me. When Iselin took over the institution's *Atlantis*, he inherited the crew of the *Carnegie*, a nonmagnetic schooner that had burned in Samoa after a lengthy scientific life. "I had four Scandinavians: a Finn, a Swede, a Norwegian and a Dane. The Swede was Eddie Roos, whose father was the captain of a Swedish icebreaker. Eddie came here, but he was just too much sailor for Woods Hole.

"He was interested in going to the Antarctic, so I sent him to Admiral Byrd. Thus he became the oceanographer on the second Byrd Antarctic Expedition. He found Iselin Bank and named it after me. The last time I heard from him, he was a respectable captain for the Moore-McCormack Lines."

Iselin relived for me the days when the Oceanographic's campus consisted mainly of the wet decks of *Atlantis*. Alfred Woodcock was also on his original crew. "He was an ordinary seaman, not even an A.B., but we soon recognized that he was much more than that. He had been taking notes at sea on different phenomena. He had noticed that the Portuguese man-of-war nearly always sails on the same tack and he wondered why. He put out a row of small numbered bottles and compared their drift to that of the jellyfish. From that he reasoned that the jellyfish was tacking against the Coriolis effect. In the southern hemisphere, he predicted a mirror image. He said jellyfish should be on the opposite tack there and he was 80 percent right.

"Then he began to observe the flight tactics of the lazy herring gull. I was so stupid that I told him he was wasting his time. But he kept looking up as well as down. He watched where the gulls were riding updrafts

Diagram of Sea Spider, showing (circled) the area in the photograph on page 291.

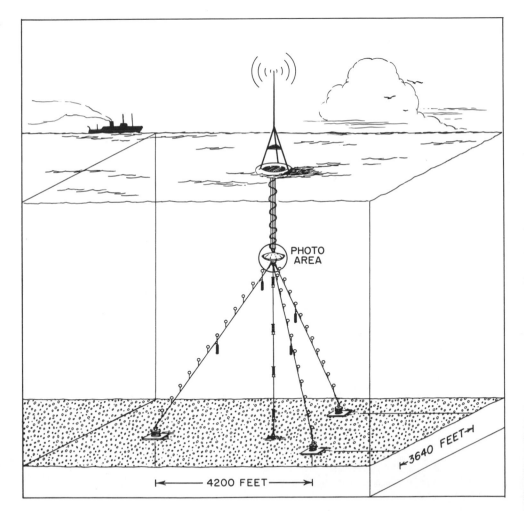

PHOTO
AREA

4200 FEET

3640 FEET

and he was able to show how convection was occurring in the lower atmosphere."

Woodcock is now a professor at the University of Hawaii and a leading authority on cloud physics. "He noticed that his windshield was covered with salt particles when he parked his car on the wharf in winter. He wondered this time how salt got into the atmosphere, and he found the answer. Air is trapped in water when whitecaps are formed. Then when a bubble comes up, it explodes into droplets that send salt particles into the air. He began to measure the size and distribution of these particles. He found salt in the air as far inland as Chicago. Salt particles are a primary reason why clouds rain out. I think he went to Hawaii because he can drive a car into a cloud there."

Iselin fervently hopes that the Oceanographic will go on producing Woodcocks. "The reason this place exists," he said to me, "is that we have a little money of our own, about $300,000 per year. It's nice clean money, not like the money you get out of Washington. On those damned contracts, you practically have to give your results before you start your research. I ought to know, I've collected many millions of it myself."

The focus of his own scientific interests has not varied very much since he made his studies of the Gulf Stream aboard the *Atlantis*. He has always cried out for buoy stations as the only sensible way of keeping track of the ocean weather, and he does have the satisfaction these days of no longer crying in the wilderness. "Twenty-five years ago, I asked the Weather Bureau in Washington to put out buoys. They told me they couldn't; they said the ocean belonged to the Navy. But buoys are now respectable. NATO has a little buoy factory in Norway at Bergen and they're about to wire up the Mediterranean with a network to study air-sea interaction."

His other main line of work is precise navigation. He had learned by sad personal experience that an oceanographer must know his own position before he can tell very much about the position and speed of ocean currents. The Oceanographic has pioneered in navigation by satellite for research ships and also in a system based on very-low-frequency radio waves using the accuracy of atomic clocks. Iselin spared me a detailed explanation, but he emphasized that VLF navigation has the advantage of low cost. "It's way down in price compared to navigation by satellites. The system is not for sale yet, but we hope to drop the price to $6,000.

ATLANTIS, *campus of the self-taught oceanographer.*

Precise navigation must be brought into general use. It's not much scientific good if only our own ships have it."

Iselin could not resist telling me a story about imprecise navigation. "We were sailing back from England in September on *Atlantis* and we had made only 300 miles in a week. I was a lazy navigator. The sky had been clouded over and I really didn't know where I was. Then a ship came over the horizon. She turned out to be the *Bremen,* and she was making a noise like an express train. I had no radio aboard, so I hoisted a flag to ask my position. They wrote it on a big blackboard and held it up for us. Later, the sun came out and I was able to fix my own position. It was eighty miles south of the one that the *Bremen* had given me."

"You mean, the *Bremen*'s captain was as lazy a navigator as you were?"

"No, he didn't want me to know that he was out of his lane. He was cutting across the Grand Banks to set a record. He did, too."

I enjoyed listening to his stories and I soon got the point that he was unconsciously making. Iselin's influence comes from the way he has of looking at the ocean not merely as a fluid on a rotating sphere. It is alive with the navigators and the fishermen who were the first to use it. The Oceanographic keeps them in mind. A "V-fin" developed to follow the temperature of the Gulf Stream from a fast-moving ship is now marketed commercially by Braincon in Marion, Massachusetts, for tankers anxious to use — or to avoid — this oceanic jet stream. Iselin told me how one biologist started to trawl for lobster on the edge of the continental shelf at a depth of 2,000 feet and passed the word along to a Woods Hole fisherman, who broke the market by bringing up 3,000 pounds of lobster a day. Another biologist, Frank Mather, experimented with Japanese fishing gear and found that he could catch swordfish, usually seen at the surface only in July. New Bedford fishermen adopted the gear and brought the swordfish to market out of season. "The housewives didn't want it at first," Iselin said. "They couldn't believe it was fresh."

This is definitely not the answer, however, to the much bigger problem of making efficient use of the ocean's resources. "If you keep fishing nothing but selected species, you're weeding the garden in reverse," Iselin said. In his thinking and his writing, he likes to emphasize that the ocean differs from the land in its capacity to renew its biological and chemical resources. He and Dr. Kenneth Emery at Woods Hole have estimated that its productivity, in terms of dollars invested, could be three times higher per acre than that of dry land if . . .

The if concerns him most of all. In an essay he wrote for an educational advertisement run by Alcan Aluminium Limited, Iselin had said: "The traditional lack of ownership of existing or potential resources of the salt water environment impedes practical experimentation [in aquaculture]. The concept of freedom of the seas, which developed gradually because the waters were considered almost worthless except for transportation and naval warfare, is diametrically opposed to their wise utilization." In our conversation, he added: "This looks like a role for the United Nations or some international organization. A wise efficient fishery has to be managed — and an American fisherman is hard to manage."

Time went by quickly with Iselin. I had my usual guilty feeling about wasting it, but one more question had to be asked. On the wall facing the wheel of *Atlantis*, there was a painting of a black sea raging up against a gray sky. It was signed by Frederick Fuglister, who has been studying the Gulf Stream for the Oceanographic almost as long as Iselin.

It led to one more story. "I found Fritz Fuglister when he was a WPA artist in the 1930's," Iselin said. "I was looking for a man with a strong stomach just to go out on *Atlantis* and give me a hand. He was making his living as a painter at Provincetown, but the going must have been pretty slim because he jumped at my offer."

Iselin stared at the painting as he must have done often before. "I had a hard time hanging the damn thing. I think I've got the sea level straight, but I still can't tell where the wind is coming from."

18. *The Ocean Is Like the Stock Market . . .*

"I had just finished painting a mural for the Brockton Public Library," Fuglister was saying. "The librarian moved to New Bedford and I knew he wanted another mural there. But the local library board turned it down. They decided to spend the WPA money to clean the outside instead of decorating the inside. So I came to Woods Hole and I went out on a Georges Bank cruise as assistant to the chief scientist. They didn't pay me anything. I just got something to eat."

Art's loss was science's gain. It was a loss for art, too. I liked the painting in Iselin's office; it was dramatic, yet understated. "Oh, I sell a painting about every other year now. I do submit to the first show of the season of an art association in P-town. I know the jury, they're all old friends."

So Fuglister went to sea, disregarding the advice of Samuel Johnson that I heard quoted in Woods Hole: "No man will go to sea that has the wit to get himself into jail. And in jail, the food is better and the company just as good." During World War II, the threat of enemy submarines drove Fuglister ashore and he worked for the Oceanographic as a draftsman. He began to produce temperature charts of the Atlantic, and his name is now attached to a widely used atlas of this ocean that he completed in the 1960's. To hear him explain it, that part of his career was another accident. "There was a great demand for oceanographers during the war. I processed temperature data while the others were teaching classes. I couldn't teach because my clearance was bungled for a year, perhaps because of my Swiss name. I felt like a big fat spider caught in its own web."

Fuglister was head of the department of physical oceanography at Woods Hole when I met him, and I am sure that he must have been shanghaied into the job. He makes no secret of his aversion for the administration game. Frankness comes up spontaneously from behind the undergrowth of his magnificent black beard. (I had sworn not to mention beards anymore, but Fuglister's is too archetypal to be omitted.) He learned oceanography on the campus of the *Atlantis*'s deck.

Nearing his sixties, ballasted by a title and honorary degrees, Fuglister still manages to cast off from his desk and go to sea in his eternal pursuit of the Gulf Stream. He no longer needs to track it. The U.S. Naval Oceanographic Office does this much more quickly by plane with an airborne thermometer that measures radiation from the sea surface. It immediately detects the current's warm northern boundary and this information is used in a monthly Gulf Stream summary. Fuglister is concerned with finer points. The more closely he looks at the Gulf Stream, the more convinced he is of its complexity. His detailed measurements even make him wonder if the Gulf Stream as such actually exists.

"I do not think there is a single Gulf Stream, but rather very swift currents not all moving in exactly the same direction," he said. "On the chart, they look like a shingled roof: the end of one current overlaps the beginning of the next. We used to think of the Gulf Stream with an average speed of one knot. That was how Columbus Iselin saw it at first. He would run a cross section and estimate his total drift when he reached Bermuda. Later we went out with accurate radio navigation. We found filaments of currents moving as fast as three to five knots. But the old average is good."

Having demolished everyone's favorite image of a mighty river of the sea (the Gulf Stream transports seventy times as much water as all the world's rivers combined), Fuglister lit a pipe, got it going under forced draft and then began to talk about some of the Gulf Stream's whims. The most striking are the eddies that it throws off. From the Straits of Florida north to Cape Hatteras, the Gulf Stream is a narrow current. When it leaves the continental shelf to head northeast for Europe, it resembles a lazy river meandering in loops over a plain. Such a river will shortcut its loops, turning them into isolated oxbow lakes. The Gulf Stream does the same, with one difference: the "lakes" that it sheds are not stagnant pools. They retain the momentum of their parent current. At first, they are seen as loops entrapping cold water from the northern edge of the Gulf Stream. Then they evolve into eddies nearly 100 miles in diameter, whirling in the middle of the ocean. Fuglister and his associates at Woods Hole keep watch on them as part of a study to learn exactly what happens to the Gulf Stream's energy as it decays from a strong current off North America to a slow drift near Europe.

Fuglister asked me to imagine an eddy as a spinning phonograph record, on a turntable that is moving west a few miles a day. He does not know what finally happens to the eddy because he has never been able to follow one through its complete life, which he thinks may last a year or more. That is what he is now attempting to do.

To hear what his record has to say, Fuglister plants a buoy in its middle, with a parachute drogue 600 feet down so that the buoy will drift with the deep current, not with the wind. "We've got a buoy out there now," he said. "We left it 300 miles from Woods Hole and it will be a week before we go out to look at it again." Then he will be able to see how far the buoy has moved from the center of the spinning record and, at the same time, measure the drift of the whole turntable. Each buoy is painted in screaming colors and carries a radio transmitter to give a homing signal to the searching ship. Fuglister and his crew are now on such familiar terms with eddies that they can find a buoy even when its radio transmitter breaks down. Among the hazards buoys face are whales. "We nearly always see whales in eddies. Around a buoy, they may act like big playful dogs."

An undisturbed buoy towed by its deep sea-anchor will circle at a good three knots inside an eddy. Fuglister knows this because he has been able to ride eddies himself aboard a research ship. It's best not to fight them. "We have to go with the current because we can only make eight knots when we tow our V-fin. If we bucked the current, it could take us four or five days to go around an eddy."

With the V-fin, he can find an eddy and brand it with a buoy. But he claims that he can sense one himself just by the change in the motion of his ship as the water becomes rougher at the eddy's edge. That may be why he uses the *Crawford*. A 125-foot converted Coast Guard cutter, built in 1927 for service on the Great Lakes, she is long, narrow and rakish. When I visited her at Woods Hole, I almost felt a change of motion at dockside. But her first mate told me firmly that she can do anything that *Atlantis II* or *Chain* can do, even if they outweigh her sevenfold. On her foredeck, she carried two red-and-white striped buoys with sharklike hulls for slipping through the water. Every inch of her laboratory space was stuffed with electronics. Her mess room, with red-and-white striped tablecloths matching the buoys, looked like an informal marine *bistro*. A sign begged guests not to use coffee mugs for ashtrays or paint containers. At sea, the cook told me, the officers sit on one side, the crew on the other. Scientists sit anywhere.

Fuglister's stomach must be as strong as it was when Iselin hired him thirty years ago. This is an asset in getting the ship time he needs to study the history of an eddy. *Crawford* has few takers for North Atlantic work in midwinter, when he and his group use her. He is particularly anxious for a study to be made of the effect of eddies on marine life. "We really could use a biologist for five or six months. I think they're waiting until we get a more comfortable ship, but I'm not sure."

I asked Fuglister how the eddies influence the Gulf Stream's heating system for western Europe. "The Gulf Stream is not as simple as it sounds," he answered. "I don't think that one could follow a parcel of warm Gulf Stream water from here to England. Even if there were no Gulf Stream, England would be warmer than we are. They have a maritime climate that comes across the ocean. On this side, our atmospheric weather comes from the continent."

Yet if a warm Gulf Stream flows through a cold ocean, how can it fail to affect the climate of Europe? I received the answer to this question not from Fuglister but from *The Gulf Stream*, a book by Professor Henry Stommel of M.I.T., who has been on the scientific staff of the Oceanographic since 1944. "The Gulf Stream is not an ocean river of hot water," he states. Then what is it? First of all, it is a misnomer. In the sixteenth century, its source was held to be the rivers emptying into the Gulf of Mexico. Stommel notes that this theory was finally discarded only many years later when comparative measurements showed that the flow of the "mighty" Mississippi was only one-thousandth that of the Gulf Stream through the Straits of Florida. But the name had stuck forever. Secondly, it is not a "river" at all. This sort of analogy goes back to the kind of thinking typified by an early theory of oceanic circulation that Stommel quotes: "At the North Pole one finds four large islands . . . between which are four deep and broad channels. The water flows together near the Pole, but at the Pole itself is a great Black Rock, 33 leagues in circumference. Ships which once enter one of these channels never return, not even with the most favourable winds, and next to the Black Rock all the water is engulfed into the bowels of the earth, whence it flows through springs and river sources once again into the light of day."

Much more prosaically, the Gulf Stream is only the westward edge of the carousel turning clockwise in the North Atlantic. On the western sides of virtually all oceans, there are such swift narrow currents, an effect of the earth's rotation. So the Gulf Stream would exist without the Gulf of Mexico, or the Straits of Florida where it actually begins. In the open ocean, it is not a river but a boundary between cold northern waters to its left and the warm Sargasso Sea in the middle of the Atlantic. Stommel calls it a "dynamic dam."

As such, it may influence climate, but not in the way that is generally believed. Variations in the Gulf Stream could affect the strength of the dam and, consequently, the Sargasso water corralled behind it. Iselin had speculated as long ago as 1940 that an increase in the Gulf Stream's flow might actually chill Europe by squeezing this warm water mass down to a greater depth and into a smaller surface area. The converse would then be true for a weakening of the Gulf Stream. Nearly thirty years later, the question remains open. Stommel observes: "There is no convincing evidence to prove that this (or any other) sequence of events actually takes place."

He brings out that theorizing about the Gulf Stream began almost immediately after its southern "headwaters," more accurately known as the Florida Current, were described in 1513 by Ponce de León, who had bucked them unsuccessfully. Two years later, the Italian scholar Peter

Martyr thought about the problem and just about hit the nail on the head. He reasoned that the North Equatorial Current reported by Spanish navigators had to go somewhere when it reached the American mainland and that it must have been deflected northward as the Gulf Stream. But his successors in theoretical oceanography did not separate science from folklore. Some looked to those rivers feeding the Gulf of Mexico, others saw a heap of water blown by the wind against the American coast and running "downhill" to the north.

As for the science of descriptive oceanography, it progressed much more thanks to seamen than to scholars. By the end of the seventeenth century, their reports had led to the first charts of the Gulf Stream and the current system of the North Atlantic. The charts, Stommel says, "were far superior to the theories advanced to explain them." One explanation, for example, held that the sun's heat built up by day a mountain of water at the equator that collapsed at night to keep the currents of the ocean alive. Physicists began to catch up with navigators only in the eighteenth century when the foundations of fluid mechanics were laid, and fictional oceanography went into a decline.

Gulf Stream research was still spurred by practical considerations. When Benjamin Franklin was deputy postmaster general of the American colonies in 1770, he wondered why service from the mother country was so dreadfully slow. On the westbound run, English mail packets were taking two weeks longer than ordinary merchant ships. Stommel relates how Franklin talked the problem over with a Nantucket whaler, Timothy Folger, who had the answer. The whalers knew where the current was because the whales, "which keep to the side of it but are not met within it," had shown them. Crossing the Gulf Stream, Folger had often met mail packets plowing through water running three miles an hour against them. He wrote Franklin that he had told them of their error, but their masters were too proud to learn from whales and "too wise to be councelled [sic] by simple American fishermen." Franklin had no such prejudices. From Folger's indications, he had a chart of the Gulf Stream engraved and it was published by the General Post Office.

In the nineteenth century, scientists themselves sailed into the Gulf Stream and began the survey work that is still going on. They saw a much more complex phenomenon than the bold river on Franklin's chart. The position of the stream shifted, its width changed, cold filaments kept appearing (they probably were eddies), and the stream's northern "bank" (that is, the face of the dynamic dam) was more permanent than its southern one. As more and more temperature readings were acquired, many scientists were tempted to attribute the driving force of the Gulf Stream and other major currents to differences in density between warm and cold water. Seamen stuck to their old conviction that the winds were running the ocean, and it was only after World War II that this belief was vindicated at the highest scientific level by the work of Walter Munk and Stommel himself.

As for the amount of water that the Gulf Stream actually moves, this is a question that has yet to be answered satisfactorily. Measuring the flow through the Straits of Florida is relatively simple. There, at least, the Gulf Stream flows between banks of solid earth, in a channel of known dimensions. At this point, it has been found to carry about 30 million cubic meters of water per second. (By way of comparison, the discharge rate of the world's biggest river, the Amazon, is 225,000 cubic meters per second.) What happens in the ocean is something else. Up to about fifteen years ago, oceanographers always assumed "a zone of no motion" below 2,000 meters (6,561 feet). On this basis, they said that the Gulf Stream moved about twice as much water in the open sea as in the Straits of Florida. Their certainty vanished when measurement of deep currents became feasible.

Here, I must be forgiven a digression across the Atlantic (advances in oceanography are never the monopoly of a single institution or country). Credit for the discovery of a practical way to prove the existence of deep currents belongs squarely to Dr. John Swallow of the National Institute of Oceanography in Britain, the inventor of the Swallow float.

When Swallow, a Yorkshireman, came to the institute in 1954 from Cambridge, where he had been working in geophysics, he joined a group that was trying to learn if the zone of no motion was really all that quiet. They had experimented with a pinger that was supposed to take a whole day to settle to the bottom at the end of a parachute while a ship traced it by listening to its sound. Some results had been obtained, but the method quickly came to a dead end. As Swallow told me when I met him in the chief scientist's cabin of *Discovery,* his institute's ship, at Plymouth (Devonshire, not Massachusetts), one must measure for more than a day to get beyond the influence of the tidal cycle on deep currents. The pinger on the parachute was the equivalent of a balloon that just

Frederick Fuglister

John Swallow

went up and down in one day. What was needed was a balloon that could reach a predetermined level, stay there and drift with deep currents for days or weeks.

The problem was handed to Swallow, who first went at it from the viewpoint of the hot-air balloonist. He toyed with an oil-filled float heated by batteries to keep it at a desired depth, then gave up when he saw the power required. He took a different approach. "Most people think that water is incompressible," he said. "It isn't." Water is just less compressible than what we usually put into it. A conventional submarine cannot be weighted to stay at a certain level: it must either go up or down. When it dives, its hull compresses faster than the water and its density becomes greater. So water ballast is pumped out, but then the submarine will tend to rise . . . until water is let in and the balancing act starts all over again. Swallow needed an underwater float, less compressible than water. Then it would hold a predetermined depth.

At this point, he remembered his work at Cambridge, where he had been studying the transmission of acoustic waves through varied materials. He knew, of course, that the speed of sound rises with the incompressibility of the medium that it goes through: sound travels four times faster in aluminum than in water. "On the face of it, it was not a daft idea," said Swallow. The shop at the National Institute of Oceanography made the first Swallow float, an aluminum tube nine feet long and three inches in diameter. Into the tube went the pinger and overboard went the Swallow float . . . along with the conviction that there really is a "zone of no motion." Far below 2,000 meters, the float moved and a listening ship could follow it. Charting currents that inch along in the deep, however, was and still is another of the oceanographer's headaches that can be cured only by precision navigation. "You can get into a situation in which you know where the ship is in relation to the float, but you don't know where the ship itself is," Swallow said.

Work done with the floats has shown that the Gulf Stream extends to the bottom even after it leaves the continental shelf. Consequently, the estimate of the amount of water that it carries along south of New England has been raised to about 150 million cubic meters a second, five times the flow through the Straits of Florida. Where the added water comes from and why its volume varies are among the many discoveries still to be made in oceanography.

Dr. John Beckerle at Woods Hole thinks he may have the glimmer of an answer. Beckerle is a large pleasant man in his mid-forties who decorates the wall above his desk with his children's drawings of various oceanographic devices. He had just come off a month's trip aboard *Chain* in the area of Bermuda, and he went out of his way to show me pictures of a cookout he had held on deck with his students and fellow scientists to give them a change of pace. Beckerle and his collaborators regularly ride a circuit of ocean stations where they measure changes in the speed of sound in the water, using an instrument that sends an acoustic pulse singing around a four-inch circular path.

What they learn is important to antisubmarine warfare, but we did not talk about that. Variations in the speed of sound indicate that something is happening to the oceanic environment. Beckerle, who described himself as in a "continual Eureka state," had been drawing maps to show these changes in time and space on the stations that he occupied. Contours represented "iso-sound velocity lines" like the isobars of atmospheric pressure on a weather map. He and others at the Oceanographic have noticed that these contours are periodically bent as if a westbound wave had jarred them. He estimates that the wave must be 250 miles long, and theory suggests it has a period of three and one-half months.

Moving west in the Atlantic, such a wave encounters the Gulf Stream. "I think — this is only conjecture for the time being — that when it does, it forces the Gulf Stream to meander and kick off eddies. Look what happens to the water from a garden hose if you hit the nozzle." Long-period waves, Beckerle speculates, might hit the Gulf Stream every three months or so and account for the extra water that it somehow accumulates between the Straits of Florida and the vicinity of Cape Hatteras. By bending the Gulf Stream, they could also affect the climate of the eastern United States. In a relaxed moment, Beckerle had drawn for his children a sketch showing the impact of a snaky long wave on the stream. His caption read: "Out of the east, the FIERY DRAGON warms our coast with the comfortable waters of the Gulf Stream."

The Oceanographic worries the Atlantic from all sides and in all ways. Ships tracking Swallow floats or lowering sound velocimeters are a valid method; so are bottles cast into the sea to study long-term surface drift. Dean F. Bumpus, an investigator at Woods Hole since 1937, has used pop and beer bottles containing postcards for this purpose.

Over a period of fourteen years, 150,000 bottles were released into the ocean by ships, planes, and even blimps. Sixteen thousand postcards came back with reports of where and when they were found. They enabled Bumpus and a Canadian scientist, L. M. Lauzier, to coauthor an atlas of surface circulation over the continental shelf off the east coast of North America for the benefit of ocean users, whether racing yachtsmen or engineers wondering what will happen to sewage dumped into the sea. They also gave the Oceanographic an opportunity to let the general public participate directly in research. As an incentive, a 50-cent reward was offered for each bottle returned. Writing in *Oceanus*, Bumpus reported that many finders waived the reward. But not a certain Scotsman in the Outer Hebrides. He insisted on being paid in English currency because the bank would have charged him a shilling to cash half a dollar. His request was granted.

Bumpus tells many a story about his bottles. He has gotten some more out of his recent experiments with seabed drifters, which consist of a labeled saucer on a plastic stem. He used over 7,000 to measure residual drift along the continental shelf, and 24 percent of them were recovered. He showed me a letter from one of the finders. It contained the drifter's label and a note: "Found $2\frac{1}{2}$ miles west of Brigantine Beach, New Jersey, while looking at a piece of feminine pulchritude in a yellow bikini. While the 50 cents will be appreciated, this chick cost me $27.85 to entertain her, all because she came over closer to see what I found."

Beer bottles and plastic drifters can track water movements at the surface and over the bottom for many months. They are the sturdy forebears of a technique that is being developed at the Oceanographic to acquire similar information about the intermediate deep waters. It was explained to me by Dr. H. Thomas Rossby, the 30-year-old son of the late Carl-Gustaf A. Rossby whose name is a byword to research meteorologists (it was he who discovered the long-period Rossby waves that Beckerle was investigating). An M.I.T. researcher, Rossby is carrying out Stommel's long-cherished dream of putting a Swallow float down into that deep sound channel where a noise travels almost indefinitely in the ocean. Three tracking stations on Bermuda, Puerto Rico, and Eleuthera in the Bahamas listen to the float when it pings four times a day, and fix its position to within less than a mile. The float is like an articulate water particle. Daily oscillations of deep currents can be learned, and total movement plotted over a much longer period. The float is designed

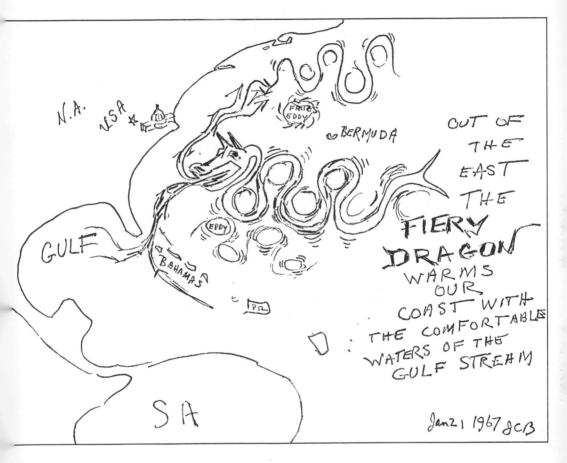

John Beckerle's sketch for his children

to operate for a year. I asked Rossby how it was recovered. "We don't recover it," he said. Then it's expendable? He hesitated. "I hate to say that anything costing $8,000 is expendable. At times, it is frustrating to live at two different economic levels. You return home from the lab and you wonder whether there will be steak or hamburger."

There is a cheaper solution for deep-current measurements of shorter duration. Rossby told me of plans to send down a float, costing about $100, that will just emit one loud signal after a week or a month. "We call it the 'abyssal drift bottle,' but unlike a surface bottle, we will know when it is located and hence its drift rate. A number of such floats in a large area would allow us to construct synoptic drift charts of the abyssal circulation."

It is Stommel, the inspirer of these experiments, who is the most outspoken critic of the "persistent though erroneous notion that all worthwhile problems will eventually be solved by some simple ingenious idea or gadget." Rossby's floats, like Bumpus's bottles, take only a slice of the Atlantic. No one slice is sufficient to describe an ocean, and nobody really can say how many slices are needed nor how often and how closely they should be taken. This leaves the modern physical oceanographer in a state of highly creative frustration. He knows that the ocean varies; it does not behave the same way from one moment to the next. He is reasonably certain that this variability determines weather. The frustration comes when he tries to detect a long cycle, to catch a rhythm, to decide what is cause and what is effect. Operating on the ocean are some forces that move water only a few inches in a few seconds, others that are planetary and last over a year.

Setting up an observation network is also frustrating. Professor Robert Stewart of the Institute of Oceanography at the University of British Columbia in Vancouver once remarked to me in envy: "The meteorologists were just damn lucky. They took simple temperature and pressure measurements on a horizontal scale governed by the spacing of major cities. They found they could make sense of them. It was only a fortunate accident. In the ocean, the time scale of events is longer than in the atmosphere, but the space scale is smaller. The ocean is more stable than the atmosphere. It is not improbable that the proper mesh for an observation network might be stations only ten miles apart or less. This is completely impractical, of course. It would mean sending out so many ships that there would be no ocean left and one could walk over it."

Dean Bumpus draws off water from a Nansen bottle for analysis aboard ship.

Stewart, a leading ocean theoretician, is in his forties but he told me: "I do not think that the problem of variability in the ocean will be solved in my generation . . . nor in my grandson's."

It is one that holds great appeal for physical oceanographers. The practical difficulties of wresting this sort of information away from the sea are equaled by the challenge of interpreting it. Such an experiment was begun by the Oceanographic as a major effort. Since 1966, it has been measuring the vagaries of small currents with an array of four to six moored buoys. They have been strung out to the south of Woods Hole at intervals of about fifty miles along 70° west, the meridian that jabs the elbow of Cape Cod. Dr. Nicholas Fofonoff, originally from Canada (a country whose production of oceanographers is out of all proportion to its population), is the senior scientist on the experiment. He was summed up by Paul Ferris Smith, who makes the Geodyne current meters used on the buoys: "Fofonoff has the brains of a theoretician and the physical stature to handle equipment at sea."

Six current meters are strung out along the mooring cable of each buoy, from the surface to a depth of about 6,000 feet. They could be called the equivalent of a weather station's wind gauges, except that no meteorologist ever lost an anemometer through fish-bites or the zeal of mariners who must pick up anything they see floating. What Fofonoff is trying to achieve in the sea is the reliability of an unmanned weather station on land. After the buoys are moored, they are left on their own. Fofonoff takes ten days aboard *Chain* to visit his array. The buoys, painted shocking orange, with radio masts sprouting from their squat hulls, look like potted trees waiting to be planted in the ocean. Back in the buoy laboratory on the Oceanographic's pier, Fofonoff can tell if they have been uprooted. By radio, they report to him on the tension they exert on their anchor lines (high tension can mean a hurricane; no tension means that a mooring has parted). He told me that Woods Hole is able to leave buoys out for two months and bring back 65 percent of them with their taped recordings of currents. The recovery rate, however, must go up to 90 percent or better before the technique can be fully exploited.

The current meters tape events on a scale from a tenth of a cycle an hour to as high as 1,800 cycles an hour. "It's a whole new field," Fofonoff said. "It has little to do with the water-bottle oceanography that has given us the permanent or long-term features of ocean circulation.

T. Ferris Webster (standing) and Nicholas Fofonoff go over the computerized data compiled by their current meters.

We're now in an exploratory phase. It's fun, but it's discouraging to lose instruments. Still, we're improving. Six or seven years ago, we only recovered 25 percent. We now measure temperature as well as currents and we would like to record salinity changes as well."

Fofonoff turned me over to Dr. T. Ferris Webster for an interpretation of the records that have already been gathered. In his early thirties, Webster has not lost any of the bright spunkiness he must have had as a student when he earned the first doctorate ever awarded by M.I.T. in oceanography.

"Our aim has nothing to do with buoys," he began, almost aggressively. "We're not trying to play with buoys, we're trying to understand the dynamic processes of the ocean. We want to get measurements so that we can ask the theoreticians to explain them to us. We use buoys only because it would cost too much to study variability with ships. But don't kid yourself, buoys won't replace ships. They're like automation, they generate work. Right now, we need more ships to set buoys."

I asked Webster why the array had been anchored on its present site. "We started with the assumption that the ocean is just too big to study all at once. So we tried to get an unbiased sample. We wanted to avoid the strongest currents. Along 70° west, there is the Hatteras abyssal plain. We know the bottom topography is flat there. You might say that we want to see what happens where nothing is happening. It's one thing to clobber the Gulf Stream with current meters, but it's only a single feature of the ocean. If you study the Gulf Stream and understand it, you're still not home."

And why were the stations spaced about fifty miles apart? "We really don't know the number of stations we need nor how they should be spaced. In oceanography, one usually runs a fishing expedition or an experiment. This program is a combination of both. We cannot yet say what the experiment will be. Our first aim is to sample the whole spectrum of time scales. Our ultimate aim is to understand oceanic variability. The classical oceanographers were describing mean conditions. Although a mean is a valuable concept, it can be completely inadequate as a description of instantaneous conditions. It's like saying today's mean temperature is sixty-four degrees when asked about the weather outside."

Fofonoff had mentioned how instruments have already recorded a shift of a one-knot current from due north to due south in a single day at a site twenty feet below the surface. Was this a step forward towards a solution? "I have a feeling that we've only got variability by the tail. We haven't grabbed it. What goes on every three weeks? What happens every season? Will our program lead to an understanding of the ocean comparable to that of the atmosphere? I don't know. Meteorologists are forced to make predictions, and this is a good thing. We hope that in ten or fifteen years, oceanographers will have good enough information to try."

The buoy array would not produce results before then? "We've already got results. A single tape from a single current meter contains 150,000 measurements. We use more computer time than the rest of the institution put together. We have found that deep ocean tides are not uniform as once was thought. We have been able to show that at frequencies shorter than the tides, the ocean is mostly turbulent. That is, it has no recognizable frequency; the details of the motion cannot be predicted for such a period. We have learned that currents are always changing. The ocean is like the stock market; it never stops fluctuating."

The final attack on variability will depend on what is now being learned. "This program is experimental," said Webster. "At present, we are able only to obtain time series of measurements at fixed locations. And we only handle a vertical scale. Before we can go further, we must know how closely we will have to sample in space. I would foresee buoys a mile apart in an initial attempt."

He gave me a paper he had written to suggest a large-scale program of oceanic observations. In it he proposed to set up a row of two-dozen buoys, spaced a mile apart, in one of those regions where nothing happens: no major currents, no storms, no seamounts, and at a latitude where the Coriolis force is not a determining factor. After a year or two, the row could be bisected by another to form a cross. Then the area between the arms of the cross could be filled in with buoys, leading to a cube that could put out tentacles until a fairly large region is covered.

Webster warned in his paper that such a program is neither adventurous nor dramatic. Here he reflected a basic attitude towards the study of the sea that Stommel expressed in his book on the Gulf Stream: "Many catastrophes of an economic kind, such as the failure of the rice crop in Japan, or of a certain fishery, or years of unusual numbers of icebergs in shipping lanes, are attributed to fluctuations in ocean currents. Very little is known about such fluctuations. It takes years of careful and expensive observation to produce even a very crude description of them. A well-planned long-term survey designed to reveal fluctuations in ocean currents would be expensive and time-consuming. It might even fail, because of the inadequacies of the tools we have at hand. But until this burdensome and not immediately rewarding task is undertaken, our information about the fluctuations of ocean currents will always be fragmentary."

It is the hard way. To those who are temped to cut corners, there is the threat of receiving the William Leighton Jordan Esquire Award, set up by the Society of Subprofessional Oceanographers (with only three members: Stommel, Fuglister, and L. Valentine Worthington of Woods Hole) and named in honor of an Englishman who tried to disprove the *Challenger* reports at the end of the nineteenth century because they disagreed with his own ideas about ocean circulation. The citation reads:

"The William Leighton Jordan Esquire Award is given infrequently to the oceanographer who has made a most misleading contribution to his field. Ignorance and utter incompetence do not automatically qualify.

"The work cited must be distinguished not only by being in error but it must be outstandingly bad: wrong both in fact and in principle, and revealing the most mistaken intuition and the most faulty insight. It should be overambitious. It should be well and plausibly presented. It should be artfully written and totally misleading and false."

19. *In Search of Absolutes*

Into a lifetime of fifty-odd years, Dr. William S. von Arx has crammed three major lines of research, none of them cut-rate breakthroughs. His name is constantly cited as the inventor of an electrical method of plotting ocean currents from a ship moving at full speed, a reducer of oceans to laboratory-sized models and, most recently, a geodesist-astronomer photographing stars and measuring slopes in the sea surface from a ship heaving and rolling to wave action. He combines teaching at M.I.T. with research at Woods Hole or at sea. Somehow, too, he has been able to consult for industry, serve on committees in Washington and write one of the first modern introductory textbooks on physical oceanography.

I first saw him on the Oceanographic's pier. Wearing torn khaki trousers and looking like a frail longshoreman, Professor von Arx was prowling over the roof of a small portable laboratory van that had just been unloaded from the *Chain*. I was waiting for him when he came down from his inspection and he agreed to talk about the prospects of oceanography. The matter of his multiple interests came up and he disposed of it immediately: "I just think there are two kinds of scientists:

those who build a little empire around one early discovery, and those who keep experimenting with something new. In the latter case, you remain the same individual but grow a little wiser . . . and, perhaps, sadder because so many opportunities exist."

The techniques associated with von Arx are only ways to give the oceanographer the advantage of precise observation enjoyed by the laboratory physicist working in controlled conditions. Von Arx, as he once put it, is among those who are trying to "transcend the discrepancy of 10-billion-to-one between man's physical bulk and that of the earth." A technique is worth trying if it promises to do this, whether by shrinking an ocean into a room at Woods Hole or expanding the scientist's reach to the dimensions of the sea.

Then oceanography can approach its ultimate goal. In his office-laboratory, with a workbench and an electric furnace behind his desk, von Arx seemed quizzically boyish. He talked with his guard down; he spoke of his current interest in the processes of learning; he told me of the string quartet that he and his wife formed twenty-two years ago with the Fuglisters and that still meets weekly on winter evenings on Cape Cod. But he never drifted very far from the aims of oceanography.

"Originally, the methods of oceanography were directed toward finding codfish or icebergs," he said. "Oceanography now has more exacting responsibilities. It needs measurements that are absolute. It needs more basic methods, and these in wider variety. Oceanography is quiet science, despite the recent use of words like 'inner space' to describe it and the popular preoccupation of the press with its hardware and ships."

He has practiced it quietly. For about ten years, starting in 1950, he walled himself up at Woods Hole to concentrate on the physical modeling of the sea, in all scales from a bay to a hemisphere. Here he was seeking a "useful middle ground" between mathematical theory, in which many details must be left out, and the actual ocean, in which they can be overwhelming. Von Arx's private ocean was a circular tank thirteen feet in diameter. He could spin it up to ten revolutions per minute to create his own Coriolis effect. The surface of the tank was covered with rubber continents and oceans at an average depth of an inch and a half (representing the wind-driven layer of the actual sea). Blowers sent breezes over it, reproducing the earth's wind system. Effects of wind could be measured by the drift of Ping-Pong balls floating on the surface and shuttlecocks suspended from thin wires overhead. He used ink and chemicals as current tracers. He used dyes that sank, others that floated so that a camera loaded with color film could follow the circulation of his tagged water masses. In photographs, the Gulf Stream appears as a swift boundary current that meanders in the tank as it does in the Atlantic. So does its counterpart in the western Pacific, the Kuroshio off Japan.

"It was an intriguing experiment," von Arx said. "I enjoyed every minute of it. Every oceanographer yearns to hold the earth in his hand. We were able to model the effect of the earth's rotation and how it varies with latitude. We could see what happened to the surface currents with a change of wind stress. Since we used homogeneous water, we had to leave out density as a factor, but our results showed surprising fidelity to nature. We could change conditions: we plugged up the Straits of Florida to learn what that would do to the Gulf Stream, we opened the isthmus of Panama, we studied paleoceanography by looking at the circulation under wind fields of the past."

When von Arx completed his work on miniature oceans, he went back to his original concern for measurements at sea. It was after he had returned from Bikini in 1946 that he had devised his geomagnetic electrokinetograph, more handily known as "the GEK," that enables a scientist to record ocean currents while a ship is under way. "It was just based on a footnote that Faraday had given in 1832," he remarked. In a lecture to the Royal Society, Faraday suggested that seawater, which is an electrolyte, should generate an electric current when it flows through the earth's magnetic field. Movement of water through the English Channel could be learned if Dover and Calais were connected by "a circuit of conducting matter." Faraday actually tried his idea in the Thames, but as was true of other nineteenth-century geniuses, his ideas were far ahead of his contemporary technology. The effect he predicted was later observed when submarine cables appeared. Then after World War II, rugged instruments developed primarily for industry became available and von Arx was able to put Faraday's principle to work at sea in the GEK. It has been used both by scientists and, in a practical application, by the International Ice Patrol in the North Atlantic.

Another jump in technology is responsible for von Arx's present interests. The gyroscopes of the space age can correct for the motion of a ship. Placed in a small observatory, they provide a stable, level platform upon which a telescope can be mounted to photograph the stars or to make a geodetic survey at sea. Von Arx had just come off such an expedition when I saw him for the first time on top of his laboratory van. It was about the size of a pickup truck and it could have been mistaken for a steam cabinet except for the astronomer's dome on its roof. Inside the van, he can mount a telescope on a table that holds still, no matter what the ship is doing. It is the heart of a system that has a number of uses. He can navigate with his telescope to a precision of a fifth of a nautical mile. It can serve as a shipboard astronomical observatory. Von Arx, a part-time astronomer himself, has been able to take hour-long time exposures of the sky at night without a blur.

Spray, the dust of the sea, is kept away from the telescope by a steady blast of filtered air inside the dome. His head at the eyepiece, his feet on a heaving deck, von Arx practices astronomical navigation and marine geodesy. Everything moves all the time in the observatory. The telescope seems to be moving, but the gyroscope keeps it steady and level. "At first, it's hard to get used to," he said, indicating the small telescope on his desk. "You see the observatory going like this and the telescope going like that. Then you look through the eyepiece and find that star images and the horizon are rock steady. That is how we can now survey the ocean with the same techniques that we use on land."

The concept of surveying the ocean is not an easy one to get across. Why survey it at all? What could be more level than sea level? Von Arx threw me a line and hauled me out of a semantic rip current. The sea is not always level. It tilts under the thrust of tides and winds. The earth's rotation alone, von Arx said, exerts a force sufficient to raise the right side of the Gulf Stream a full three feet higher than the left side. That means a gradient of about a foot in twenty miles. He thinks this slope can be surveyed from a ship. He has already found a "spectacular dent" in the ocean. Aboard *Chain* over the Puerto Rico Trench, he set up his theodolite and measured the deflections of vertical as the ship steamed along at ten knots for sixteen hours. He found that the elevation of the "geoid" — the actual shape of the earth based on mean sea level — is ninety-two feet lower over the trench than in San Juan harbor on Puerto Rico. Reporting on his results in *Science*, von Arx characteristically called them "relatively crude," and added: "The accuracy attained is barely comparable with that achieved by Eratosthenes two millenia ago when he estimated the circumference of the earth." Eratosthenes was 16 percent off in his calculations based on the shadows cast by the sun at two points in Egypt and the distance between them (which he estimated on the basis of a camel's average speed).

Once accuracy is achieved, the technique could help the oceanographer answer certain broad questions. One of the biggest is whether or not sea level is rising (it should be if the earth's climate is becoming warmer and glaciers are melting). From land, he cannot be sure. He knows that continents move up and down at uneven rates along their shores. If the sea could be surveyed for decades to within a vertical uncertainty of one meter (39.37 inches), von Arx thinks that a start could be made. With a hundred times greater precision, one could detect the "slopes" in the ocean along which water flows and how they vary with time. As a start, an experiment is being made to measure the tilt in the Gulf Stream across the Straits of Florida between Miami and Bimini.

"We can look at problems that no one was ever able to solve before," he said. "Scientists are living on the fruits of military technology and the space age. That's where the lovely gyros that we use for our telescope have come from. I think it is part of the scientist's business to adapt such new developments to the uses of science, and as good citizens, to help the military when we can. But only up to a point. When anything becomes classified, I usually duck out. I don't want to know anything that I can't talk about to my students and colleagues."

Von Arx himself was a student not so long ago: he received his doctor's degree in 1955 at the age of thirty-nine. He had started his education in a nonaffluent society. "I spent four years working in a law office and illustrating catalogs for Montgomery Ward so that I could have a year at Brown. I saved up $1,000; I just wanted to trade four years of intellectual starvation for that year at college. When I did, it opened a whole new world."

He studied oceanography the way everyone else did at the time. He studied everything: geology, physics and chemistry at Brown; geology, physics and astronomy at Yale for his master's; meteorology and fluid dynamics at M.I.T. for his doctorate. "I was trying to understand all I could about the earth: its rocks, the ocean, the atmosphere, the astronomical environment. Oceanography is an intellectual quincunx. You keep bouncing off people until you have a chance to be in the clear."

He would like to see it remain that way at M.I.T., where he has been teaching since 1956. "Oceanography at M.I.T. is a can of worms. It is made up of pieces from the whole institute. We want to keep it that way." And not too big. "As a teacher, I don't like closed-circuit television. I want to see faces. I want to know if a student is with it or not, I want to walk up and down the aisles. Even with a class of seventy-five, it can still be a Socratic dialogue. Education is a scramble of people thinking."

Von Arx expressed what he expects from an oceanography student in an article he wrote for M.I.T.'s *Technology Review:* "It is necessary to maintain a childlike appreciation of new phenomena and at the same time bring to bear a full measure of scholarly skepticism in seeking a physical explanation for that which has been observed." Such an attitude must grow spontaneously. "Lots of good science is still being done today in backyards and basements the way it was 150 years ago," he said. "Most people who are driven to think originally about problems are loners. Oceanography has its share of them. We must recognize this administratively, we must learn how to manage the unmanageable. So far, no department of oceanography has been set up at M.I.T. Yet, in ten years it has produced a dozen innovators. If you can turn out one Ferris Webster a year, you're doing fine."

One of his students at M.I.T. took a political job in Washington. Von Arx did not think the less of him for that. "We must develop a breed of people in political office who can take responsibility for science in a technological society. The scientist should know how his work spins off into the social structure. There is a place for him in the centers where political decisions are made. He can exercise a reasoned judgment there. His effect on public policy is almost negligible, but it can be positive.

"Decisions must not be left to computers. The computer works by rules, but man does not live by fixed rules. His law is a living, breathing thing. One cannot program subjective changes. They must come from the gut, not the head."

Von Arx spends thirty days a year himself in Washington, partly on the executive committee of the National Research Council's division of earth sciences, and he has served on the weather modification commission of the National Science Foundation. "The most important social use of oceanography is to remove the surprises from the weather, which spends three-quarters of its time over the ocean. The problem is this: we simply do not know what happens when winds blow over the ocean. They rumple it, they increase the area of its surface. We do not know how much. It may be ten or a hundred or a thousand times. Yet this is

William S. von Arx

where the interaction is. We should be studying this, we should be studying both violent storms and situations where nothing happens, where huge masses of air just sit over huge masses of water."

Von Arx raised the possibility of man-made changes — voluntary or involuntary — of climate before the prerequisite basic research is done. "We could blow bubbles on the bottom of the Straits of Florida and cool the Gulf Stream. This is conceivable, but we're not in a position to state exactly what would occur. There is the more immediate question of a sea-level canal from the Pacific to the Atlantic. Such a canal would certainly bring water and organisms from the Pacific into the Atlantic. Exactly how much would depend on the latitude of the canal. At 8° north, one would have maximum transport from the Pacific.

"Pacific water is warmer. With a canal 100 kilometers wide and 50 meters deep, one could warm the North Atlantic without much effect on the Pacific. The means exist to tear a piece out of the isthmus of Panama. The flow through the canal would be 10 million cubic meters per second, and with such a depth, there would be no problem of bottom erosion. Water would just slide over water. If such a canal were equipped with gates that could be opened and closed, one would have a valve on enormous potential energy . . . for good or evil. It could be geophysical engineering or just geophysical blundering."

In *Effective Use of the Sea*, the report of the Panel on Oceanography of the President's Science Advisory Committee set up in 1965, a strong recommendation was made for biological research at both ends of a future canal before it is too late. The report stated: "If a sea-level canal is opened across Central America, many biological problems of great potential consequence will emerge. A number of species have close relatives on opposite sides of the present land mass which has existed for 80 million years. What will happen if the barrier is breached so that organisms can move between oceans . . . ? Will changing selection pressures and competition eliminate species? Will present populations resist invasions unchanged, or will serious disruptions occur . . . ?"

No such considerations were in the minds of the excavators of the Suez Canal, which was opened in 1869. A century later, a biological upset had occurred. Eight months a year, the current in the canal flows from the Red Sea to the Mediterranean, carrying fish and larvae with it. The high salinity of the Bitter Lakes killed off immigrants at first. Then, as the flow of the canal washed out the salt beds on the bottom of the lakes, Red Sea organisms were able to survive the trip. Some colonized the eastern Mediterranean, driving out commercially profitable species unable to compete with them.

Von Arx brought up the Red Sea in another context. He referred to that oft-bruited project to dam it at Bab el Mandeb, allow the Red Sea to evaporate hundreds of feet down and then produce hydroelectric power at the head of the dam. "It has been calculated that such a dam would amortize itself in two or three decades. But what would happen if all that weight of water were removed from the earth's crust? It might buckle and snap. This is a region of active volcanoes and hot springs. Has anyone thought of geological consequences? It's time that we did. If a man can dream of damming the Red Sea or cooling the Gulf Stream or warming the Atlantic, it will come up sooner or later as a practical problem."

The conversation had meandered far from physical oceanography. Von Arx made no excuses. "You realize, I'm an anachronism. I want to live an eighteenth-century culture as well as in a technological environment. In the eighteenth century, science and culture were one. The present polarity between science and the public mind worries me."

20. Brains in the Sea

Everybody in Woods Hole knows *Alvin*. Within three years, *Alvin* found an H-bomb, lost (and recovered) an arm, spotted a World War II airplane at 5,214 feet (down, not up), and survived a spearing by a swordfish before it was lost at sea in October 1968. To some, it was a bright child; to others a spoiled brat. Anthropomorphism aside, *Alvin* was a bulbous-nosed little submarine, the smallest of the research vessels sailing out of Woods Hole.

Alvin and other deep submersibles are involved in a healthy controversy over man's place in exploring or exploiting the sea. In shallow water, man has three choices: he can swim down as a diver, ride down inside a submarine, or remain on the surface, televiewing and telecontrolling what is happening below. Each approach has its fierce partisans and its undisputed domain. No one queries the advantages of a diver for precise work at shallow depths. The submarine is undeniably the best way to take the scientist into deep water to look for the unexpected. A robot on a cable is needed in a dangerous situation requiring great strength. Still, the domains overlap, and wherever they do, intelligent arguments are heard. I shall try to give the reader the gist of them without attempting a complete review of the achievements of divers and submariners, who deserve all the books that have already been written about them at first hand.

Cost is usually a paramount factor in undersea work. Unlike outer space, the ocean does not operate on government budgets running into the billions and it is expected to provide a return on economic investments in a shorter length of time. The oceanographer looks at any technique and estimates how much each datum will take out of his funds (assuming that there is more than one way to get data of good quality). The oilman must remain competitive with drillers on land; the fisherman is up against the price of hamburgers. Cost, of course, is less important if a submarine lies disabled on the seabed with its crew trapped inside or an "object" of strategic value goes astray.

Alvin was out at sea during my visit to Woods Hole, but I had a chance to talk to Frank Omohundro, chief engineer of the Oceanographic's Deep Submergence Research Group, and a retired Navy submarine builder. He was straightforward: "At first, we were worried because *Alvin* was not available throughout the year for scientific research work. The amount of data that it gathered was not impressive, although, fortunately, things improved in 1967. But the few who used it at the very start were enthusiastic about its possibilities. A marine biologist could go down with plankton nets rigged on a tray so that he could sample life a few inches off the bottom. Here is a whole new area that simply cannot be touched by a surface ship. A geologist used *Alvin* in the Tongue of the Ocean in the West Indies. The Tongue of the Ocean is a hole in the continental shelf between 4,500 and 7,500 feet deep; it looks just as if the bottom had dropped out of the shelf. In *Alvin*, the geologist was able to climb one of the underwater cliffs that forms the Tongue. He might have been scaling a mountain. He was able to look around, see the texture of the rocks, ignore the poor samples, then ask the pilot to take the right sample there . . . and there. When a geologist on a ship makes a dredge haul, he cannot choose a sample and he can never be sure that it had not fallen down from another outcrop a thousand feet up. The scientist must ask himself not only how much does a bit of information cost but how much it is worth if he cannot get it in any other way."

Alvin, carrying a pilot and one scientist, was about as expensive to run as *Chain* or *Atlantis II* with nearly thirty scientists aboard. What drove up the cost per working day were the days lost waiting for good weather. *Alvin* was handled by *Lulu,* a catamaran mother ship that no yachtsman can look at without shuddering. Its hulls, a pair of pontoons ticketed for the scrap pile and donated instead to Woods Hole, lie low in the water, giving it the same sluggish motion as the submersible. Within and above them are accommodations (they once included a house trailer) for the crew and the hoisting gear that lifted *Alvin* out of the water after divers put lines on it. This feat can be performed in waves no more than five or six feet high.

The bigger the submersible, the more it can do underwater. If it grows over a certain size, however, no ship can handle it and it must be towed to and from the job. Omohundro favors small submersibles and he was outspoken about a new *Alvin* that has been built for the Navy. "It's better in some ways, but it's bigger, heavier and more awkward. That's often the case when the military write specifications. They think in terms of large combatant submarines. *Alvin* was successful because its weight was kept down. It's only thirteen tons; the new one is over twenty."

When *Alvin* was delivered to Woods Hole in 1965, it was one of the world's nineteen research submersibles. There are now over forty and the second generation has benefited from the trials and errors of its predecessors. The greatest step forward in the new *Alvin* is a pair of mechanical arms: one to do the work, the other to get a purchase. If a one-armed sub like *Alvin* tries to twist a bolt, it may twist itself instead. If it is not resting on the bottom, it is somewhat like a weightless astronaut working outside a space capsule.

Some newer submarines also have larger windows than *Alvin*'s portholes that require an observer to keep his eye no more than a few inches away. "After a few hours, it can be tiring," Omohundro said. "If you've spent eight hours in that little rascal, you're glad to get out of it."

Alvin's certified working depth was 6,000 feet. It had two lift propellers for vertical movement and a stern propeller that drove it at a fair walking speed. Slowness was compensated by maneuverability, the quality that helped bring success to *Alvin* during the H-bomb search off Palomares in the spring of 1966. At the surface, sonar devices using acoustic waves were helpless: they were unable to distinguish the bomb among the rugged features of the terrain where it had fallen. *Alvin*'s

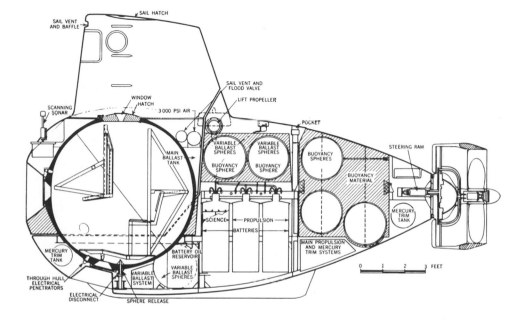

SAIL HATCH

SAIL VENT
AND BAFFLE

SAIL VENT AND
FLOOD VALVE

WINDOW
HATCH

LIFT PROPELLER

SCANNING
SONAR

3000 PSI AIR

POCKET

STEERING RAM

MAIN
BALLAST
TANK

VARIABLE
BALLAST
SPHERES

VARIABLE
BALLAST
SPHERES

BUOYANCY
SPHERES

BUOYANCY
SPHERE

BUOYANCY
SPHERE

BUOYANCY
MATERIAL

SCIENCE

PROPULSION

MERCURY
TRIM
TANK

BATTERIES

MERCURY
TRIM
TANK

BATTERY OIL
RESERVOIR

MAIN PROPULSION
AND MERCURY
TRIM SYSTEMS

THROUGH HULL
ELECTRICAL
PENETRATORS

VARIABLE
BALLAST
SYSTEM

VARIABLE
BALLAST
SPHERES

0   1   2   3 FEET

ELECTRICAL
DISCONNECT

SPHERE RELEASE

ALVIN *in cross-section (note scale at right):* "*Anyone who could drive from Boston to New York in a big car shouldn't think twice about going down in a little submarine.*"

pilots reasoned that the bomb might have left a track while sliding down a slope. So they first looked not for a small object but for a track perhaps a thousand feet long in the mud. When they found the track, they followed it, backing down a slope. "It was like flying a helicopter in the Rocky Mountains on a dark night," Omohundro said. "A mud slide coming down the slope could have given them a bad time." Another peril awaited *Alvin*'s pilots at the bottom of the track. There, they saw the bomb enshrouded by its parachute. As the submersible approached, the parachute billowed in the wash of its propeller. *Alvin* risked being enshrouded with the bomb.

The risk was considered to be so great that the bomb was finally brought to the surface by a tethered robot. Still, *Alvin* and its pilots had done a good day's work. Omohundro showed me the original of a Houston *Post* cartoon. In the conning tower of a big nuclear submarine, one gold braid is saying to another: "I wouldn't be so embarrassed if the *Andrew Jackson* or the *George Washington* or the *Nathan Hale* or the *Woodrow Wilson* had found it . . . but *Alvin!*"

Alvin was named after Allyn Vine, who has been with the Oceanographic for a quarter of a century. He has devoted much of his time to thinking up unorthodox but more efficient ways of going to sea. He was one of the inspirers of FLIP, he collaborated with Maurice Ewing on a deep-sea camera, he has advocated putting roadways on the sides of ships to make it easier to haul things out of the water, he once mounted an airplane wing on a destroyer to get hydrophones away from the noise of the ship's hull. Vine, a stocky man who enjoys talking quotably, disclaimed any undue credit for *Alvin*. "There were half a dozen of us working on the idea and the Europeans had already done much of the early work," he told me. "My name just happened to make a cute acronym." His main contribution to *Alvin* came when he helped convince Woods Hole and the Navy to experiment with a research submersible. *Alvin* was then built by a division of General Mills (which later became a division of Litton Industries) and financed by the Office of Naval Research, its owner. "The parts played by the Office of Naval Research and the manufacturer were obviously as important as the early role of the Oceanographic," said Vine. "Basically, it was a three-way gamble that won."

Vine goes on convincing, a task for which he is eminently suited. "The principal problems with submersibles are, in this order, emotional,

ALVIN *rammed by a swordfish.*

political, economic and technical. It is wonderful that we're finally getting past the first and most difficult emotional phase. Anyone who would drive from Boston to New York in a big car shouldn't think twice about going down in a little submarine. In a car, you can't even stand up to change your shirt. Even rescue submarines don't pack people in as tight as we did when we used to go out on double dates in a Model A roadster. But conservatism dies hard. *Alvin* was built by a nonmaritime company like General Mills because the traditional maritime companies weren't seriously interested at that time."

Traditionalism, Vine thinks, must also be overcome if small submersibles are to be successfully handled at sea. Though it is named after his mother, he does not think that *Alvin*'s tender, *Lulu*, is the only or even the best way to handle a submersible. "As a mother ship for submersibles, a vessel like the old *Constitution* has much to offer over the ships we now use. She had a job of carrying big sails in heavy weather; she had enormous stability built into her. In 1930, Woods Hole ordered their ketch, *Atlantis I*, with a mast and sails 130 feet high, partly for stability. Today, we spend much bigger sums, but we hesitate to put a stabilizing mast below the surface, such as a sliding centerboard 100 feet deep that would give us stability. Ship people seem almost obsessed against putting anything outside a ship's hull. FLIP is a textbook example of how a radically different but technically sound tack has led to an entirely new concept of stability. Her 600 tons of steel are more stable than a 50,000-ton battleship or the biggest liner afloat."

Vine believes that a great many other constructive changes or additions can be profitably put into ships for research or special purposes. The new craft being built for the oil industry are typical examples. Vine has suggested a research vessel with a second bridge below its keel to facilitate the docking of a submersible or other equipment. Small boats should be taken aboard ships not by davits but via a ramp lowered from the stern: "It's been a common idea for fifty years, but let's do it!"

He wants to see a long bowsprit on submersibles. "Our submersibles now carry lights close to their windows. That violates elementary optical principles when used underwater or in fog. If we put a twenty-foot bowsprit on a submersible, then we can get the lights out where they belong. The best ways of handling submersibles will probably be determined by such requirements as finesse in the use of instruments — and not by the relatively mundane problem of handling twenty tons at sea.

LULU, *catamaran mother ship of* ALVIN

"Surprisingly little of this is new. We now have submarines that use wheels to run on the ocean floor or that take divers down in lockout chambers. Simon Lake built and used those ideas fifty years ago. The main difference is that today there are more accepted uses and customers for what used to be peripheral technologies. We're in a business where very much is new. Yet if one starts beating his chest and telling himself how good he is, someone is apt to come along and show him the same thing in an old copy of *Popular Mechanics* or a nineteenth-century report."

Vine thinks that the problem of getting proper use out of submarines will solve itself. "Right now, we use submersibles for some things that we used to do with cables. In the future, many things that we are now trying to do with submersibles probably will be done more cheaply by tethered devices. For example, I would guess that at least 90 percent of underwater work would be done from surface ships for a long time. But that other 10 percent done from submersibles can be very interesting, valuable and essential. It may be that in underwater construction jobs, the boss will do his checking and troubleshooting with a submersible even though the bulk of the work is done with tethered unmanned vehicles. No instrument can equal the human eye for versatility in exploration and of course a human being is far more than just an eye. For example, what instrument could have taken Darwin's place on the *Beagle?*"

At long last, man's reluctance to go down and into the sea in ships is waning. "What is interesting to see is the transition from a generally negative to a generally positive attitude towards the ocean. Perhaps the trouble started with Homer, who was generally negative about the 'wine-dark sea.' It was easy for him to explain why Ulysses was away for the first ten years. But the second ten years were harder . . . he had to make the ocean sound as tough as the Trojans."

The president of the Deep Submersible Pilots Association, Larry Shumaker, would agree with Vine. Shumaker, whom I had met in San Diego, started piloting submersibles for the Navy in 1959 and went down to 20,000 feet in the *Trieste II* bathyscaphe. He did not think it was very Homeric. "Deep submersibles don't need skill, but you've got to know them inside out," he said. "You have to be familiar with every nut and bolt. There's no crew chief aboard to pull you out of a jam." He is now chief pilot of *Deep Quest*, the 52-ton submersible launched by the

Lockheed Space and Missiles Corporation in 1967, the year that the Deep Submersible Pilots Association was founded. Shumaker scotched any rumors about a *sub aqua* union. "We just need a chance to compare notes. We want to kick things around so that we can avoid making some mistakes. Perhaps one chemical isn't as reliable as another for absorbing carbon dioxide. Then why wait until someone writes a report about it?"

Shumaker's newest charge, *Deep Quest*, betrays aeronautical parenthood. It looked like a small blimp when I saw it on skegs aboard *Trans Quest*, its tender docked at the Lockheed Marine Terminal in San Diego. *Deep Quest*, one of the most ambitious of the newest crop of submersibles, carries four persons and can cruise at half-speed, two knots, for twenty-four hours. "Scientists don't want to go fast," Shumaker said. "You see more at low speed. It's like walking instead of driving through a town." Range counts for more than speed. The *Trieste II* bathyscaphe could run for only five hours at two knots and it was considered mainly as an elevator. *Deep Quest* covers fifty miles of ocean floor in a dive. Behind the two linked spheres that house its pilots and observers is a compartment that can carry either geological coring equipment or divers operating out of the hull.

Trans Quest, the mother ship, is prettier than *Lulu* and just as odd. It has the bow of a river barge, the beam of an ocean liner and a split stern that looks like the after end of a catamaran. Frank Chmelik, a marine geologist with Lockheed, took me aboard and explained that docking *Deep Quest* is something like landing a plane on a carrier. The mother ship floods its stern compartments and keeps moving to maintain steerage way. First, *Deep Quest* sails into the split stern; then a submerged platform operated by a high-speed hydraulic lift snatches it out of the sea from below. Chmelik and I were talking on deck when the captain of *Trans Quest* called out to us: "Don't go near that lever! It's activated! If you push it, down she goes!" We retreated and the captain took over for a test. "I'm coming up," he announced into a bullhorn. The platform moved slightly. "Going down," said the captain, like an elevator operator in a department store. A massive piston inched the other way and *Deep Quest* settled until water covered its skegs. The rehearsal was over. Subsequently, Lockheed's submersible went down to 8,310 feet in diving tests off the coast of California.

The first American commercial firm with the temerity to finance a large submersible on its own was the Reynolds Metals Company, which built the *Aluminaut* in 1964. It was, and still is, a unique craft. Louis J. Reynolds set out to prove that lightweight aluminum could be used for a large submersible. Instead of a small sphere where passengers must assume a more or less fetal position, *Aluminaut* boasts a roomy cylinder of a pressure hull. Fifty-one feet long, it accommodates a horde of six and weighs seventy-three tons. *Aluminaut*, which is towed out to sea before diving, has done some unusual work. One of its exploits was a trip on wheels over a highway of manganese oxide on the continental shelf off Florida. It came up with a 200-pound slab of pavement that it had wrenched loose. Its endurance of thirty-two hours enabled it to baby-sit the H-bomb at Palomares when *Alvin* had to surface and recharge its batteries. It also has to its credit the discovery of an immense bed of scallops off the east coast of Florida. *Aluminaut* was designed to operate down to 15,000 feet.

The current trend in submersibles is away from the greatest depths. Ninety-eight and a half percent of the ocean floor lies no deeper than 20,000 feet, now considered the ultimate target for vessels that not only descend to the bottom but keep busy once they get there. A more immediate goal is the first 6,000 feet of the ocean, covering the continental shelf and the upper continental slopes. This constitutes only 15 percent of the bottom but an overwhelming percentage of the sea's mineral and biological resources.

Early in the day, the late Professor Auguste Piccard developed his bathyscaphe, essentially a steel sphere supported by a gasoline float. In 1960, his son, Jacques Piccard, and Lieutenant Don Walsh of the U.S. Navy set a long-standing record when they took the original *Trieste* down to 35,800 feet in the Mariana Trench off Guam. At present, many submersibles aim no deeper than 1,000 feet, enough to gain access to the continental shelf and the market represented by the offshore oil industry. Emphasis is placed on visibility and dexterity; some vessels carry a tool rack outside their hulls so they can change the function of their arms without surfacing.

National economics affects the design of submarines. Japan and the Soviet Union were the first to use them for fisheries research. Since 1960, the Japanese have been operating *Kuroshio II*, a tethered manned submersible that works down to 650 feet, making biological observations and watching nets in action. In 1957, the Soviets took a 500-ton military submarine, the *Severyanka*, and converted it for fisheries research, transforming a torpedo room into a scientific laboratory. Size never frightens the Russians: the *Severyanka* carries eight scientists and a crew of sixty. It has been used in extensive studies of the herring fishery in the Norwegian Sea, it has acted as a scout for fishing fleets, and it has been able to hold position behind a trawler's net underwater to observe the proportion of fish that get away. The *Severyanka* descends to only 600 feet, but the Soviets have developed a *Sever II* to go down ten times as far. According to available information, it is a small two-man craft along the lines of *Alvin*.

Frenchmen have done remarkable work with submersibles while under financial as well as hydrostatic pressures. Cousteau's *Denise*, the first diving saucer, went into operation in 1959. It is neither very capacious (one passenger) nor very fast (one knot). Propulsion by water jets gives it extraordinary maneuverability: it floats through the depths with the same ease as a skin diver. Weighing only two and a quarter tons, it does not need a specially constructed mother ship. The saucer skims down to 1,000 feet. Thirty thousand feet below this depth, the French conduct biological research with *Archimède*, a bathyscaphe possessing considerably more range and endurance than *Trieste II*. It was used in the Japan Trench in 1967, but it usually works closer to home in the Mediterranean and Atlantic for economic reasons.

The erstwhile ruler of the waves has been late in getting under them, also because of cost. The first British deep submersible went into the water at the end of 1967. The SURV (Standard Underwater Research Vessel) is intended to ply to 1,000 feet for prospective employers in the oil fields of the Middle East, the gas fields of the North Sea and anywhere on the continental shelf off the British coast. It was built privately at the modest cost of $100,000 to give its owner a chance to recover his stake in a year or so of chartering.

Switzerland would not be ranked as an undersea power if her five million-odd population did not include the Piccard family. Jacques Piccard has taken over where his father left off. He has built the world's largest civilian deep submersibles. He can not only walk around in them, but stand comfortably at his full height of six feet six. In 1964, he launched the *Auguste Piccard*, a 167-ton craft, 93 feet long with a 13-foot ceiling. Inside it were armchairs for forty passengers, each with an individual porthole. That year, the *Auguste Piccard* was put into service as the star attraction of the Swiss National Exhibition at Lausanne. It made 700 dives, giving 20,000 people a tour of Lake Geneva 900 feet down. When the exhibition ended, the *Auguste Piccard* was put up for sale and, at last reports, was still awaiting a buyer.

In many respects, it is similar to the *PX-15*, later named the *Ben Franklin*, which was developed jointly by Piccard and Grumman. Both boats were built by Giavonala Frères, a Swiss steel-working firm that usually goes in for ski lifts and cable cars. Piccard selected it because it also makes giant pipes for hydroelectric projects and his submersibles are something like a piece of pipe. The *PX-15* is 10 feet in diameter, 48 feet long and weighs 130 tons. For its Gulf Stream drift mission, it was equipped to keep a crew of six alive and happy for a maximum of forty-two days. I saw it in Switzerland only a few days after its outer hull had been completed. Red lids were still masking its twenty-nine portholes and the hull was in two halves, waiting for equipment to be installed before it would be bolted together.

Piccard explained his craft to a group of visiting oceanographers who had been attending an international meeting in Bern. Like the Swallow float used to track deep currents, it is less compressible than water, and therefore it can hold any predetermined depth. Thus, said Piccard, it could drift in the Gulf Stream like plankton (he called it "human plankton"). Floating noiselessly in mid-water, it could record the background of sounds in the ocean while photographing the life around it.

After Piccard's talk, a representative of Grumman took the floor to tell of future plans. Following the Gulf Stream drift mission as an underwater Kontiki raft, the *PX-15* could be converted into an "undersea workboat" by unbolting its hull and substituting a new half. Then it would be able to handle heavy loads with a crane on its nose and provide a home for half a dozen divers on the sea floor for two weeks at a stretch. The oceanographers listened with an interest that slackened perceptibly when the Grumman man, in answer to their first question, told them that charter rates would be $10,000 a day.

Not all "workboats" are the size of the *PX-15*. General Motors has kept its DOWB (Deep Ocean Work Boat) down to seven tons. Weighing in at only eight tons is *Deep Diver*, the first submersible to lock a diver outside at a depth of 415 feet. Built by Perry Submarine and operated by Ocean Systems, it is destined for maintenance work on undersea

Grumman engineer goes to sea in a tub to observe a model of the BEN FRANK-LIN *in a test tank.*

oil and cable installations. Diving marine biologists have also used it for fish surveys and it took Walter Cronkite and a TV cameraman below for CBS's "The 21st Century" show.

Whether it carries dry or wet toilers of the sea, the submersible is primarily a way to get a man into the ocean. There is a school that wants to keep him on the surface, except for exploring. Its members reason in this way: beyond the depth range of the free diver, a man cannot use his hands anyway. He has to sit behind the pressure hull of a submersible and work a manipulator. It's not easy when submersible and manipulator are moving simultaneously (*Alvin* once took eleven hours on a task that could have been done in five minutes on land). So why not let the man sit on a ship and operate his arm remotely?

Dr. Victor C. Anderson, associate director of Scripps's Marine Physical Laboratory, thinks that he would be no clumsier controlling a manipulator from the surface. There, he is protected against pressure by all the water under his ship. The manipulator is down below at the end of a cable bringing it far more power than a submersible can store in batteries. The cable transmits commands, it reports on how they are obeyed, it sends up data. In a shipboard control room that could be stabilized by gyroscopes, the operator watches his distant hand on television. Two screens provide binocular vision; a loudspeaker gives him hearing. He cannot use his sense of touch, but neither can a submersible pilot.

Nuclear research laboratories are the main users of telechiric (Greek for "distant hand") devices. There, too, a human needs a shield between his brain and his tools. H. A. Ballinger of the Atomic Energy Research Establishment at Harwell has given an idea of what the manipulator is up against in duplicating human movement: "Consider, for example, the seemingly simple process of quietly closing a door. The hand proceeds through three dimensions in space, to reach and grasp the door knob. It must then describe a true arc, which is parallel to the plane of the floor and centered on the door hinges. As the door approaches closure, the rates of the integrated movement must be selectively diminished, and a rotary motion applied to the door knob through changing axis angle. At the right moment, when visual, auditory and force feed-back confirm, the knob is released." Ballinger, who is not without humor, observes that door-closing is among the few operations "that can with deterioration of performance quality, be reduced to a simple kick."

A manipulator is not very good at this but it is tireless. Anderson has calculated that a diver or a small submersible can only do four hours of actual work a day. With all the "support" required, a diver runs to $200 an hour and a submersible to $500. A "substitute man" at the end of a cable could be slave-driven twenty hours a day by operators manning a surface panel around the clock at a cost of $150 an hour.

All this is still in the future. As a start, Anderson has built a Benthic Lab as an undersea control center for long operations. It is a ten-ton beehive that stands on the sea floor and shelters electronic circuits protected from water by a bath of kerosene. It repairs itself: when a breakdown occurs, a manipulator replaces the guilty circuit card with a spare.

Benthic Lab serves as a base for a Remote Underwater Manipulator (RUM, they call it at Scripps) that can perform chores in the area. In its first version, the manipulator was mounted aboard a surplus gun carrier clanking on caterpillar treads. Anderson likes to keep the feet of his substitute men on the bottom so they can place instruments like current meters within an inch of where they belong. RUM tended to bog down and it was far from an unqualified success. Anderson thinks he has licked this in a brand-new RUM operated from a floating platform that can hoist it over soft spots. If the bugs are eliminated, it could be used commercially on such jobs as the inspection of oil pipelines, straddling them to seek flaws with its television cameras.

Anderson avoids polemics with defenders of the submersible. "I'm lazy," he had told me at Scripps. "I'd rather not go down into the sea if there is another way of doing things. Our devices have their disadvantages. They can only work on the bottom, they must drag a cable through the water. But they're so much more economical."

Not all telechirists stick to the bottom. There are distant hands that swim. At Palomares, the dirty work of grappling for the bomb behind its menacing net of parachute lines was entrusted to a Cable-Controlled Underwater Recovery Vehicle that the Navy usually uses to pick up spent torpedoes and missiles. CURV sees with television and sonar, moves with propellers and wields an arm that it can shed to get out of a predicament (crawfish capability, the professionals call this). Working with Shell, the Hughes Aircraft Company has made several MOBOTs (Mobile Robots) to service underwater wellheads. In its most recent form, the MOBOT has four arms, two for taking hold, two for turning wrenches. The French Petroleum Institute has a *Télénaute* for the same purpose, but with fewer arms. *Télénaute* carries a movie camera and did some exploring in the summer of 1967 when it was sent down into the Fountain of Vaucluse in southern France as a speleologist. In the fourteenth century, Petrarch wrote of this cave from which the Sorgue River surges, and divers have been looking for the river's mysterious source since 1878. *Télénaute* was able to penetrate nearly 350 feet down and film a new hall with its camera.

In Britain, an interesting idea exists on paper. Ballinger from Harwell has suggested a "sextapus," a six-limbed swimming sea creature on a cable leash. Two of the limbs are manipulators, the other four are retractable legs that allow the beast to stand on the bottom. If one leg were to sink into the mud, it could be washed free with a squirt from another. For geologists or prospectors, the sextapus would use a sting coming out of its belly to core sediments. Ballinger also suggests putting suction pads on its legs so that it could cling fly-like to the vertical plates of a wrecked ship or hang from the underside of a submerged cliff.

The British have not built a sextapus, but their National Institute of Oceanography is putting down a tethered seeing ear, a 32-foot captive unmanned submersible to take acoustic pictures of the deep ocean bottom over a strip twelve miles wide. GLORIA (oh, well . . . Geological Long-Range Inclined Asdic) is to be towed at ten knots at the end of 600 feet of cable. It does not have much of a brain, only a steering system to keep it on an absolute even keel so that it will not mar its picture by twitching during the twenty-six seconds that an acoustic impulse needs to make a twenty-four mile round trip.

The best-known underwater device is man, the envy of the telechirists and the submariners. Even on land, a remotely-operated manipulator is up to sixty times slower than what an engineer has called "the Mark I eyeball-computer-manipulator combination," meaning us. Man is far from obsolete. According to another definition that Richard Terry quotes in *The Deep Submersible*, he remains "the only 150-pound servomechanical system that can be mass-produced by unskilled labor."

The system is being upgraded all the time. Scuba gear has freed man from air hoses, helmets and weighted shoes. It came into general use with the regulator that Emile Gagnan and Cousteau invented in 1942 to keep the diver's lungs at the same pressure as the water surrounding him. With air in his aqualung, he can descend to about 250 feet. The nitrogen in the air befuddles his brain and he experiences what Cousteau named "the rapture of the deep," as dangerous as it is exhilarating. Helium elimi-

Above, Scripps's original bottom-crawling RUM (Remote Underwater Manipulator). Below, diagram of a "sextapus," the six-legged robot suggested by H. A. Ballinger.

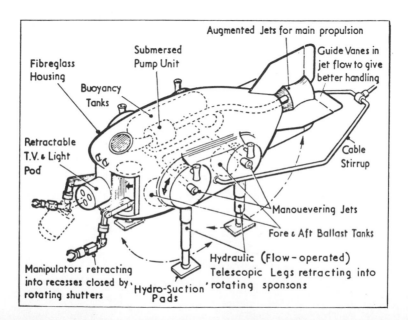

Augmented Jets for main propulsion

Fibreglass
Housing

Submersed
Pump Unit

Guide Vanes in
jet flow to give
better handling

Buoyancy
Tanks

Retractable
T.V. & Light
Pod

Cable
Stirrup

Manouevering Jets

Fore & Aft Ballast Tanks

Manipulators retracting
into recesses closed by
rotating shutters

Hydro-Suction
Pads

Hydraulic (Flow-operated)
Telescopic Legs retracting into
rotating sponsons

nates the risk when it is used to replace nitrogen as the inert gas to be breathed along with oxygen. An oxyhelium mixture allows the diver to work at depths beyond 600 feet, enough to command the continental shelf. Physiologists think that it will be safe down to 1,000 feet, a depth first reached in 1962 by Hannes Keller, a Swiss mathematician, in a dive that took the life of a companion.

Beyond 1,000 feet, there is the already-tested possibility of oxygen-hydrogen mixtures. Way beyond, there are artificial gills. Dr. Johannas A. Kylstra in the Netherlands has conducted experiments with mice and dogs in which, like fish, they have gotten their oxygen out of a saline solution (enriched with oxygen because seawater does not contain enough to support life for a mammal). Captain George F. Bond of the United States Navy has predicted that man will be able to reach 10,000 feet, his lungs filled with a liquid solution and oxygen fed directly into his bloodstream. At the time of writing, no human has volunteered for conversion over to fluid lungs. But someone will. The history of diving shines with the courage of physiologists experimenting on themselves.

Time limits man in the sea even more severely than depth. The diver lives by the iron law of the decompression table. The longer and deeper he stays down, the more time he must spend coming up to allow dissolved gases to escape slowly from his blood. If he breaks the law, the gases bubble out like uncorked champagne, crippling him with the bends. According to the U.S. Navy Diving Manual, the diver who works two hours at 100 feet must take another two hours and twelve minutes to come to the surface. For a three-hour stay at 300 feet, says the manual, over nineteen hours would have to be spent in decompression.

Decompression time rises in a sharp curve that suddenly breaks. After twenty-four hours, the diver's blood is saturated with gases. It absorbs no more, even if he remains at depth twenty-four days. This is the principle of saturation diving, first demonstrated in a compression chamber on land by Captain Bond and Navy divers. Put into practice, it has brought about the establishment of underwater homes for varying lengths of time. Divers live in a dry house under the same pressure as the sea and swim to work as in Cousteau's Conshelf stations, the Navy's Sealabs and the Man-in-Sea outposts planted by Edward Link and Ocean Systems. After a few days or weeks below, the diver is taxied up to the surface in a capsule pressurized to the depth of his home. There, the

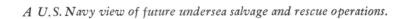

A U.S. Navy view of future undersea salvage and rescue operations.

capsule is bolted to a deck decompression chamber where the diver waits out his return to normal atmospheric pressure. The time required depends on the depth at which he was saturated: occupants of Sealab II who spent two weeks at 205 feet in 1965 needed thirty-one hours; Robert Stenuit and Jon Lindbergh were only down two days and four hours at 432 feet on a Man-in-Sea experiment in 1964, but their decompression took four days. The system has been used commercially to great advantage. A diver can remain in the chamber on deck between shifts on the bottom, undergoing decompression only at the end of the job.

I must confess that the nearest I ever got to a saturation dive was a talk with Earl A. Murray, a tattooed ex-Navy gunner's mate who has been diving with Scripps for over fifteen years. Murray spent two weeks in Sealab II, where life in a high-pressure oxygen-helium atmosphere had its good and bad points. "We had plenty of room. There were only ten of us down at a time. On a submarine in wartime, they put seventy men in the same space. It was a good thing mentally to be able to swim out of the ship."

The aquanauts could not swim very far up. Murray explained that a saturated diver has a ceiling over his head. During the Sealab experiment, he could not rise more than thirty-five feet (representing one atmosphere of pressure) from the depth where he was living. "As soon as you went up twenty-five feet, you became worried. So you tended to hug the bottom." This, by the way, has led to the chilling suggestion of underwater penitentiaries. Ronald Sweig, an imaginative Navy writer in San Diego, thinks they would be escape-proof. The saturated prisoner could not get up to the surface without decompression. "It would be an incredible deterrent for a drylander: Seaweed Prison, 400 feet down, with sharks and killer whales on the other side of the wall as wardens." Capital punishment seems much more humane.

On Sealab, every man was a volunteer and the company was good. "Underwater swimming sorts out people," Murray said. "No matter how varied their background, they must love the sea, they must feel comfortable in water. There was more good feeling in Sealab than on a normal project. Except for Scott Carpenter, who stayed a month, we were down for only two weeks. After twelve or thirteen days, people began to talk about sunlight and walking in dirt. It was so wet down there. The temperature was comfortable, between 80 and 83 degrees in the house compared to about 50 degrees outside, but the humidity was

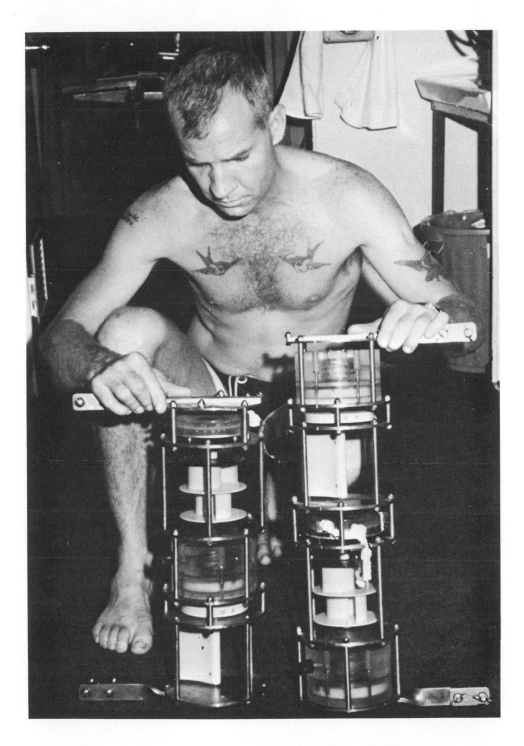

Earl Murray prepares two current meters for the underwater weather station operated during Sealab II.

terrible. It was like a summer in New London, where I did my basic training in the Navy. Everybody sweated, mold grew in the diving equipment. When you looked around, you could see it was pretty rotten. We all got fungus infections in our ears. Finally, we rigged up a woman's electric hair dryer. At the end of the day, you'd stand in line for a chance to blow hot air into your ears and dry them out for an hour or so."

Murray was with a team of divers and scientists from Scripps who set up an underwater weather station 165 feet away from Sealab, a good distance for a man carrying tools and swimming at only half a knot. It measured currents, pressure, temperature and variations in light. Murray himself was able to sense heavy swells on the surface in his ears for the first three or four days before a fungus infection impaired his hearing. "The currents were greater than we had thought and they changed much more often," he said. Divers occasionally ran into gusts as strong as two knots, the equivalent of bucking a hundred-mile-an-hour gale on the surface. The station did not operate long enough to produce conclusive results, but it did show that weather only a couple of hundred feet down could not be predicted on the basis of what was occurring up above. Plankton samples were also taken to see how marine life reacted to weather changes and fish were cased and observed on the bottom.

France and the United States have led in long underwater stays at depths of several hundred feet, while the British and the Soviets are carrying out more modest projects in shallow water. What struck me in various conversations is a change in the attitude of oceanographers towards diving. As technical and physiological problems are solved, it becomes more and more feasible for a man to go underwater and concentrate on other matters besides keeping alive. Credit for the first scientific dive is generally given to another Frenchman, Henri Milne-Edwards, who went down in 1844 to twenty-five feet in Sicilian harbors to collect living marine animals. His air supply came from a pump first intended to cope with flooded cellars in Paris. Milne-Edwards, according to the late James Dugan, author of *Man Explores the Sea*, was a "stout, solemn man of forty-four with a monocle." His exploit off Sicily proved that the sea bottom would not remain the monopoly of sponge divers and other supermen.

Scientists shied away from the inconveniences of helmet diving and Milne-Edwards had few imitators until the appearance of the aqualung.

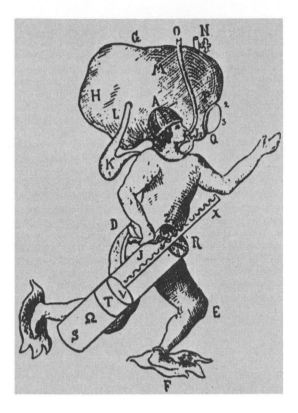

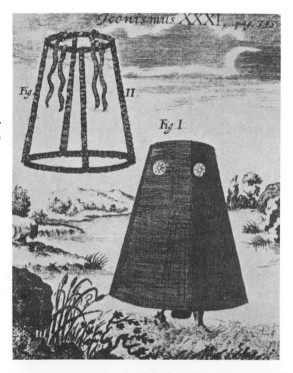

Seventeenth-century idea for a diving rig. The diving helmet (right) was already in use.

Then many took the plunge. While it certainly cannot be called a branch of oceanography, archaeology is perhaps the science that has benefited most from diving. A sunken ship buried under mud that protects it from the destructive forces of the sea can be a time capsule of the civilization that sent it on its last voyage. Dr. George F. Bass, an underwater archaeologist from the University of Pennsylvania, has written that "virtually everything made by man, from tiny obsidian blades to huge temple columns, was carried at one time or another in ships, and much was lost at sea." The more ancient the civilization, the easier it is for the archaeologist to get at its wrecks. Early vessels, hugging the shore to stay in sight of land, were particularly vulnerable to hidden reefs in the Mediterranean. They went down near the coast in depths well within the range of divers using aqualungs. There is no reason, Bass believes, why archaeologists should not use them. In his book, *Archaeology Under Water*, he says: "Some of the hardships of working under water can be compared to those faced above water. The underwater archaeologist protects himself against cold with a rubber suit rather than a coat. The infections he suffers from cuts and bruises are serious, but no more so than those he has contracted in steaming jungles. Divers searching for ancient sites have been frightened out of the water by sharks, but more than one surveyor on foot has been chased by wild boars and savage sheep dogs. The diver-excavator must beware of moray eels which live in empty wine jars, but no land-based excavator would in certain areas put his hand under a rock or a piece of pottery without first checking for the scorpion which might linger there. Poisonous fish are to be avoided, as are equally dangerous snakes on land, and annoying worms that sting are the horse-flies of the underwater world."

Bass, who led a team in Turkey that carried out the first complete underwater excavation of an ancient wreck, believes that the archaeologist-diver must be first a scientist. It takes years to train an archaeologist but only a little more than a week, he writes, to turn him into a diver who can work under proper supervision.

Divers were rare among the older generation of oceanographers that I met. Some had dived earlier in their careers, then gave up when they saw the time they lost in frequent physical checkups to keep up their "diver's license." It was not so much a question of age as of priority: they had more important things to do on land. Younger scientists, however, came into their intellectual majority at a time when diving was already a proven technique. In quite a few cases, it has affected the choice of their careers.

In Britain alone, the Underwater Association has twenty-five full members despite the clubbiest of admission requirements. To join it, one must (1) possess a Ph.D. and (2) conduct actual research under water. I learned about it from one of its founders, Dr. Nicholas C. Flemming of the National Institute of Oceanography. A small, wiry young man, who flaunts a drooping moustache that must trail in his wake like seaweed, Flemming thinks that the scientist-diver is in a category by himself among "subsea systems." The scientist has all the advantages that Flemming lists for the ordinary diver — low running cost, simplicity, land transportability, agility, versatility — and he also takes a specialized brain beneath the sea.

To join the Underwater Association, he must use it. "We have an obsession about performing the experiment right on the sea floor," Flemming explained. "The scientist who just dives is not automatically eligible. We do not count the biologist who scrapes stuff up and analyzes it in the lab. We have biologists who study photosynthesis *in situ.* Instead of taking the plant into an artificial environment on land, they study it in the sea. They put a jar of seawater containing radioactive carbon over it and measure its carbon uptake at various depths down to sixty meters. We have a fisheries zoologist who tags fish in deep water. If one does it on the surface, there is always the danger that the swim bladders of the fish will burst. Our geologists go down with a 40-pound hand corer. That is the only way to put three holes next to each other in a straight line on the bottom . . . unless one is willing to spend half a million dollars to try it from the surface."

Flemming has the unofficial title of foreign secretary of the Underwater Association, which is not a very official body. It calls itself the Underwater Association of Malta because, he said, "Underwater Association of Great Britain would have sounded too grandiose" and the Maltese government has been a big help. Malta is a favorite swimming ground in the sterling area for British scientist-divers. Its waters are warm enough for long experiments and it offers diving facilities maintained by the military.

Flemming himself began diving with the Royal Marines — "limpet mines and that sort of thing" — and then went to Cambridge, where he started the university's underwater exploration group and did his Ph.D.

on changes of sea level in the Mediterranean. He has written a book on drowned cities in the Mediterranean and he has found one off the Greek island of Elaphanisos that dates back nearly 4,000 years. "My central core of interest is the geomorphology of the continental shelf. I'm an amateur diver and an amateur archaeologist. I just do things." Among the things he does are experiments with gas mixtures and decompression schedules. He has suffered the bends and spent ten hours recovering from them in a decompression chamber. He is interested in oxyhelium mixtures because a nitrogen jag makes it hard for the scientist to focus on such problems as distinguishing ribbons of sand from ribbons of shingle over a few yards.

"It's unfair to expect professional divers to do this," Flemming admitted. "You've got to be able to find the sand grains that you want, then spend a week taking six cores in a straight line across a flat lens of sediments. If you are in the wrong sand, you must start all over again. It is difficult for an unscientific mind to find any motive for this. Professionals won't do it. One is better off with a Greek linguist or an historian, a mind that can focus on apparent triviality and stay on it for a week.

"People won't do it for fun, either. Scientific diving takes staying power and perseverance. It has no attraction for the sport diver who wants to tell his girl friend about the kicks that diving gives him. When one must get up at six in the morning, spend two hours filling cylinders, then drag a boat into the water, the kicks are few and far between."

The Underwater Association of Malta is always looking for new recruits that come up to its unyielding standards. Students working on their Ph.D.'s are accepted as associate members and Flemming estimates that the association influences a community four times as large as its roster. Whether scientist-divers grow plants at thirty fathoms or photograph dyed internal waves breaking at the boundary between warm and cold water, they get along swimmingly.

"We find that the diver is a physical character type who is not unathletic but who dislikes organized games, the kind of person that would go in for skiing or mountain climbing and thinks that hitting a ball about is a bloody waste of time. In games, one plays against human rules; here, we're playing against natural rules."

21. Money in the Sea

Among scientists, one seldom hears a voice joining the chorus about the boundless treasures of the sea. No one mentions mineral hoards for the taking or blue pastures awaiting the lucky herdsman. To the oceanographer, the sea is a reserve of resources that is coming within our reach only now, hopefully at a time when we know enough to use them wisely.

Businessmen, too, do not subscribe to the folk definition of the sea as a mixture of salt water and easy money. They take a cool look at it as an economic asset, not boundless but well worth serious investigation. Such an attitude is exemplified by a Commercial Oceanology Study Group that has been formed by six of Britain's largest firms involved in mining, construction, food, chemicals, aerospace and oil. Flemming had got away from his Greek scholars in scuba gear to spend eighteen months as the group's chief consultant. His report was so confidential that he only showed me the cover, but the group's very existence indicates a faith that the business side of the ocean in Britain will grow beyond its present figure of $1.2 billion a year.

Flemming did not think that it would grow into the blue sky. He saw immediate gains in workaday pursuits: construction of harbors, dredging of channels, piercing of tunnels, high-speed transport, improved fishing methods. The most precious mineral in the sea around the British Isles is humble gravel. "We're on an island, we've dug up all the gravel on it. We are already getting gravel with suction dredges 100 feet down."

His slant on marine technology was the opposite of what I had heard expressed in the United States. Beleaguered by requests to use submersibles or satellites in their observations, many American oceanographers tend to regard such techniques as "a solution looking for a problem." Flemming, on the contrary, envied them. "The United States can develop technology for its own sake, then wait a few years to find a use for it. Given the general economic picture, the American manufacturer makes a gadget first and puts his faith in an expanding market. Unfortunately, we haven't got that kind of money in Britain. We must find the problem and the solution together."

It is also much harder to put a figure on the economic importance of the ocean to the United States. The discrepancies in various estimates run well into the billions of dollars. They make good reading, but I caught myself regretting dull scientific journals with their references in illegible print and their cautious qualifying of "raw data." In a series of articles in a reputable financial journal, the total of offshore oil production was multiplied by ten from one day's edition to the next. Two sources disagreed by $2.5 billion on the amount that the oil industry has invested in the Gulf of Mexico, but, I suppose, that's the oil business.

The most serious study of the ocean as an investment has been made by Robert L. Clark and Stuart H. Clement Jr. for the Wall Street firm of Hayden, Stone. They found that "oceanography" in the United States added up to $7.7 billion in 1967 and that it should grow to $23.45 billion by 1977 (in their figures, they do not include shipping and direct military spending by the Navy). Petroleum makes up the largest chunk: $4.5 billion in 1967 and $16 billion in 1977. Wall Street, of course, has its own interpretation of oceanography. At a Hayden, Stone Forum on Oceanography, a drilling contractor remarked that his company was engaged in an oceanographic project, the mining of undersea deposits of hydrocarbons. "The interesting thing," he said, "was that we had been doing the same thing for ten years under the more prosaic term of 'offshore drilling.' It's no wonder that our stock didn't move up at that time."

According to Hayden, Stone, the oil industry has already spent $7.5 billion on exploration and production wells. Sixteen percent of the oil consumed by the non-Communist world comes from the ocean, where 25 percent of the world's reserves are believed to lie. At least 10,000 wells have been drilled on the continental shelf, starting in the Gulf of Mexico and spreading from the Caspian Sea to Nigeria and Cook Inlet off Alaska. One hundred fifty mobile rigs, the oddest craft to float since the Ark, are seeking new oil fields to conquer. Some can drill in depths up to 1,000 feet, an illustration of the American way that Flemming spoke about. From what I gathered in the trade press, wells below 300 feet cannot be brought into production because divers are unable to work at such depths. But the deep drillers know that men, or substitute men, are being improved.

Offshore oil drilling is another of those success stories in which people make many millions out of a paltry few millions. It is no place for the little fellow. The newest of the mobile rigs run to $10 million. Operators scream about their insurance premiums: Lloyds raised the rate to 10 percent following a nasty streak of accidents that within six months sank five of the eighty rigs insured by the company. As a rule, drilling costs four times more per foot at sea than on land; as an exception, it can run to thirty times more. On the other hand, offshore exploration ends in fewer dry holes and taps larger reserves. Since oil consumption cannot go anywhere but up, the future rewards to the offshore driller seem to compensate him for his present risks. In June 1967, oil companies paid $512 million for 745,000 acres at an auction of federal leases off Louisiana (in 1803, the first Louisiana Purchase of 828,000 square miles was swung for only $15 million). Hayden, Stone thinks the companies were protecting their future against the endemic political upheavals that threaten their low-cost foreign sources. At present, so I was told, it is cheaper to haul oil from Kuwait to California by tanker than to pump it out of the Pacific in sight of shore.

In this respect, North Sea gas has been a true gift of the ocean to Britain. It lies within easy pipeline range of an energy-hungry country whose only domestic source of fossil fuel had been its coal mines. British Petroleum's *Sea Gem*, a mobile jack-up rig, made the first strike in September 1965 forty miles off the English coast. Since then, Britain has staked out in the North Sea a gas field that is expected to produce 4 billion cubic feet a day by 1975. Drillers have worked under murderous conditions. *Sea Gem* went down three months after its exploit when two of its eight legs collapsed. The North Sea has made many an oilman regret the Gulf of Mexico, where at least he knows hurricanes happen infrequently. In the North Sea, tides constantly scour the footing out from under the legs of rigs, and a quiet day on the surface is a memorable one.

The oil companies ran into their worst perils on land. In Britain, gas is a nationalized public utility; the sole supplier is the National Gas Council. It paid British Petroleum five cents a therm (a therm is about 100 cubic feet) for gas from the first strike, with the understanding that this was a "promotional" rate. The Gas Council had a good bargaining position for later negotiations and used it. In March 1967, the council and a major group of producers agreed on a rate of 2.87 cents a therm. The companies did not like the game, but it was the only wheel in town. According to the London *Sunday Times*, several drillers reacted to the "dreary battle over the price of natural gas" by moving their rigs off the Scottish coast to look for oil, which unlike gas, they could market themselves.

As soon as one turns away from oil and gas, zeroes must be lopped off the figures on marine resources. Hayden, Stone added up offshore mining by American companies the world over and came to a total of only $150 million in 1967. They say it should rise to $750 million by 1977. This is the most disconcerting branch of ocean economics, the one with the bravest optimists and the chilliest cynics. Almost simultaneously, one source can state that DeBeers is "obtaining several times as many diamonds from the sea as its land mines are producing" and another can claim that the Marine Diamond Corporation, now controlled by De-Beers, lost $6 million in five years. It was Sammy Collins, a flamboyant Texan, who started mining diamonds off western South Africa in 1962. Weather took a terrible toll of his dredgers and he was bought out handsomely by DeBeers in 1966. A new dredging fleet is now in operation.

Hayden, Stone remarks that half the dredging now done by Americans is for nothing more than sand and seashells to go into cement mills. Traces of gold are often found on drowned beaches off the Alaskan placer deposits that were worked in earlier days, but the question again is one of how much must be put in to get anything out, particularly in the kind of weather that Alaska promises. Sulphur is being taken successfully from the seabed by plants on two huge artificial islands off the Louisiana coast. They inject hot water into the deposits and pump the sulphur out in molten form. A world shortage keeps demand high and the market steady.

Outside the United States, tin is being dredged regularly from the continental shelf off Thailand and Indonesia, while the Japanese are bringing up iron ore from a shallow bay. What seems to brake the growth of sea mining is the cost of prospecting, just as high as for petroleum but with lower potential returns. Sea miners, so I was told, tend to clamor for government surveys of the continental shelf, while oilmen do their own surveying and keep the results to themselves.

Extracting minerals from the ocean's water instead of lifting them out of the bottom can be more profitable. Hayden, Stone rates American production of salt, bromine and principally magnesium from seawater at a tidy $200 million a year. According to Dr. John L. Mero, formerly with the University of California's Institute of Marine Resources, these are the only three substances that are presently taken from seawater in substantial quantities. Salt was all alone until antiknock gasolines created a demand for bromine. As for magnesium, nearly all of America's consumption now comes from the ocean.

Mero has arrived at a total of 166 million tons of solids in every cubic mile of seawater, and there are 330 million cubic miles in the ocean. In his book, *The Mineral Resources of the Sea*, he estimates that the seas contain six million tons of gold. He does not recommend trying to remove it. Since the end of the nineteenth century, the prospect has tempted scientists, who first thought that a ton of seawater contained at least six milligrams of the metal, a ratio that implied eight trillion tons of gold in the ocean. Research in Germany brought the figure down almost to the vanishing point. Mero reports that the Dow Chemical Company once tried to see how much gold it could recover from fifteen tons of seawater. The result was .09 milligrams, worth 1/100,000th of a cent. So far, no one has done any better.

Ocean gold will never replenish Fort Knox, but Mero thinks other minerals can be extracted more economically when big desalinizing plants come into widespread use. Here, one man's waste is another man's resource. The brine pouring out of the plants will offer a much more concentrated ore than raw seawater. Desalinization will pay for pumping the ocean onto land, a heavy charge in mineral extraction where it is the water that is the waste product.

Certain elements are concentrated by the sea at no cost at all. The presence of widespread bottom deposits of phosphorite and manganese lumped into nodules has been known for the past hundred years. Mero studied the economic possibilities of both. In the case of the phosphorite nodules, a billion tons are supposed to lie off the coast of California. Mero thinks they could compete for the local fertilizer market with phosphate rock now sent by rail from Utah. Transportation doubles the cost of the land phosphate, but the phosphorite nodules could be dredged offshore and hauled directly by ship to San Francisco or Los Angeles. California would get its fertilizer at little more than half the present price and the sea miner would enjoy a 40 percent annual return on his investment.

Mero is best known for his work on the economics of manganese nodules. They run in size from marbles to slabs and they come in staggering quantities. Manganese nodules cover 20 percent of the floor in a single layer that, for some reason yet undiscovered, is not buried by falling sediment. No one has seen all of them, but on the basis of samplings and sea floor photographs by scientists, Mero calculates there are 1.5 trillion tons of manganese nodules on the floor of the Pacific Ocean. They represent a renewable resource: six million more tons form there every year. Nodules accumulate around a shark's tooth, a whale's earbone or simply a piece of grit, building up in layers like the skin of an onion at a rate that varies widely from place to place. The highest yet found has been nearly four inches a century, a figure based on a coating of iron-manganese oxide around a naval shell fired during the Second World War.

Manganese nodules, Mero says, also contain nickel, cobalt and copper in commercial quantities. He wrote in his book: "Assuming that only 10 percent of the nodule deposits prove economic to mine, there are, in general, sufficient supplies of many metals in these sea-floor deposits to last for thousands of years at our present rates of consumption."

Then . . . what are we waiting for? First, a way to bring the nodules up. They lie two or three miles deep, and the usual offshore dredge is stretching when it works at 150 feet. Mero has proposed a deep-sea hydraulic dredge, a sort of monster vacuum cleaner operating down to 10,000 feet, with its machinery submerged well below the tumult of the ocean surface. It would sweep the bottom in circles, sucking up 4,200 tons of nodules a day and dumping them into ore carriers moored alongside in mid-ocean. The vacuum cleaner could bring up 1,220,000 tons of nodules a year at a cost of $3.55 a ton. Mero's figures have not been unanimously accepted by any means. Some critics compare his idea "to trying to suck up milk from a saucer on the pavement using an extremely long drinking straw while standing on top of a 20-story building in a gale."

Secondly, no one is quite sure of how to handle the nodules if they ever do come up. The U.S. Bureau of Mines, after five years of research, was forced to admit that there is no way to run them profitably through existing plants built to process land ores, whose composition is not at all the same. I happened to talk to Mero in La Jolla, where he now runs a consulting business known as Ocean Resources, Inc. His optimism had been dampened, but not quenched. He foresaw a gradual advance of miners into the deep sea, starting with present dredging off the beach and, in ten years or so, moving out to depths of a thousand feet for phosphorite. In twenty years, the mining of manganese nodules in 15,000 feet of water should be a sound business proposition. He did not advise manganese nodules as an immediate investment. "The best place to prospect," he said guardedly, "is in the library."

Mero's caution doubtless saved my money, but it was not good copy. Such words of prudent wisdom could be heard everywhere. I spoke to an investment counselor in the hope of taking a flyer, perhaps, in uranium on the Mid-Atlantic Ridge. He had nothing better than fishing for flavors and scents, or converting plankton into cosmetics. Scientists have more imagination. It was with relief that I picked up *Sea Frontiers* to read of future mines under the seabed. Dr. Carl F. Austin wrote about men living in self-contained units cut into hard rock. They would enter their mine through an access lock and tunnel into mineral deposits. The idea is not sheer fantasy. Over a hundred mines have already been dug under the bottom from shafts starting on land or artificial islands. Austin says that the English were getting coal in this way as early as the sixteenth century. A mid-ocean mine would simply be cut off from land. It could amass manganese nodules and store them until submarine freighters came to haul them away. The entire operation would be carried out in the stillness of the deep, with never a day lost because of storms.

The more that oceanographers look at the problems of operating from the surface, the more appealing such ideas become. A British scientist, Dr. Robert Morgan, ventures that the sea is a good place for the sort of factories that nobody wants on land. Writing in the *New Scientist,* he listed the advantages of a chemical plant on the bottom: no land costs, unlimited water for cooling, easy storage of gases or liquids under high pressure (the pressure of the sea would do most of the work and a thin container the rest), and no objections from the neighbors. Hydraulic power to run the plant could be sent down from the surface or the shore; in certain cases, strong currents, like the four-knot Gulf Stream off Florida, could turn underwater windmills.

A natural chemical factory exists on the bottom of the Red Sea, where it has piled up $2.3 billion worth of metals waiting to be taken away. As far as I can determine, the financial journals have not gotten around to it yet. Its existence is known mainly to oceanographers who were motivated only by their usual curiosity when they discovered it. And it serves to illustrate, as if any new illustrations were needed, the danger of judging the pure scientist on the basis of immediate payoffs. One never knows what he will come up with.

The discovery was made by ships under many flags over several years. Oceanographers going through the Red Sea had occasionally observed a puzzling patch of warm salty water which they were tempted to attribute to faulty thermometers. The Swedish Albatross Expedition of 1947–48 logged a small temperature increase of a few degrees at this spot, although it reported that its Red Sea cruise was "uneventful." In 1958, Woods Hole's old *Atlantis* found a similar occurrence of suspiciously warm water and there the matter stood.

During the early Sixties, the Red Sea became a main highway for research vessels bound for the International Indian Ocean Expedition. In 1963, *Atlantis II* and the British *Discovery* passed over the area and reported abnormal temperatures. The following year, *Discovery* was en route from the Suez Canal to Aden when her scientists took a longer look. A string of Nansen bottles with their thermometers went over the side in 7,200 feet of water. No one quite believed the thermometers when they came up. Six hundred feet from the bottom, the water was at 71 degrees F.; just off the bottom, its temperature was 111 degrees. John Swallow, the chief scientist on board, was even more surprised by the contents of the Nansen bottles: "When water was being drawn from bottles that had been near the bottom, it seemed to run out more slowly than usual, and any that got spilt on deck immediately dried up, leaving a thick white patch of crystals." Analysis showed it to be seven times saltier than the rest of the Red Sea. These findings were confirmed two months later by *Meteor*, the new flagship of West Germany's oceanographic fleet, when she stopped at what was now known as Discovery Deep. The hot salty water near the bottom showed up as a distinct layer on her echo sounder.

In 1965, *Atlantis II* dropped a thermometer into the hot hole she had found two years before, the Atlantis II Deep. It came back reading 133 degrees F., the most unlikely of all observations that had yet been made. If it could be confirmed, this would be the hottest water in the world ocean. Another bottle cast was taken with the same result. Two Woods Hole scientists, Dr. Egon Degens and Arthur R. Miller, put a corer down on the line. It brought up, so Degens and Dr. David Ross reported in *Oceanus*, "a black ooze which, on first sight, had the physical appearance of tar and was too hot to touch." When it cooled, they saw that it was more like a fine black face powder. They wanted to learn more about it, but their shipboard chemical laboratory was equipped to handle only seawater. Expedients had to be used: peroxide from the sick bay, sulphur from the darkroom (hypo contains thiosulphate), a stainless steel cauldron from the galley while the cook wasn't looking. At Aden, the scientists landed and they did a more thorough job in the laboratory of a small Arabian school.

In 1966, the National Science Foundation gave Woods Hole a grant of $167,000 to study the hot holes thoroughly, not just as a stopover on the way to the Indian Ocean. That fall, *Chain* crisscrossed the area dozens of times, taking sixty cores. On board, she had American, British, German and Swedish scientists. Dr. John M. Hunt, chairman of the chemistry and geology department at Woods Hole, was chief scientist for part of the cruise. "People kept working until they dropped into bed," he said. "We knew this was our only chance. We weren't off Cape Cod." *Chain* discovered and gave her name to another hole but spent most of her time over the Atlantis II Deep, the biggest of the three that have been detected. It is eight miles long and three miles wide.

The cores taken on this cruise bore no resemblance to the usual drab ooze. Degens and Ross thought they were some of the most colorful sediments that had ever emerged from the depths of the sea. They wrote in *Oceanus:* "The individual layers are well-defined even down to layers of less than one millimeter. The color variation is fantastic; all shades of white, black, red, green, blue or yellow can be observed. Perhaps some of the more colorful Indian sand paintings and Mexican rugs faintly match these sediments in the variation and intensity of their colors." The sediments, once they had been dried, consisted of "approximately 90 percent of heavy metal oxides and sulfides of which the most abundant ones are those of iron, manganese, zinc and copper." Degens and Ross think they are produced by a chemical reaction between the hot brine and the overlying normal waters that precipitates the minerals to the bottom. A full account of the academic and economic significance of the hot brine area is presented in a 650-page book, *Hot Brines and Recent Heavy Metal Deposits in the Red Sea*, published by Springer-Verlag, Inc., New York, and edited by Degens and Ross.

No one is certain why the factory exists nor how long it will keep running. Measurements over three consecutive years lead Hunt to the conclusion that the Atlantis II hole is warming up, but there has been no spillover into the Discovery hole, because the latter is cooling and becoming less salty. Degens regards the brine as a "recent event" of the past few centuries. It may stop and start all over again.

After analyzing eight samples brought back from the Red Sea, Dr. F. T. Manheim of the U.S. Geological Survey at Woods Hole estimated that, in the Atlantis II Deep alone, the sediments might contain $1.5 billion in copper, zinc, silver and gold. This estimate turned out to be conservative. Later, Dr. J. L. Bischoff of the Oceanographic made a thorough study of the chemistry and mineralogy of the sediments. He and Dr. Manheim now estimate a total value of $2.3 billion, including $780 million in zinc, $1.1 billion in copper, $280 million in silver and $50 million in gold.

Future work may make even these figures conservative, for they are based on the upper thirty feet of sediments and the total thickness is at least twice as great, although the metal grade is still unknown. Since the sediments are soft, they should be easier to work than manganese nodules, even at their 6,000-foot depth. As geologists, neither Manheim nor Degens felt competent to decide who owns this wealth in the Red Sea. Geographically, the deposits are on the Sudanese side of a line drawn through the center of the Red Sea, suggesting that the Sudanese are the legal owners.

When it looks up from the oil and minerals on the bottom, Wall Street becomes much less bullish about the ocean. Under the heading of fishing, Hayden, Stone could find only one American firm, a fishmeal distributor, to recommend to investors. In its seventy-page report, it disposed of fish-farming in a three-line paragraph. I thought I had killed it myself when I spoke to its detractors in California, but I couldn't get rid of the corpse. Every time I looked at it, signs of life appeared. I would run into reports of a Japanese salmon ranch or a Spanish mussel farm. Growing fish in Asia is no more outlandish than growing rice and has been going on just as long.

Shellfish, rather than fish, make the best farm animals because they stay in one place like vegetables. French oyster beds are an estimable resource and an old one. The newer way is to raise shellfish on ropes or wires, a form of three-dimensional farming. Dr. John Ryther, chairman of the Woods Hole biology department, has estimated that an acre of water used in this manner can yield 10 tons of oysters or 100 tons of mussels a year by keeping shellfish away from natural enemies on the bottom.

Ryther saw the rafts from which mussels are grown on Vigo Bay in Spain. He thinks that a similar operation in an area the size of Long Island Sound could produce a tonnage of mussel meat equal to the world's total landings of fish. There are many reasons why this will never be tried. Among them is the American aversion to mussels, probably because the breed has not been changed to improve its color and kill its taste. Native food habits are the despair of American sea farmers. Off the California coast, kelp growers are looking for an absolute weapon against the sea urchins that destroy the roots of their crop. In restaurants on the French Riviera, sea urchins fetch a price that stings as much as their spines.

I know of one fish farm bold enough to try to grow a product that finicky Anglo-Saxons will eat. Since 1963, the British have been hatching and rearing plaice, a haughty relative of the flounder and sole, in an experiment supported by their Ministry of Agriculture, Fisheries and Food, and the White Fish Authority. The White Fish Authority levies a tax on landings of "white fish" (which means almost everything except herring) and uses the proceeds to improve ways of catching and preserving fish, to propagandize housewives with recipes for "Fish the Big

Dish" and, on a modest scale, to investigate the economics of fish and shellfish farming as part of its brief to assure an adequate future supply of fish in Great Britain. Like the BBC, it is one of those bodies in which the British display their genius for providing government support while leaving people alone so they can get some work done.

When I met Ian Richardson, the Authority's research secretary, in his London office at Lincoln's Inn Chambers, I broke the ice·by telling him that I was already familiar with the thoughts of Wilbert Chapman and Milner B. Schaefer on the subject of aquaculture. An eyebrow went up. "I do accept their view that the seas must supply more of the world's protein requirement in the future. I also accept their view that to make the maximum use of the ocean's productivity, it is sensible to fish lower down the food chain for oily fish to be converted into oil and meal. But I do not think they do full justice to the possibility of cultivating fish and shellfish to supply high-grade protein for direct human consumption. One thing they have done — and this has helped us — is to get rid of such science fiction ideas as plowing the seabed. That type of approach cannot get us anywhere."

I also mentioned to Richardson that I was interested mainly in the basic scientific side of oceanography. Up went the other eyebrow. "That's fair enough, but far too little attention is paid to development of ocean systems and techniques. Basic research might start because of somebody's interest in a problem or desire to produce a scientific paper. These are not our criteria. We are carrying out development based on a scientific appreciation of the situation and the need.

"We are not seeking the highest possible survival rate of fish but maximum production at a minimum cost. We knowingly cut corners to try to increase profits. Our purpose is to demonstrate where the problems are, and at the same time, to create a technique that can be used commercially. There is nothing new in fish-farming, but I believe we have the first truly marine farm where fish are grown from the egg through the larva to the adult."

The fish farm's first requirement, he explained, had been a sound seed supply (this also applies to raising oysters, clams and other shellfish). A supply of baby plaice and sole became available following twelve years of work by a research group under J. E. Shelbourne, a British fisheries biologist. They began by taking plaice eggs from the open sea, then feeding newly hatched larvae with brine shrimp as the Norwegians had done previously. By 1962, Shelbourne was no longer dependent on the sea. He and his co-workers, starting with captive plaice as parents, raised a generation of postage stamp-sized plaice that had metamorphosed from larvae to fish. Antibiotics were added to water in the tanks where the larvae were reared and the survival rate was impressive: 66 percent, compared to 99.999 percent mortality of plaice from egg onwards in the ocean.

The next step moved the fish farm from research into "research and development." The Ministry of Agriculture and the White Fish Authority jointly set up a pilot plant hatchery at Port Erin on the Isle of Man. It was intended to hatch plaice and other fish on a large scale and to give a picture of costs.

In 1964, when operations began, 160,000 plaice came out; then 400,000 in 1965. The graph collapsed a year later: only 3,000 plaice and 5,000 sole. Baby fish are as uncooperative as baby chicks. If anything displeases them, they take revenge on a farmer by dying. The disaster was traced to a change in diet. Usually, the larval shrimp had been treated to brine shrimp flown in as eggs from San Francisco, but the normal supply failed and a substitute had been brought from Great Salt Lake in Utah. By 1967, production was back to normal.

The plaice raisers hesitated to release their stock in the sea, where anybody would have the right to catch them in the free-for-all fishery of international waters and where pampered hatchery fish would stand a poor chance in the struggle to survive. So they tried two approaches: extensive and intensive farming. One site is a five-acre pond dammed off at Ardtoe in Scotland at the head of a tidal inlet, known locally as a sea loch. This farm was first stocked in 1965, when 200,000 plaice were shipped by sea from the Port Erin hatchery and put into the pond.

They were greeted by a day of drenching rain. Water streaming into the pond reduced its salinity. Organic matter washed down from the hills, decomposed in the pond and robbed the fish of their oxygen. No sea farmer ever prays for rain.

The farm had its pests — hungry crabs and eels that fed on the young plaice. "At Ardtoe, we spent two years growing a few fish and overcoming many problems," Richardson said. "We have much to learn about salinity and oxygen requirements. The answers are just not available in the literature. If we had waited until there was sufficient information, we never would have gone ahead — nor would we have discovered what the real problems are."

The exercise goes on at Ardtoe, with a new dam to keep rainwater out and an aerating system to give the fish more oxygen, Richardson thinks that aquaculture's near future lies in intensive farming rather than just putting fish out to pasture. Scientists are beginning to move in this direction at Ardtoe. Instead of letting fish roam the pond, they are kept first in nursery tanks, then in cages or enclosures. There, the fish can be husbanded, given additional feeding and harvested cheaply.

The other line that shows promise is rearing sole in small heated tanks at an electric power station in Scotland. The heat is waste from the power plant and so costs nothing. It gives the fish summer temperatures all year round and they respond by reaching a marketable size in two years instead of four. Researchers were worried at first about chlorine in the waste water from the power plant, but the fish do not appear to mind in the least.

Sole in the heated tanks have been fed on mussels to simplify the experiment. Mussels are an expensive dish in Britain even for humans, and one writer has calculated that mussel-fed sole cost $4.20 a pound. The next step, therefore, will be to raise them on a diet of crude fishmeal just like chickens.

"The sole that have come out of the power station tanks so far are the most expensive fish ever grown," Richardson said. "But they may turn out to be the cheapest. After two years, we already know that we can raise fish from the egg to marketable size in only two years. Now we have to do this in quantity. That means we must develop husbandry techniques and cut costs each year until we can make an assessment of the true price of a pound of flesh.

"If costs are competitive, then we will have a technology to offer any commercial firm willing to take the risk. The Authority itself is not a producer, we're more like an agricultural research station."

I asked Richardson when he thought that fish-farming would be a good risk. He reeled off the figures: "To land 3,000 tons of fish a year today (and remember, stocks of fish in the North Atlantic are heavily fished, so you might not meet this target in a few years time), you need the catch of a long-range freezer trawler. Capital cost is approximately $1,200,000, amortized over twenty years. The trawler costs about $1,200 a day to run 200 days a year. A trawler operator receives subsidies, but you won't. If you can grow 3,000 tons of fish a year for less — and unsubsidized — then you're in business, particularly if you can produce a high-cost species."

22. *Blight in the Sea*

As a Cloaca Maxima, the sea offers a resource that is neither underexploited nor overpublicized. Raw sewage, dangerous chemicals, radioactive wastes, crude oil from tankers, fuel oil from bunkers, unwanted explosives, detergents, pesticides, obsolete war gases, the leftovers of industry . . . anything is considered safely out of the way once it has been poured or pitched into the ocean by what *Punch* once called the effluent society.

Oceanographers regard this sadly and realistically. They have demanded, and they are getting, the establishment in the United States of "marine preserves" so that, at least, they can have a relatively protected reference point from which to measure the ruin that is being wrought elsewhere. At the same time, they recognize the irresistible call of the sea as a sewer. When he was director of Scripps, Roger Revelle observed: "The fact that the ocean basins are great holes in the ground and that we, as land mammals, tend to think of the ocean as somehow alien to our normal lives makes it seem logical to us that we should hide our wastes in the sea." Within carefully imposed limits, this can be done without wanton destruction of other resources.

"Within limits" is the catch. In the sea as on land, we pollute first and ask questions of our scientists afterwards. True, this is not the case of radioactive wastes, where the danger is clear and present. Dumping is controlled, registers are kept and marine life is watched for any ill effects. The International Atomic Energy Agency operates a laboratory at Monaco to get basic information on how radioactive wastes move in the sea, whether in the water or through the food web. The agency's activities "are motivated not so much by any existing problem as by the necessity of thoughtful planning for future circumstances, including the substantial growth of nuclear facilities of various kinds, nuclear ships, etc."

In most instances of "conventional" pollution, the scientist is called in not to calculate the risk but to assess the damage. We are already befouling the sea. It is impossible to say how badly. The story of marine pollution lies scattered in bits and pieces; no one seems to be able to put them together. In an attempt to get some kind of global view of the problem, the United Nations sent a questionnaire to 102 countries and totted up the results in 1967. The general statistics were of the usual sort: 66 countries responded, 47 considered sea pollution a problem, 20 a health hazard, 10 a "reduction of amenities," etc. It is the details that stink to high heaven. Most countries glossed over them in prudish generalizations, but a few described the kind of conditions that apply to many of the others.

The United States was the most specific in its replies, yet not even the world's leading scientific and technological power was able to come up with a total assessment of what is put into the Great Lakes and the coastal waters, around which 75 percent of its population lives. However, it gave several examples to provide a "general impression" of the degree of the problem:

— Into the Hudson River and down to the sea go raw sewage from a "population equivalent" of 4,297,000 and sewage receiving only "primary treatment" from 3,760,000; industrial wastes, mainly from petroleum, paper, meat-packing and chemical industries, are produced by 53 sources in the state of New York and an "unknown number" in New Jersey.

— The Delaware River estuary takes over a million pounds a day of "first-stage carbonaceous wastes" — and it is also used for pleasure by boat owners in eighty-six marinas. Two beaches there have been closed (public health authorities in the United States have little faith in the "self-purifying powers" of the sea under such conditions).

— In Chesapeake Bay, sewage has encouraged the growth of the unwanted Eurasian milfoil weed to the point where it is a serious problem; more sewage destroyed a prospective site for oyster beds on Humboldt Bay in California; nine million fish died in a case of mass mortality in the Potomac River in 1963; 38 million in another case in San Diego Harbor in 1962; half of South Carolina's blue crabs have been wiped out by a "massive kill of yet undetermined origin."

Norway's reply to the UN told of the fishermen's side. They have become involuntary scavengers. Drums dumped from ships to dispose of waste forever keep coming up in their nets. So do plastic containers, cheap enough to be disposable but stubbornly resistant to the processes that break down natural materials in the sea. The Norwegians fear that if this goes on, they will not be able to fish at all in a few years. Fishermen themselves are responsible for a cruel and unusual form of damage to marine life. Nylon nets break loose, and instead of rotting, they go on catching fish blindly for years. Victims die in the trap, decay, and pollute the waters.

Along with the usual problems, the United Kingdom has one all to itself. Waste from whiskey distilleries around the Moray Firth used to be discharged into rivers. Since this is now forbidden, the wastes are hauled instead by tank truck to the coast and deposited onto beaches or into nearby sewers. This sums up the normal march of water pollution everywhere: from still water to rivers and now into the sea.

The UN's questionnaire is not light reading and it can be put aside with no great difficulty. Occasionally, however, a few voices speak out loud and clear on the issue of marine pollution. At first, it is a relief to hear them; then one almost wishes they had remained silent. I felt such an uneasiness at Scripps when I talked to Dr. Edward Goldberg, a top-ranking geochemist whose name is usually associated with research on the chemical composition of seawater, marine organisms and sediments. He has also turned to waste. "Man has left his fingerprints upon the chemical composition of the world ocean," he said. "In any fifty-gallon sample of seawater taken anywhere, traces of artificial radioactivity can be found. Lead from high-test gasoline gets into the atmosphere and precipitates out into the sea. The discharge from cars in the United States alone is 300,000 tons of lead a year, about ten times all the lead carried into the ocean by the world's rivers. We are now dispersing lead at a level close to that at which we mine it.

"Pesticides, primarily the chlorinated hydrocarbons such as DDT, are a recent entry into the ocean. The amounts found in the bodies of deep-living fish are similar to those in land organisms, including man. The carbon dioxide that we put into the atmosphere by burning fossil fuels is changing the composition of seawater. On the sea floor, our artifacts are everywhere: beer bottles, inserts of cork from bottle tops, welding beads. Man's dust is going into the sediments. The big question is how long can we continue to alter the composition of the ocean without causing any perceptible effects."

Goldberg had participated in an experiment in 1965 on Barbados. There, half a dozen scientists from the Liverpool Institute of Technology and Scripps built a tower to collect dust samples from the air and learned that material from the Sahara was being blown over the ocean. The purpose of the experiment was to test Darwin's idea that the atmosphere could transport large amounts of solids from the land into the ocean. As usual, Darwin was proven right.

But talc kept turning up on the tower as well, the same talc that one finds in baby powder. "The Russians have seen it in the air, too," Goldberg said. "We know how it gets there. It doesn't come from babies' bottoms. Every year, 100,000 tons of talc are used to 'carry' insecticides when they are sprayed."

Insecticides are spread so thinly in the atmosphere and the ocean that it is impossible to detect them by analyzing samples of air or water. Since the talc is more obvious, Goldberg thinks it can be used to plot the trail of the insecticides. To measure the "standing crop" of talc — that is, the amount of it around at any given time — Goldberg proposes to sample the comparatively clean air over the ocean from a ship. He also wants to study slices taken from land glaciers to see how much talc has accumulated since insecticides first came into common use. "People don't care about this," he said. "Finding support for unpopular research is a terrible problem. Who wants to be a scientific garbageman, a public accountant for garbage? I'm not saying there is a danger as yet. But we must be aware, we must monitor. What goes into the ocean doesn't come right out. That is what I am screaming about."

A few other scientists are raising their voices. Traces of insecticides, they say, have been found in the tissues of Antarctic penguins and Arctic seals. So far, so good. It's tough on the penguins and seals, but we're all right, aren't we? Then the voices become disquieting. A report in the *New Scientist* relates how Charles Wurster of the State University of New York at Stony Brook became curious about DDT's effects on phytoplankton. He learned that DDT in infinitesimal concentrations can cut photosynthesis — that is, oxygen production — by certain species of marine plants as much as 25 percent. What a pity for the phytoplankton . . .

Dr. Lamont C. Cole, a professor of ecology at Cornell University, told the American Association for the Advancement of Science in December 1967 that the oxygen balance in the atmosphere is becoming very shaky indeed. *Science Journal* explains that "a drop in the amount of oxygen in the atmosphere could come about quite suddenly as the result of gradual destruction by toxic garbage of planktonic diatoms in the ocean, which produce 70 percent or more of the atmosphere's oxygen by photosynthesis." Cole expressed the fear that we may be poisoning the diatoms right now, "thus bringing disaster upon ourselves." What to do about it? Stop reading the *New Scientist* and *Science Journal* . . .

Oceanographers have their biggest quarrel with the prevalent — and convenient — belief that the sea's capacity for waste is boundless. Dr. Pieter Korringa of the Netherlands Institute for Fishery Investigations breaks a lance against it whenever he can. Korringa has been chairman of a panel on marine pollution set up by the Intergovernmental Oceanographic Commission, an offshoot of UNESCO, and his main focus of interest is the North Sea. He admits that the North Sea looks like a temptingly large trash can. Shallow as it is, it contains 54,000 cubic kilometers of water. If 54,000 tons of anything were dumped into the North Sea and perfectly dispersed, it would show up in a concentration of one part per billion, nothing to be afraid of. But, says Korringa, "the sea is not one tub of water mixed every day by wind and tide." He tells how, in the spring of 1965, a large number of dead fish were found on a beach north of The Hague. An alert chemist from his institute spotted blue crystals on the beach and a hunch told him they might be copper sulphate. He ran an analysis and found there was 500 times too much copper in the water off the beach.

How much copper had to be put into the North Sea to achieve such concentration? Only twenty tons, Korringa has estimated, by a clandestine dumper on a beach at low tide. The waste did not go into one big tub but remained concentrated by tides and currents. It flowed north along the coast as a narrow river about 200 yards wide. Two weeks after the fish had died near The Hague, the river had moved only forty miles to the north and its copper content was still 100 times above normal. Now it was off the entrance of the Wadden Zee, where the Dutch were growing 60,000 tons of mussels. "Fortunately, north winds drove the water away from our coast," Korringa told me. "It is also fortunate that mussels were threatened, not clams or oysters. Mussels take up elements, then get rid of them, but clams and oysters practice biochemical inflation. They can accumulate some heavy metals to as much as 500,000 times the amount present in the sea." Copper has one saving quality: it turns oysters so green and unpalatable that no one dares eat them. Not all poisons issue such loud warnings.

Another handy belief holds that sewage is good for the sea. As a nutrient, it should turn barren waters into marine gardens. Korringa has many reservations about this. "One cannot just fertilize the sea anywhere. When we enrich waters that are already rich, we get into trouble. We do not want to grow all forms of phytoplankton. Dinoflagellates, in particular, are a world to themselves; they live by waging chemical warfare. The red tides caused by certain species of dinoflagellates do not occur only in subtropical waters. They have been seen in the ports of Hamburg and Liverpool. One in the Bruges-Zeebrugge Canal in Belgium led in 1937 to deaths from poisonous shellfish. Waste from Long Island duck farms allowed dinoflagellates to flourish in Great South Bay and affected the rich oyster beds there.

"We biologists have come to the point where we think man should be considered a biological catastrophe. Wild field mice go mad when they are subjected to such population densities as ours. Medical science has made these densities possible, but now we are hindered by the density of the waste that we produce.

"Industry will always try to get rid of its wastes into the air and water as cheaply as possible. We cannot stop industrial development, it is the basis of our standard of living. But we must learn to live with industry, we must frame adequate measures. It is incredible that we have such problems when solutions are technologically possible."

Pulp mills stand out prominently as sources of industrial pollution.

Their wastes are enormous. The Canadian expert on Korringa's international panel, Dr. Michael Waldichuk, has estimated that a sulphite paper mill producing 500 tons a day will spew out organic waste that is the biological equivalent of sewage from a city of two million. Like sewage, the mill's spent liquors take dissolved oxygen from the water and leave little for marine life. Waldichuk, who is with the Fisheries Research Board of Canada, keeps an eye on nearly a dozen large pulp mills working on the coast of British Columbia. In particular, he has followed one at Port Alberni Inlet, a long narrow fjord on Vancouver Island. Dr. J. P. Tully had begun to survey the inlet in the late Thirties, and terminated his study with a Ph.D. thesis in 1948 on the oceanography of the inlet and prediction of pollution there. Waldichuk has continued the watch since 1954, six years after the pulp mill went into operation. The purpose of their study was to reconcile the interests of two of British Columbia's major industries: pulp and fishing. The owners of the Port Alberni mill cooperated and kept production down to a point where, theoretically, there would always be enough oxygen in the inlet to dispose of waste and still allow migrating salmon to get through.

However, the mill's effects were cumulative. Everything was not being flushed out to sea. As the years went by, sludge built up on the bottom of the inlet while wastes were discharged on the surface. In the dry summer of 1965, the salmon had to run through a suffocating vise between old pollution below and new pollution above. Waldichuk sampled the thirty-foot-deep waters of Alberni Harbor: there was enough oxygen to keep salmon alive only in a layer five feet thick. He reported what the fish were up against: "In the northeast corner of the harbor, gases could be seen bubbling to the surface everywhere. There was a distinct odor of hydrogen sulphide in the area. Our stainless steel and brass sampling bottle, set near the bottom, came up severely blackened from the effect of sulphide." He has since recommended to the mill that it should improve its treatment of wastes and, specifically, recover chips and fragments for fuel instead of letting them settle as sludge.

Across the border, as I happened to learn from another member of the international panel, Dr. Leon W. Weinberger of the Federal Water Pollution Control Administration of the U.S. Department of Interior, the same problem exists. The Department of Interior and the state of Washington's Pollution Control Commission have made careful joint studies of the effects of waste from seven pulp and paper mills on Puget

Sound. In three areas — Bellingham, Everett Harbor and Port Angeles — pollution was shown to be harmful to oyster larvae, flatfish eggs and young migrating salmon. Two cities, Everett and Port Angeles, were making an additional contribution of sewage. In the case of Port Angeles on the northern shore of the Olympic Peninsula, two miles of waterfront were considered "bacterially contaminated for water-contact use." The agencies spelled out recommendations for the cities and the mills: treatment of wastes, dredging of bottom sludge, discharge into deeper waters. Puget Sound supports a $10 million a year commercial fishing industry, while 300,000 sportsmen spend five or six times as much annually to fish for the fun of it. The agencies could place no estimate on the value of the Sound's beaches and scenery as "important and highly treasured benefits for employment and residence in the region."

Neither Puget Sound nor Alberni Inlet should be considered as isolated cases. On the contrary, they were mentioned at an international meeting in Paris precisely because steps are being taken to study and solve their problems before further damage is done. The danger is far greater wherever pollution is accepted or ignored and no machinery exists for investigation and control.

Only nine countries replying to the UN's questionnaire cited pulp and paper wastes, but thirty-two mentioned oil. This is not unexpected: five million tons of oil are spilled into the ocean every year and they must go somewhere. When the *Torrey Canyon* piled up on the Seven Stones off Cornwall in March 1967, 117,000 tons of oil were lost, only a fraction of the annual total. Yet the circumstances were so dramatic and the object lesson so severe that one is tempted to say the end result has been beneficial. A cry went up for more stringent policing of the movements of giant tankers (there were a dozen larger than the *Torrey Canyon* at the time she was wrecked) and for sterner enforcement of existing rules against the discharge of oil into the sea. Major oil companies that come under the full glare of public scrutiny use a "load-on-top" system that eliminates the need for tankers to wash their tanks at sea, a practice that means pumping out one percent of their cargoes. Pressure is building up against less scrupulous operators who pollute to shave costs.

The International Convention for the Prevention of Pollution of the Sea by Oil has existed since 1954, and in its amended form, it covers all ships over 150 tons and prohibits any discharge of oil within 100 miles from shore. Its sponsor, the UN's Intergovernmental Maritime Consultative Organization, aims at an ultimate ban on any oil dumping anywhere. The convention has been honored more in the breach than in the observance. As the U.S. National Council on Marine Resources and Engineering Development says candidly, it was only the *Torrey Canyon* that "brought widespread recognition of the severity of damage that could result from oil spills." An immediate consequence in the United States was the inspection by the Coast Guard of four tankers sunk on the continental shelf during World War II to see if they were likely to become a source of delayed-action pollution (so far, they are not). More attention is being called to the danger of blowouts in offshore drilling operations. Several have already occurred.

The loss of the *Torrey Canyon* gave a considerable fillip to research on new ways of cleaning up spilt oil. Proposals have been made to soak it up with shredded plastic foam that could be collected by a trawler or to mop it up with a big rotating sponge mounted on a catamaran. A British firm has suggested sinking it in the deep sea with silicone-treated fly ash (an unwanted by-product of power plants burning pulverized coal) that repels water and attracts oil. Jersey Standard has announced a new spray that breaks up oil slicks, cleans beaches and is said to leave marine animals unscathed.

All these approaches seek a way out of the dilemma that the *Torrey Canyon* raised: at the time, the only known hope of keeping beaches clean for tourists lay in detergents that rendered them lethal to nature. Quick decisions had to be taken on the basis of scanty knowledge. A survey in 1966 by the Organization for Economic Cooperation Development showed that none of the ten countries that replied, among them Britain and the United States, had any institutes working solely or mainly on marine pollution.

Here and there, scientists had been able to look at oil pollution on a smaller scale. A team from Scripps knew of a small cove on the Mexican coast of Baja California that had never been touched by man. In the spring of 1957, a tanker carrying diesel oil was wrecked at the entrance of the cove. Dr. Wheeler J. North, a member of the team who is now at California Institute of Technology, reported that three months after the wreck the cove was fresh and clean, with no visible traces of oil. Life took much longer to come back. At first, only two species of animals and four species of plants survived. Nearly a decade went by before species returned to something like their former abundance, and, North believes, the cove is still not the same as it was prior to the wreck.

Nature had been allowed to take its course on a deserted Mexican shore, but the Cornish coast was due to receive swarms of vacationers in less than four months. To clear the beaches of 14,000 tons of Kuwait crude oil that had come ashore from the *Torrey Canyon*, the British used 10,000 tons of detergents. There was no time for research. The job was done and scientists, once more, could only conduct a postmortem.

It fell principally to the Plymouth Laboratory of the Marine Biological Association of the United Kingdom, the nearest scientific institute to the scene. On the face of it, the Plymouth Laboratory would not appear a likely candidate for such a role. Man's garbage in the sea is not its main concern by any means. It has been wrapped up in basic research ever since it was founded in 1888. Its twenty-three staff scientists are outnumbered by twice as many visiting researchers, and all of them, insiders and outsiders alike, do pretty much as they please in deciding on their research. Dr. J. E. Smith, the laboratory's director, described to me how it is run: "We have an odd way. We plan in general terms, but we do not lay down a program and then get people to fit it. We want people to come here and see what interests them. The best work gets done if you can get the best people. We are given our budget, a little more than $500,000 a year, then told to get on with the job according to our lights."

Somehow, it works. The bents of individual scientists add up to a coherent picture of the manifold forms of marine life, starting with the plants five-thousandths of a millimeter in size that come under the laboratory's electron microscope. Considerable work is done on the physiology of sea animals, and it was largely at Plymouth that a Nobel Prize was won for research on the nerve axons of squid. Physiologists there are now looking intently at the buoyancy control mechanism of the squid and its relatives. I spent an enjoyable hour with Dr. John Gilpin-Brown, who with Professor Eric Denton has learned how the cuttlefish effortlessly changes its depth. As he dissected a specimen, he showed me the way it uses osmotic pressure to vary the amount of water in the minute chambers of its cuttlebone that serves as a ballast tank (a better-known function of the cuttlebone is to sharpen the beaks of pet canaries). I spent an equally enjoyable hour with Dr. Leslie Cooper, a chemist and physical oceanographer who has been at Plymouth since 1930, patiently studying long-term changes in the ocean. Terms like "applied fisheries research" are never used in the laboratory, but Cooper was able to explain the disappearance of the English Channel herring fishery forty years ago. He traced it to mild Arctic winters: they reduced the thrust of cold water into the depths of the Atlantic and weakened the stirring process that had brought up phosphates to fertilize the plants on which small animals grazed before they became food for the herring. The laboratory has also found that a change in fish population can be heralded a year or two in advance by a change in certain species of zooplankton, particularly arrowworms that come and go in advance of the herring. It has records almost as long as its history. Specimens have been collected at one station ten miles off Eddystone Light since 1902 and the laboratory now conducts half a dozen cruises a year to keep an eye on the waters of the western English Channel and their inhabitants. Such routine checking on normal marine life took on immediacy when oil and detergent were poured abnormally into the environment.

For ten weeks, the Plymouth Laboratory abandoned its research pursuits and plunged into the reeking mess left by the *Torrey Canyon* over the waters and the shores that its scientists knew so well. New techniques had to be improvised for an unheard-of situation. To learn how life below the oil surface was affected by fallout, the laboratory's largest research vessel, the 120-foot *Sarsia*, stood off to windward of heavy oil patches, lowered open sampling bottles, then drifted into the oil. The bottles thus could be closed and brought up without surface contamination. To the relief of the biologists, analysis of these samples showed that subsurface life in the open sea was less affected by the mixture of oil and detergents than had originally been feared. In its report, *"Torrey Canyon" Pollution and Marine Life*, the laboratory attributes this unforeseen boon to evaporation of the detergents' toxic components after two or three days. Scientists even ate bottom fish taken by trawl under a thin oil patch and enjoyed them with no aftereffects. Birds, massacred by the thousands, were the main victims of oil in the open sea.

On the shore, a different story had to be told. In its report, the laboratory regretted that it was unable to compare detergent-treated areas with others that had been hit by oil alone. In the afflicted region, hardly any beaches or coves, no matter how isolated, were spared by detergents, which, the laboratory notes, dispersed the oil but did not destroy it. They did destroy life. Algae became bleached and brittle, mussels gaped in death, limpets vanished from rocks and left their empty "seats" behind them. Destruction of the limpets, in retrospect, seems to have been particularly needless. On rocks overlooked by the detergent sprayers, the limpets eliminated the oil themselves . . . by eating it. Kuwait crude did them no harm. At one beach where these grazers had been thoroughly wiped out by detergents, rocks were covered in the summer of 1967 by a carpet of bright green algae proliferating in the absence of its natural enemies. The laboratory commented with restraint: "On this sunny July day Porthmissen Beach was crowded with holiday-makers and children were happily playing even in the still stained and still slightly smelly sandy patches . . . For them the shore was back to normal."

The French took a different tack. At first, they hoped that the beaches of northern Brittany would be spared by the southwest winds that normally prevail at this time of the year. There was only one chance in ten that the wind would back to the northeast. It did. Fifteen thousand tons of oil came ashore. The French press called it a "black tide." To preserve Brittany's rich oyster beds, the oil was not sprayed with detergents at sea. It had to be attacked on shore with not much more than shovels, buckets and bulldozers. This was only the first wave. Two months after the wreck of the tanker, 30,000 more tons were lying offshore. First, the French unsuccessfully tried to sink it with sawdust. Then, to the surprise and admiration of the British, they used powdered *craie de Champagne*, the blackboard chalk of French schoolboys. This variety of chalk contains one percent of sodium stearate, which enabled it to be attracted to the oil and to convert it into large football-sized lumps that sank to the bottom. The Plymouth Laboratory estimated that 3,000 tons of chalk disposed of all but 100 tons of the oil mass at sea. An interesting and still-unelucidated sidelight appeared when Plymouth's *Sarsia* steamed into a mass of chalk-treated oil and found it rich in dinoflagellates: the "black tide" may have been turned into a red tide. No evidence has yet been found to indicate that this was more than a coincidence.

In concluding its report, the Plymouth Laboratory stated that the effects of the *Torrey Canyon* disaster on marine life were not as catastrophic as had originally been feared. But this is no guarantee that we will get off as lightly after the next accident nor that we are getting off lightly at present. As the laboratory remarks, most forms of pollution are not accidental and many are thought to be necessary. The mild, professorial

Dr. Smith edited the laboratory's report and he is responsible for its conclusion:

"If we ask why they are thought to be necessary, there can be but one answer: it is because the easiest and cheapest way of disposing of unwanted materials is to throw them away. If materials so disposed of are harmless and unenduring no one minds very much. But, if they are injurious and persistent, acceptable means of disposing of them must be found even though it may be expensive to find the answer.

"We are progressively making a slum of nature and may eventually find that we are enjoying the benefit of science and industry under conditions which no civilized society should tolerate."

23. The United Oceans

As the ocean thrusts itself into our affairs, it creates situations that demand new political and juridical answers. Its present and future uses are incompatible with the old assumption that beyond the three-mile limit it belongs to no one. For all intents and purposes other than navigation, the assumption is as anachronistic as the shore batteries upon whose range the limit was based. At least seven nations have claimed jurisdiction over fishing rights 200 miles off their shores. Under the Convention on the Continental Shelf, adopted by a United Nations conference in 1958 at Geneva, all coastal nations now have a clear title to the bottom resources of their continental shelves down to a depth of 200 meters (656 feet), a boundary that can run as far out to sea as 250 miles, depending on the hazards of submarine geography. It is as if a continent larger than Africa were added to their area.

Within it, states the convention, they own "the mineral and other non-living resources of the seabed and subsoil together with living organisms belonging to sedentary species, that is to say, organisms which, at the harvestable stage, either are immobile on or under the seabed or are unable to move, except in constant physical contact with the seabed or the subsoil."

Certain "organisms" slip through this legal barbed-wire entanglement. In international disputes since the adoption of the convention, marine biologists have been drafted as experts to determine whether lobsters and king crabs swim or crawl. If the animals swim, then the lawyers must consider them as fish and anyone can catch them; if they crawl, they belong to the owner of the continental shelf.

Ownership of the shelf is not at all that clear, either. In 1958, the Geneva convention's framers expected that twenty years would go by before anything worthwhile could be mined beyond the depth boundary of 200 meters that they had drawn. Oil drillers are already capable of surpassing it; the miners of phosphorite and manganese nodules are waiting in the wings. They can make use of a purposely opened loophole in the convention's definition of the continental shelf as "the seabed and subsoil of the submarine areas adjacent to the coast . . . to a depth of 200 meters, or beyond that limit, to whether the depth of the superjacent waters admits of the exploitation of the natural resources of the said area."

In other words, exploitation of the natural resources is nine points of the law. Dr. Kenneth O. Emery, a Woods Hole geologist, is among those who note that "exploitation" is not defined in the convention. He has asked several provocative questions that cannot as yet be answered: "Does the recovery of a few manganese nodules as curios constitute exploitation? How many tons of nodules per year per unit area constitutes exploitation? Is profit on a free and open market required, or will large governmental subsidies substitute for profit? Manganese nodules with their content of cobalt, copper and nickel are the chief deep-sea resources that generally receive mention, but does the recovery of a few million dollars worth of these metals per year warrant assignment of sovereignty to huge areas of the earth?"

There are other questions. What is the status of the country with a deep trench near its coast that separates it from what would normally be its continental shelf? Norway was in such a position when drilling rights were apportioned in the North Sea, but Great Britain allowed her to extend her claim across the trench. In the Pacific Ocean, the long arm of American law reached over waters 10,000 feet deep to prosecute an ingenious group that had tried to put a man-made island on Cortes Bank,

110 miles off San Diego, to reap a crop of abalone and lobster. To start their island, they decided to sink an old troopship on the bank, but their plans went awry and the ship was wrecked in 35 feet of water. They were charged with creating a hazard to navigation on the continental shelf off California.

The convention's least controversial provisions are becoming obsolescent. It declared as a matter of course that the legal status of the seas above the shelf remains unaffected. Serious doubts are now being expressed about allowing freedom on the top of the sea. Dr. John P. Craven, chief scientist of the Navy Special Projects Office in Washington, does not see how fishing and shipping could continue in areas where divers are working for long periods at a stretch. "The saturated diver is in a precarious position with respect to man-made perils. He cannot tolerate explosive detonation in his near vicinity; he cannot tolerate extensive pollution; he cannot tolerate interference by trawls or dragnets. He will be chary of even normal merchant ship transit overhead because of the danger of jettisoned debris."

Craven raises a point of criminal law. On his ship or in an underwater house, the diver is under the jurisdiction of his own country. But what if saturated divers of different nationalities meet under unpleasant circumstances? "It is relatively easy for one diver to impose conditions on another which force him above his saturation depth or which force him to become saturated or which separate him from his life support. . . . In extreme situations where life itself is clearly imperiled, desperation attempts to turn on a fellow swimmer or any swimmer in the vicinity and to physically vie for control of life support equipment are an inevitable scenario of some future underwater undertaking."

Such prospects are plausible in the context of a legal vacuum. There is a growing sentiment that the vacuum cannot be allowed to exist much longer if we are not to repeat in the ocean the same grievous mistakes that have left us in our present predicament on land. In July 1966, President Johnson said what many are thinking: "Under no circumstances, we believe, must we ever allow the prospects of rich harvests and mineral wealth to create a new form of colonial competition among the maritime nations. We must be careful to avoid a race to grab and to hold the lands under the high seas. We must ensure that the deep seas and the ocean bottoms are, and remain, the legacy of all human beings."

In several quarters, the President has been taken literally. Senator

Claiborne Pell of Rhode Island (a state, as he has said, with 156 of its 1,214 square miles under water and a shoreline of 384 miles) introduced into the Senate in September 1967 a short resolution aimed at achieving "a reasonable legal order for the extranational world ocean." The resolution speaks of an "urgent need" for an international agreement to keep the deep-sea floor and its resources free for use by all nations. The agreement would also ban the stationing on the ocean bottom of "unproven types of nuclear or other kinds of mass destruction weapons." Pell asked that the State Department take steps leading to an ocean space treaty that would allay any fear that the United States and the Soviet Union "might attempt to carve up the oceans of the world into codominions much as the Spanish and Portuguese sought to do with the New World in their agreement at Tordesillas, signed on June 7, 1494."

Just about this time, Malta, a state even smaller than Rhode Island, dropped a similar idea into the United Nations General Assembly. In August 1967, Malta requested that the Assembly's agenda be modified to include an item on "the reservation exclusively for peaceful purposes of the seabed and of the ocean floor, underlying the seas beyond the limits of present national jurisdiction, and the use of their resources in the interests of mankind." In an accompanying memorandum, Malta suggested that the "net financial benefits" that would come from use of the sea floor should be used "primarily to promote the development of poor countries." An international agency could be created to assume jurisdiction over the ocean floor as a trustee for all countries.

One of the main proponents of such a solution has been Dr. Francis T. Christy, Jr., of Research for the Future, Inc., in Washington, a non-profit corporation financed by the Ford Foundation. Christy discounts the feasibility of simply extending each country's continental shelf as it is exploited. Under such a "national lake" approach, the French and the British could lay claim to vast areas of the Pacific, Atlantic and Indian Oceans because of their island holdings (the Geneva Convention gives islands the same rights as the mainland). The Soviet Union, with its comparatively small coastline, would be short-changed and, Christy remarks, no ocean regime can be set up without its agreement. The second possibility he mentions is that of the "flag nation." Anyone could operate on the ocean floor under the protection of his own country, but competition and conflict would inevitably call for supranational rules anyway.

Christy concludes that the answer is an international authority that could collect royalties from the seabed miners in the deep ocean, and in return, guarantee their exclusive rights to a deposit.

The UN General Assembly started to discuss Malta's idea in November 1967. Dr. Arvid Pardo, the Maltese delegate, provided more details about the international agency that his government had in mind. The ocean floor, he believed, could not very well become the responsibility of the UN in its present form: "It is hardly likely that those countries that have already developed a technical capability to exploit the ocean floor would agree to an international regime if it were administered by a body where small countries, such as mine, had the same voting power as the United States or the Soviet Union." Pardo suggested a new agency that could finance itself by income from rental of the ocean floor. If the agency were created in 1970, its gross income could reach $6 billion a year by 1975, a sum that could be transfused into the underdeveloped world. Two months later, the General Assembly adopted its resolution setting up a committee of thirty-five countries to study the item in view of future action.

Malta's suggestion kicked up a curious storm in the United States. Strong reactions were heard in the halls of Congress against the idea of turning the sea floor over to the United Nations (which Pardo specifically said he did not have in mind). Florida seems to have led the attack. One of the state's congressmen, Rep. Paul G. Rogers, proposed an eastward ho! alternative. He urged that the United States should occupy the sea floor out to the Mid-Atlantic Ridge by 1980. "The sea bottoms off the United States present an opportunity to expand our national borders in the same manner we did as we crossed the West in the early days." In October 1967, Florida's governor, Claude Kirk, went down in *Aluminaut* and planted the flags of his state and the United States on the bottom, eight miles off Miami, at a depth of 1,000 feet. When he came up, he explained to the press: "I didn't make a fanfare about this thing because we would have had eighteen senators and the federal government protesting. Well, it's too late now. You should dismiss the question of boundaries when talking about the ocean bottom. It is only a question of possession. That's the way the Spaniards did it. They just said 'it's mine' and took it. The United States should do the same thing." Eighty-six members of Parliament for all British parties do not see things his way.

In May 1968, they tabled a motion in the House of Commons that asked, as Pell had done in the Senate and Malta in the General Assembly, for a treaty to conserve the sea floor as "the common heritage of mankind."

Elsewhere, it has been hinted that the strongest backers of the Malta plan were large companies with a stake in the sea. Their support was attributed to their business sense, not to any sudden infatuation with the UN. Yvonne Rebeyrol, who covers oceanography for *Le Monde* in Paris, wrote: "They [industrial firms] are the most eager of all to see a settlement of the legal problems raised by the exploitation of the resources of the ocean bottom. In fact, they cannot start to invest heavily on the bottom until they are certain they will not be evicted by someone else who, for example, could claim prior discovery or rights under a national law."

The debate among parliamentarians, economists, jurists and diplomats shows that the land world is becoming aware of the built-in internationality of the ocean. The oceanographers are involved in dozens of international organizations, the oldest being the International Council for the Exploration of the Sea that dates back to 1901, when it was founded in Copenhagen by countries of northwestern Europe. Dr. Arthur Maxwell, associate director of Woods Hole, has gone so far as to say that "the oceanographers have arrived at a position where they are actively considering a public order of the sea quite independently from the efforts taking place in international law circles."

Maxwell, who is equally at ease at sea or in a UN working group, traces the first major cooperative effort in oceanography back to the International Geophysical Year, which ran through 1957 and 1958. It was based on enlightened self-interest: "While the motivation of the organizers of this effort was cooperation on a worldwide basis, its acceptance among the oceanographic community was at least in part an economic necessity. Support for oceanography had been fluctuating widely and this international program provided a salvation."

The scientists then convinced their foreign ministries to support an Intergovernmental Oceanographic Commission, which came into being under UNESCO's wing in 1960, with the late Anton Bruun, a Danish deep-sea biologist, as its first chairman. One of the Commission's earliest moves was to turn all its members' guns against a proposed international research vessel. The oceanographers knew what they were doing. Instead of one ship performing international research, they have since had dozens — their own. The Commission offers them a way to combine their resources, represented by land laboratories as well as by ships.

Such resources are not the monopoly of a single country. The United States, it is generally agreed, spends more than anyone else on the ocean. Its federal marine science and technology budget has been growing lustily: $333.4 million in the 1966 fiscal year; $409.1 million in 1967: $447 million in 1968. The proposal for fiscal year 1969 was $516 million, an increase of 15 percent, but still only 3 percent of the $17 billion that the federal government devotes to research and development. In 1967, the United States had 125 oceanographic ships.

In a report to the UN, the U.S.S.R. has stated that its annual expenditures on oceanography run to $20 million and that it operates 110 vessels. Comparisons are difficult to establish and are always being made. In the United States, there is a tendency to speak in public about "catching up with the Russians" whenever funds are being sought. American oceanographers who visited the U.S.S.R. have told me that their Soviet colleagues tend to use the same argument for the same purpose.

There is certainly a similarity in attitudes about the sea. The following quotation must sound familiar to Western readers: "More than 40 chemical elements have been discovered in seawater. There are more than 10 billion tons of gold, 4 billion tons of uranium and 270 billion tons of heavy water, to say nothing of the fact that the sea contains 97 percent of our planet's wealth in water. The ocean is a storehouse holding all the minerals of the globe. If they were gathered and spread evenly over the earth's surface, they would form a layer more than 200 meters thick." It is from an article entitled "Seven Seas," by A. Grinevitch, in *Yuni Technik* (Young Technician), a popular Soviet science magazine aimed at young readers. The issue also contains articles on the polar seas, whaling, ships of the year 2000 and a piece by Jacques Cousteau, who starts by telling *Yuni Technik*'s audience: "Mystery is a challenge I cannot resist." The main difference with the usual Western presentation of the subject is the Russian soul: Grinevitch talks of six seas (those of the physicist, the biologist, the geologist, etc.), and adds a "poet's sea." A Soviet Navy captain describes the area where he picked up the U.S. Sixth Fleet on his radar screen: "A handful of amber beads is scattered over the blue Aegean. Garlands of yellow pebbles fill the waters between the Greek and Turkish shores; their many rows cross the sea, and along the southernmost strand of the necklace of islands, there hangs the mysterious amulet of Crete."

To learn more about Soviet oceanography, I called on an old acquaintance, Dr. Konstantin N. Fedorov, a physical oceanographer from Leningrad who worked for the Institute of Oceanology of the U.S.S.R. Academy of Sciences. He now doubles in brass as head of UNESCO's oceanography office and secretary of the Intergovernmental Oceanographic Commission (and manages to do valid scientific work during his weekends). In his office, Fedorov is perpetually snowed under and we made a date for lunch. He suggested a Basque restaurant he knew near UNESCO headquarters. No interpreter was needed: Fedorov's English is as fluent as his Russian, and his French is not far behind.

He thought that American and Soviet oceanographic efforts are now running parallel, though at their very origin they stemmed from different sources: the practical needs of the seaman and the fisherman in the United States, and basic scientific curiosity in Russia. "During the eighteenth and nineteenth centuries, attempts were often made to study the ocean as part of Russia's major geographic exploratory efforts. The great Russian scientist-explorers were always assured the active support of the Academy of Sciences. Ever since its creation by Peter the Great, the academy has never been a passive club of academicians."

A major stimulus to Soviet oceanography was the early exploration of the Arctic. "Little is known outside Russia of the dramatic history of the Arctic seas. They were our only free route to the Pacific: to Japan, to the Aleutians, and to Alaska, our source of furs and gold. Beginning in the seventeenth century, Russsian explorers went east along the Arctic coast in summer. This economic drive was the basis of our present efforts in Arctic meteorology and oceanography. On the northern route, the U.S.S.R. runs one of the few existing oceanographic services in the world. It serves shipping bound from Archangel and Murmansk to Vladivostok."

Fedorov himself came into oceanography through meteorology. In 1950, he was graduated from a technical college in his native Leningrad with a diploma as a meteorological observer. "Our diplomas are narrowly specialized, true, but they are based on a very broad education. The technical college also offered a course in descriptive and physical oceanography. It interested me, and I chose it for my higher education and more advanced work for my Ph.D."

His first expedition took him to the Baltic and the Barents Seas. Later, he worked in the Black Sea and the Pacific, and in 1959, he was chief scientist aboard the *Akademik Vavilov* when she made the first Soviet research expedition to the Mediterranean. Following that trip, he went to England to study at Liverpool University and the Imperial College of Science and Technology in London on a UNESCO fellowship.

Fedorov has also sailed on an American ship, Woods Hole's *Atlantis II*, during the International Indian Ocean Expedition in 1965. This cruise — his idea of a vacation from his office in Paris — gave him an opportunity to work with Henry Stommel on the study of differences in temperature and salinity over depth ranges on only a few feet, the new field of micro-oceanography. He knew of Stommel from his writings. "His works were among the first scientific books that I studied in English. Practically every research oceanographer in the Soviet Union reads English. Later, I met Stommel at a meeting of our Commission's scientific advisory group in Moscow. He is one of those scientists — I only know a few — like Lev Zenkevich, the father of marine biology in the Soviet Union, or Roger Revelle, or Vsevolod Zenkovich, the coastal geomorphologist, or Walter Munk — who have both stature and unlimited human qualities." Stommel and Fedorov published a joint paper on their research.

Fedorov saw no difference between *Atlantis II* and Soviet vessels in the organization of work at sea and the spirit in which it was carried out. "On both American and Soviet ships, many crewmen participate voluntarily in scientific observations: bird-watching or surface fish-catching. When one of our ships is on station at night, sailors lower a lamp into the water and catch fish. It's a sport, of course, but they don't eat the fish. They give them to the scientists for their collections. I think that, like *Atlantis II*, we get the type of sailor who doesn't go to sea just for the money."

I asked Fedorov a question that keeps popping up: Why are Soviet research ships so big? The largest is the veteran *Ob*, displacing 12,000 tons, and several newer vessels run to 6,000 tons, three times the size of *Atlantis II*. "There are several reasons. The boundaries of the U.S.S.R. are such that our ships cannot keep returning to Soviet ports. It is not profitable for them to pay for supplies in foreign ports. Fuel, for example, is much cheaper at home. So voyages must be long. A large ship offers more comfort for the scientific team and much more of a cultural life for both the scientists and the crew."

Fedorov confirmed what I heard from American visitors to the Soviet Union who were struck by a solid emphasis on details in oceanographic work. "We're very pedantic in scientific work. When we make observations, we bring along not only great scientists but a host of intermediate characters. They take a student by the ear and they give him a smack if he is careless. This is an absolute must, from the point of view of methodology. You must enforce standards of observation when you deal with a changing environment — otherwise, your measurements will change more than the environment."

Marine science in the U.S.S.R., he explained, has three main bases: the Academy of Sciences, responsible for basic research in the world ocean; the All-Union Institute of Fisheries and Oceanography; and the Hydrometeorological Service, which provides forecasts for fisheries and shipping. They are coordinated by a State Committee of Science and Technology under the Soviet Council of Ministers. Fedorov, who never neglects a chance to score a point in the long and usually friendly debate that we have had over the years, reminded me that the U.S.S.R. brought the ocean into national affairs as early as 1921, when Lenin issued a decree establishing a "Floating Marine Science Institute" at Murmansk aboard a research vessel, the *Perseus*.

Behind the Soviet Union and the United States, money spent on oceanography falls off sharply, but there is no corresponding dip in quality. *Discovery* in Great Britain, *Meteor* in West Germany, *Jean Charcot* in France are every bit the equal of American and Soviet ships, and laboratories are at the same level. Unlike space — a rich man's game — oceanography can be played by the moderately well-off.

Total British expenditure on oceanography is less than $8 million a year, funded through a Natural Environment Research Council, which also finances activities in conservation, marine biology and Antarctic exploration. The National Institute of Oceanography at Wormley in Surrey must get along on an annual budget of $1,800,000 that includes operation of the 2,800-ton *Discovery*. Frills are few and far between at the institute's laboratory, where offices are spartan and secretaries a collector's item. There is no scrimping on the ship: she is fitted out as a small liner, on the theory that scientists get more work done when they live well. British oceanographers whom I met shuddered when they recalled the steel decks of American vessels and the ordeal of going to breakfast without a cup of morning tea served in one's cabin by a cheery steward. *Discovery*'s size and comfort are considered an economy: she can work throughout the North Atlantic winter, and nothing costs more than a ship in port.

West Germany is on pretty much the same tack as the British. The Ministry of Scientific Research pays the bills for the new $4-million *Meteor*, a magnificent 2,740-ton ship equipped with a dozen laboratories to work in all branches of oceanography. The German Research Society enabled her to carry out a notable cruise that studied both the geology and the inhabitants of seamounts in the Northeast Atlantic, particularly the Great Meteor Seamount, a peak rising from a depth of 15,000 feet up to 900 feet and discovered by the first *Meteor* in 1938. The cruise was led by another marine internationalist, Professor Günter Dietrich, head of the Institute of Oceanography at Kiel University. Dietrich was elected president of the International Association for the Physical Sciences of the Ocean in 1967 and he stuffs the *Meteor* with foreign scientists (on the seamount cruise, he had sixteen aboard from France, Great Britain, Norway, Portugal and Spain). He once told a writer for *Science:* "When we were at the zero point of our existence in 1945, there was one commander who came as supervisor for oceanography from the British navy to our country. He did not come as a conqueror who drove the oceanographers in all directions . . . He gave them chances to work in Hamburg and Kiel . . . If oceanography revived in Germany, it was by his help. This was Dr. J. N. C. Carruthers of the National Institute of Oceanography."

France, as usual, must be set apart. It is trite to say that France is a nation divided into 50 million Frenchmen . . . but a government survey has counted 500 Frenchmen working in oceanography at no fewer than 100 laboratories. The statistic sums up the brilliant individualism that characterizes the French. While their country devotes but $26 million a year to all forms of marine science, civilian and military, they are present everywhere: whether in diving and underwater living, deep-sea tide measurements, biological studies in the deepest ocean with the bathyscaphe *Archimède*, or the use of manned floating islands.

A National Center for the Exploitation of the Ocean has been set up by the government to harmonize these commendable, if somewhat disjointed, efforts. The center operates the *Jean Charcot*, a new 2,200-ton ship, and is establishing a large oceanographic laboratory at Brest. As priorities, it has chosen the development of marine protein concentrates for food, aquaculture, the mapping of the continental shelf, deep-diving techniques, the prevention and cure of pollution, and air-sea interaction research. It has contracted with Cousteau's Center for Advanced Marine Studies at Marseilles for a new diving saucer that will take a pilot and two scientists down to 10,000 feet. Also under construction in cooperation with the French Petroleum Institute is a 230-ton submarine that is really a mobile houseboat for divers, rendering them independent of a surface ship and attendant risks of bad weather.

A new floating island will replace the first version that has been in the water since 1963 as a house sitting on top of 210 feet of pipe, with 160 feet below the waterline (it cannot be flipped; once it is down, it stays vertical even when it is towed). It has spent most of its working life anchored between Nice and Corsica, staying for as long as two years at a stretch. Its main user has been the laboratory of Professor Henri Lacombe, who started the first modern course in physical oceanography in France in 1948. Members of Lacombe's staff, based at the Paris Museum of Natural History, take turns living on the buoy to run an ocean data station. They try to correlate what happens in the sea with the atmospheric records kept by meteorologists less than a hundred miles away. "That is the advantage of working on air-sea interaction in the Mediterranean," Lacombe said. "It is caged by a network of land stations." To study these processes on a smaller scale, he is also creating a sample ocean 130 feet long, 10 feet wide and 3 feet deep, to be used with a wind tunnel. Professor Alexandre Favre, director of the Institut de Mécanique Statistique de la Turbulence at Marseilles, is in charge of this work.

Lacombe considers the whole Mediterranean as a miniature ocean where processes can be studied with greater ease and accessibility. He and Dr. Paul Tchernia, his assistant director, put the finishing touches to the solution of the ancient riddle of why the Mediterranean doesn't overflow despite the current that rushes into the Straits of Gibraltar from the Atlantic. The presence of an opposing undercurrent in the straits had long been known (and put to use during World War II by Italian submarines that rode it silently out into the Atlantic past British listening posts), but the Mediterranean's water budget was still uncer-

tain. Using measurements obtained by ships of five nationalities in a one-
month survey of the straits, Lacombe and Tchernia concluded that
about 31,600 cubic kilometers of water enter the Mediterranean from
the Atlantic every year and only 30,000 slip out below. The missing 5
percent represents evaporation by Mediterranean sunshine.

Despite the sun, Lacombe also finds the Mediterranean an ideal place
to study the formation of deep water under "polar" conditions normally
found only off the Greenland ice cap and Antarctica. During a cold
European winter, the Mediterranean off the Riviera behaves almost like
the Labrador Sea: surface water chilled by cold winds grows denser as it
cools, then sinks to mix with underlying water and thus contributes to
the formation of bottom water. What happens to it after that is of importance not only to physical oceanographers but to researchers in marine pollution who wish to know the fate of dangerous wastes buried in
the deep. Movements of bottom water are influenced by "sills" in the
seabed, another feature that the Mediterranean offers in abundance for
convenient examination. Lacombe told me of a study of the process of
deep water formation in the northwest Mediterranean that he hopes to
carry out with the participation of American, British and French vessels.
Very detailed observations are to be made with new techniques to follow "mini-features" of temperature or salinity characteristics and to try
to get at the underlying processes.

Lacombe served as chairman of the Intergovernmental Oceanographic Commission from 1965 to 1967. He manages to remain active in
teaching and research, yet find time for international affairs. It is something of an act of faith. He once wrote: "Will man be able to see the
ocean's unity as an image of the need for a unity of efforts, a sharing by
nations of their capacity for discovery so they can first explore and then
exploit an area that is intrinsically almost entirely international and open
to all — open to hopes but also to ambitions?"

As chairman of the commission, Lacombe was busy with legal matters. The status of buoys drifting or anchored in mid-ocean is a subject
for discussion; so is freedom of research itself, which was set back, many
feel, by the convention on the continental shelf. Under the convention,
the country owning the shelf must give permission for research there,
and scientists are complaining that it can take longer to get a permit than
to do the actual work. Lacombe sees two distinct viewpoints here: "The
Americans and the British prefer to look at an issue case by case before

trying to frame rules; the Soviets, and to some extent, the French and the Latin countries, want to study all aspects at once and move immediately to a convention."

The commission has sixty member countries, but no budget of its own, no building and no bureaucracy. Administrative housekeeping arrangements are provided by UNESCO at a cost of $50,000 to $80,000 a year, as compared to the $10 million to $20 million a year that the commission's members have devoted to international cooperative expeditions. The most recent of these expeditions is a study of the Kuroshio (its name means "black water" in Japanese), the western Pacific's equivalent of the Gulf Stream. It has been carried out by eight countries and thirty-six vessels, with Japan making the greatest contribution. In 1963 and 1964, an international cooperative investigation of the tropical Atlantic was conducted by the same number of nations using thirteen ships.

The commission's largest single effort has been the International Indian Ocean Expedition from 1959 to 1965 that launched an armada of forty research vessels under fourteen flags, with nine more countries participating in shore operations. Dr. Warren Wooster of Scripps, who preceded Fedorov as the commission's secretary, once tried to find the genesis of the expedition and gave up after he had traced it to a conversation in the bar of the Commodore Hotel during the First International Oceanographic Congress in 1959 at New York. No matter where the first spark was struck, the idea quickly caught fire. On the oceanographers' charts, the Indian Ocean was one of the last great blanks; even data from commercial shipping had dwindled since the opening of the Suez Canal. It was also the site of the kind of natural experiment that every physical oceanographer dreams of performing. To see the effect of the wind on the circulation of the sea, he would dearly love to switch it on and off. In the Indian Ocean, he has the seasonal reversal of the winds with the monsoons. Geologists wanted to learn if their ridge system continued into the Indian Ocean; biologists were interested in the actual productivity of an ocean that accounts for 25 percent of the area of the sea but only 5 percent of its fish catch.

No single nation could mount such an undertaking. The major oceanographic powers already mentioned sent ships, but so did Australia, India, Indonesia, Pakistan, Portugal, South Africa and Thailand. The expedition was started by the Scientific Committee on Oceanic Research (SCOR) of the International Council of Scientific Unions, an organization that groups scientists in their professional capacities, not as delegates of governments. Later on, the expedition was cosponsored by SCOR and UNESCO, while the Intergovernmental Oceanographic Commission took over its coordination. Its implications for weather and fisheries became the respective concerns of two UN agencies: the World Meteorological Organization, and the Food and Agriculture Organization.

The reader has every right to be bewildered by the coordination of these various bodies. They had confused me to the point where I wondered how they could ever get anything done; then I guessed the secret of world oceanography. It is a small club: the same men who sit as scientists at a SCOR meeting can turn up as national delegates at an official UN session. Wooster remarked: "I think the International Indian Ocean Expedition was the greatest uncoordinated expedition in the history of oceanography. I ought to know, I was its coordinator part of the time. It was the only way to explore such a region. Scientists with curiosity would not have come in if it had been done in any other way."

Despite, or perhaps because of, such an attitude, tangible results were produced by the free-roaming ships. The great wind experiment was a success. During the southwest summer monsoon, Soviet, British and American ships investigated the Somali Current along the coasts of Arabia and Africa. It races north at speeds up to seven knots — almost twice as fast as the Gulf Stream. When the wind reverses at the end of the monsoon, the current becomes a weak southerly drift.

The Somali Current turns sharply away from the Arabian coast. To replace it, cold water — 55 degrees F., the coldest surface water anyone has ever found so close to the equator — rises and brings up nutrients. It is roughly the same upwelling situation that feeds the anchovies off Peru in the Pacific.

It would be comforting to write that a scientific expedition has found fish for the protein-hungry populations on the shores of the Arabian Sea. It would be misleading: the 150,000 tons of fish that are now being taken off the Arabian coast go into the holds of modern Japanese and Soviet trawlers. Antiquated local dhows are unable to work this new offshore fishery.

In the short run, therefore, the expedition has failed to achieve one of its stated purposes: to bring food out of the ocean for Asia. In the long run, the prospects may not be as gloomy. The expedition has given a salutary jolt to marine science in the region, mainly in India, which now has a National Institute of Oceanography of its own at New Delhi. Dr. N. K. Panikkar, its director, also heads an Indian Ocean Biological Center that has been set up at Cochin in South India to sort zooplankton samples taken by the expedition's ships. Cochin is a nucleus for fisheries research and fishing, thanks to a little-known Norwegian aid project that has brought over $8 million in aid and moved North Sea skippers to the Indian Ocean as teachers.

The expedition brought scientists into Indian universities as teachers. Among them was Dr. Robert L. Fisher, who spent six weeks in India in 1966 giving twenty-four lectures in a training course sponsored by UNESCO and the government. Fisher is also a member of the editorial board that is producing a geological and geophysical atlas of the expedition, with Dr. Gleb Udintsev of the Institute of Oceanology in Moscow as its chief editor. When I spoke to Fisher at La Jolla, he and his staff were still charting the soundings taken by the expedition.

The soundings have revealed the Ninety East Ridge that starts in the Bay of Bengal 600 miles north of the equator and runs south 3,000 miles along the meridian for which it is named. "It's a fantastic feature," Fisher said. "It's 10,000 feet high, as wide as the Sierra Nevadas and flat on top. Unlike the mid-ocean ridges, it's not seismically active. On the map, it's a straight line . . . it looks like a big freight train."

Prior to the expedition, only isolated shoals had hinted at the presence of the ridge. Then it was surveyed by American, Australian and Soviet research vessels, whose soundings enabled Fisher to fill in his chart. Help came from amateur scientists. "A British freighter captain kept his echo sounder going for us all the way from the Gulf of Aden to Australia. We've got an echo-sounding record from Her Majesty's yacht *Britannia* taken when she crossed the Ninety East Ridge on the way to Australia for the Queen's visit."

Other results of the expedition are being charted. Scripps has brought out an atlas of the fishery oceanography of the Arabian Sea; Soviet scientists are responsible for a biological atlas of the entire Indian Ocean; Americans at the University of Hawaii are compiling physical and meteorological atlases. Another heritage of the expedition is an International Meteorological Center at Bombay that is getting an insight into the vagaries of the monsoon, upon which Indian agriculture depends. The end of the expedition has seen the start of permanent research in the Indian Ocean.

Scientific cooperation on the high seas is now focusing on areas that can be covered more intensively. The latest studies conducted by the Intergovernmental Oceanographic Commission are aimed at the Caribbean and the Mediterranean, two seas that have already been explored but now need to be understood. What is heartening about both studies is that they give smaller countries a chance to join in oceanography. The investigation of the Caribbean was proposed by the Netherlands; research in the Mediterranean is bringing together countries of North Africa and the Near East under arrangements that permit them to carry out science in the same waters, even if they are not on political speaking terms.

24. The Past and the Future

I first heard of oceanography nearly ten years ago from Roger Revelle, whose writings and statements I have shamelessly mined here. At a sleepy meeting in Paris, a big slouching man rose to his feet and began to speak of geology at sea. His voice and presence filled the committee room.

He told of oily uncomfortable ships, of the great grinding mills that destroy the sea floor in the deep trenches, of the maps of this realm that were no better than the land maps of the seventeenth century. More than any other single figure, Revelle is responsible for the introduction of oceanography into public affairs. He began as a marine geologist and geophysicist; he has evolved into a statesman of science.

As Revelle sees his science, it has already gone through three major periods, each shaped by the instruments it had at its disposal. The first was that of the classical Challenger Expedition. Wire replaced hemp in sounding lines so that the great depths could be measured accurately for the first time. The deep-sea dredge brought up scrapings from the sea floor and a catalog of the animals living on it. "But it had its limitations. At the end of two years, not even the scientists on the *Challenger* came out on deck to see what was in the dredge. It was always the same."

The second stage was that of the Nansen bottle, the reversing thermometer and accurate salinity analysis. It began just prior to the First World War and it saw German and Scandinavian scientists lead the way in determining the basic structures of the ocean's waters, the climate of the sea. Their equipment was not up to following its changeable weather.

The third period, in Revelle's view, has been that of exploration of the sea floor with geological and geophysical instruments: piston corers, precision echo sounders, gravimeters, magnetometers, heat probes, bottom photographs. "It has been one of the great ages of the exploration of the earth, but like all the others, it has been short. It lasted only about twenty-five years, the same time that elapsed between Columbus's voyage of exploration and the conquest of Mexico."

The coming age of oceanography will also be founded on new techniques: scientific submersibles, man-in-the-sea, instrumented buoys recording at all depths, satellite observations of the surface. Computers? "I am less sanguine about the computer. It is useful only when it can communicate with human beings. Amassing data on rolls of magnetic tape is not enough: there is always the danger that a complete scientific description of an object can become larger than the object itself. More than description is needed; the oceanographer must understand relationships."

Revelle was born in Seattle in 1909. Since then, he has had one of those multiple overlapping careers that are the despair of the thumbnail biographer. He received a Ph.D. in oceanography from Scripps in 1936, and in 1951, he was appointed as its director, the first graduate of the institution to run it. He held the job for fifteen years, also serving near the end of his stay as dean of research for the University of California, and during a two-year leave, as the first science adviser to the Secretary of the Interior in Washington. He led two expeditions over salt water in the Pacific; he headed an American team that went to West Pakistan to recommend ways to get rid of brackish water ruining the soil of the Indus Delta, the world's largest irrigation project.

In 1964, Revelle took his present post as the head of Harvard's Center for Population Studies. Like his mission to West Pakistan, it has brought him closer to the plight of most of the human race. Revelle once explained his interest in human fertility and agriculture: "I just don't think that our people can remain very good human beings if they are to be so callous as to ignore starving people everywhere in the world; it would produce a kind of selfishness which could break down our society in the long run."

When I renewed acquaintance with Revelle at Harvard, he was almost reluctant to speak of the sea. He considered that he belonged to the era when an oceanographer was "a sailor who used big words." But he thawed when I asked him about the start of Scripps's lawn lunchroom, where the guests had given me my own outdoor survey course in oceanography. "The main problem was to get money from the administration. They thought it was frivolous to buy tables, chairs and beach umbrellas. So I bought them anyway from my emergency fund. It was a very important thing to do. In a scientific institution, the biggest problem is communication. One of the fallacies about science is to think that it is done by individuals. It's not, it's done by conversation."

Revelle also inspired a Scripps Estates Association to give his scientists a chance to build their own homes. "That was an emergency, too. We had to get them to build homes and fit into the community. We wanted to desegregate the oceanographers; then we had to integrate them into the rest of science. That was the purpose of the upper campus, the University of California at San Diego. It was essential to get fundamental science and a broad intellectual spectrum into oceanography.

"They're all full of nostalgia for the good old days, but the oceanographers do better science when they are not isolated from physics, chemistry, and biology. The price you must pay is size . . . and a certain sense of inferiority. Oceanographers tend to feel they are second-class citizens. They're sailors, they're not as bright as molecular biologists or physicists who think that everything that does not involve fundamental matter is trivial. I know I'm not that bright. But oceanography is changing: it is becoming more fundamental, more rigorous and more mathematically oriented. As Clemenceau remarked about war and generals, the ocean is now too important to be left to oceanographers. They must forget the notion that it is the monopoly of those who hold trade-union cards as working oceanographers."

Revelle, who describes himself as "primarily an explorer rather than an experimenter or a theoretician," has less trouble than others in visual-

Roger Revelle

izing uses for scientific submersibles. "In a submersible, you can see for yourself. That is the main difference. I myself would like to see what a flat-topped seamount really looks like. No one ever has."

He suggested another project for the submersible: to verify the hypothesis of the bipolarity of marine life. "At high latitudes in the north and south, species are essentially the same in the cold waters near the surface. That is what is meant by bipolarity. But how do they move from one pole to the other through the warm tropics? Perhaps they take the path offered by uniformly cold bottom water all over the ocean. This could be investigated by submersibles in an international cooperative study. At these depths, as John Isaacs has shown at Scripps with his monster camera, there may be fish in the sea that we have never seen. There may well be sea serpents. Take the giant squid; we have mainly samples of it: sucker marks on the bodies of sperm whales or arms in the whales' stomachs."

International research by oceanographers, he feels, is urgently needed to develop a worldwide reconnaissance system for military submarines. "The possibilities of missile-carrying submarines are appalling. What if China were to develop one and fire a missile at the United States from Kamchatka? We would think that it was Russia. We must eliminate the awful opacity of the sea, we must make the ocean transparent so that the submarine has no advantage over surface ships. If we can, then we could have a reconnaissance system based on international cooperation. It should be run by the United Nations once it is foolproof. But if we do it before it is taped, more harm than good will result."

Revelle links such an underwater police mission to proposals for UN ownership of the sea's resources. "It is not the height of folly to think that our planet would be better off if all mankind exercised sovereignty over the ocean through a United Nations that would receive payment for its use. You cannot have any kind of government if it cannot collect taxes. Under the Articles of Confederation after the American Revolution, each state collected taxes. The situation then in the United States was exactly that of the UN today. The UN cannot be even a pale imitation of a world government as long as it is dependent on individual countries. What is needed is a UN oceanic agency to make the ocean transparent, collect taxes on its use, and issue licenses to operate and do science in it."

There is nothing exclusive about Revelle's ocean of the future. "I am interested in the ocean because there are many things that people can do about it. Its importance to human beings is not limited to fish or oil or manganese nodules. It offers them not only swimming and sailing but a new capacity to live under the sea and explore it themselves. You might call this recreation, but it is more than that: I call it an opportunity for people to live at the height of their powers."

Historical oceanography (a branch of the profession so new that it held its first international congress only in 1966 at Monaco) finds that awareness of the ocean is always highest when men are trying to grasp their environment instead of laying down rules for it. It was in the context of a series of recommendations aimed at halting the destruction of the American environment that President Johnson proposed an International Decade of Ocean Exploration for the 1970's. The pendulum of scientific inquiry keeps swinging between observation and synthesis. Aristotle had to resolve such a conflict: according to Sir John Murray, editor of the reports of the Challenger Expedition, Aristotle threw himself into the whirlpool of the Strait of Euripos, separating Euboea from the Greek mainland, because he was unable to explain it.

Interest in the ocean dimmed between antiquity and the Renaissance. It was stirred anew by the great voyages of exploration. They were made by seamen, not philosophers (just as astronauts have preceded scientists into extraterrestrial space), but the seamen had eyes. Murray quotes the incidental observations in marine biology carried out by the old Elizabethan sea dog, Sir John Hawkins: "Were it not for the Moving of the Sea, by the Force of Winds, Tides and Currents, it would corrupt all the World. The Experience of which I saw *Anno* 1590, lying with a Fleet about the islands of *Azores*, almost Six Months, the greatest part of the time we were becalmed; with which all the Sea became so replenished with several sorts of Gellies and Forms of Serpents, Adders and Snakes as seem'd Wonderful; some green, some black, some yellow, some white, some of divers Colours and many of them had Life, and some there were a Yard and a-half, and some two Yards long; which had I not seen I could have hardly believed; and hereof are witnesses all the Company of the Ships which were then present; so that hardly a Man could draw a Bucket of Water clear of some Corruption."

Such tales awoke the curiosity of scientists. The seventeenth century in England witnessed an outburst of speculation and experimentation that could have been called the birth of oceanography if it had not ended as suddenly as it had begun. This period is the starting point of a history of oceanography in Great Britain that is being written by Margaret Deacon, the daughter of Dr. G. E. R. Deacon, the head of the British National Institute of Oceanography. Deacon is helping his daughter write a history that he helped make, although he never would admit it. I knew him for several years before I learned by chance that he was the principal discoverer of the Antarctic Convergence, the area around 50 degrees south latitude where cold water spreading out from the ice cap sinks as it meets warm water coming southward from the Atlantic.

Deacon has always been drawn to the history of his science and he acts as his daughter's constant adviser. "It was he who suggested that I write a history of oceanography," she told me. "He said he had no time to go about doing original research." She began work in 1963, when she was only twenty-one and fresh out of Oxford with a bachelor's degree in history.

Her father, a Fellow of the Royal Society, guided her into the seventeenth century and the work of the early Fellows in marine science immediately after the Royal Society was founded in 1660. When she was only twenty-three, the Royal Society published her first paper on its original Fellows. In it, she uncovered an oceanographic facet to the career of Robert Boyle, much better-known to all students of elementary physics as the formulator of Boyle's Law. He endeavored to ascertain the "saltness" and temperature of the sea, and using his common sense for want of any satisfactory instruments, he gave the lie to "the vulgar error that, in all deep water, of which the sea is the chiefest, the lowermost are still the warmest parts." Another Fellow, Robert Hooke, tried to make up the instrument gap. He improved a sounding machine devised on the continent to dispense with the old-fashioned lead and line for depths over a hundred fathoms. The idea was to measure the time it took for a weighted wooden sphere to sink, release its weight on the bottom and float back to the surface. All the frustrations of shipboard science appeared at once. A Fellow reported that "there could be no pfect triall of ye instrument for depths at sea, the motion of the waves unhookes the lead."

The Royal Society, Miss Deacon writes, came tantalizingly close to answering the question of why the Mediterranean does not overflow. Seamen in the Straits of Gibraltar had seen that their ships would lose way if they dropped an anchor almost to the bottom. In 1661, the Royal

Society asked the Earl of Sandwich, bound for the Mediterranean on a naval expedition, to lower a bucket from a boat to see if it would be towed by an undercurrent. He never did, perhaps because he agreed with another Fellow who thundered: "Since Nature doth nothing in vain, it would be an idle supposition to think so vast a quantity of Water should be hurried into the Mediterranean for no other Reason but to be hurried out again." The undercurrent's existence was confirmed only in 1870.

In the meantime, the Royal Society had turned its attention elsewhere. "The seventeenth century was really a golden age," Miss Deacon remarked. "There was a comprehensive interest in the natural world. Navigation and the sea had been important since Elizabethan times and the practical applications of marine science were evident. But interest was falling off when Newton published his *Principia* in 1687 and wrapped up the problem of tides. It led to a general swing from environmental science into physics." She quotes Pope to illustrate the new spirit of the day. He thought it was of no use to man "to measure earth, weigh air and state the tides" when he could not "describe or fix one movement of his mind."

Willing laymen had to carry the torch of oceanography in the eighteenth century. In her subsequent research, Miss Deacon ran into instances of men like the Rev. Stephen Hales who persuaded the captain of a slave ship to make salinity and temperature experiments at different depths. "Most work was done by persons generally interested in science who had to make long voyages around Cape Horn or the Cape of Good Hope. They would do their observations in a dead calm when the captain did not object."

Purposeful investigation at sea by scientists was not really resumed until the nineteenth century, the start of the first great period that Revelle cites. It was only then that a wish expressed by Newton, and quoted by Miss Deacon, began to be fulfilled: "If instead of sending the Observations of Seamen to able Mathematicians at Land, the Land would send able Mathematicians to Sea, it would signify much more to the improvement of Navigation and the safety of Men's lives and estates on that element."

Newton's remark is still pertinent: the land is not educating enough able minds to be sent to sea. Dr. William Nierenberg, Scripps's present director, thinks that until it does, the transmutation of marine science

into big science on the dimensions of nuclear or space research is bound
to suffer. Nierenberg, a physicist who worked on the Manhattan Project
and later taught at Berkeley, makes some pointed comparisons. At the
end of the war, at least 3,000 physicists and 20,000 chemists in the United
States were on hand to usher in the atomic age. "Industrial users, scientists, students and research and development work were all there in the
right proportions," Nierenberg said. "In any field, there should be at
least a one-to-ten ratio between the number engaged in the research
characteristic of the field and the total."

He does not think that space research has done as well as atomic
energy. While there were 15,000 American physicists and 100,000 chemists when Sputnik went up, they were busy elsewhere and less available.
Nierenberg finds that only two or three percent of the scientific pool
engaged in the space program consists of basic researchers, a ratio that
may be too low. Yet it looks much better than anything he can see on the
horizon in the marine sciences. Nierenberg estimates that in 1967 there
were only 500 oceanographers in the United States. He questions other
figures that are ten times as high: "I know one company that claims they
have more oceanographers than Scripps has graduated since it was
founded. They just transferred their engineers from rocketry to oceanography on the payroll."

Taking a census of oceanographers is like counting plankton in the
sea: the result depends on the kind of net that one casts to catch them.
The finest mesh of all was used in 1966 by the Panel on Oceanography of
the President's Science Advisory Committee. It could find only 370
American oceanographers producing papers important enough to be
cited by other scientists — and thirty-seven of them accounted for half
the citations. The field has expanded since then, but not miraculously.

Nierenberg wants a crash program with emphasis on facilities for
students. Scripps now has some 180 students and turns away 90 percent
of its applicants, a percentage that unfortunately applies to other top
institutions. It could accommodate 400 if it had the buildings, but no
more if it is to keep standards. Nierenberg is no advocate of cut-rate
degrees.

Neither is Dr. Robert Abel, director of the National Science Foundation's Office of Sea Grant Programs set up in 1967. In its first year, it had
$4 million to help colleges and universities establish courses or research
projects. A few years ago, Abel reported that he had received a brochure

from a college offering a dozen courses and a master's degree in oceanography, but not a single faculty member had ever taken a course in the subject himself. It is this sort of situation that Sea Grants are intended to correct. Certainly not overnight. Of the 1,200 colleges and universities in the United States, only sixty or so teach oceanography, and no more than twenty go as far as a doctorate. To step up the flow at the start of the pipeline, the National Academy of Sciences has produced an excellent film strip series, *Understanding Our Deep Frontier*, for high school students. The Marine Biological Association at Plymouth in England is among the institutes that go a step further and take schoolboys to sea to awaken vocations.

Oceanography remains a vocation, for there are certainly easier ways for a bright young scientist to earn his living. Dr. Robert S. Arthur, a quiet, courtly professor at Scripps, finds that his students' common denominator is a love of the sea. A passing fancy is not enough: it usually takes five years, and as many as eight, for an oceanographer to get his doctorate. Some students even come to Scripps with Ph.D.'s in other fields where they had felt bored, restless and hemmed in.

How long will oceanography keep drawing them? As long as the sea remains undefeated by those who match wits with it. The RAND Corporation's Delphi study, carried out as an exercise in forecasting, does not foresee economic mining of the ocean floor before the late 1980's. Ocean farming capable of producing at least 20 percent of the world's food supply, according to the RAND oracles, is not likely before the year 2000 at the earliest. However, they expect reliable weather forecasts by the mid-1970's and regional weather control by 1990.

If these last predictions are to be borne out, physical oceanography — the study of the liquid ocean — must achieve a synthesis as clear as the sea floor spreading theory that has allowed marine geology to fit fragments of data into a coherent account of how the solid earth works. The search for such a synthesis has begun and it will be intensified in the coming years. The reader and the writer have witnessed the early stages of attempts to pin down the variability of the ocean, the key to its influence on weather and climate. The military are lending their ample resources to this effort so that they can predict the ocean's acoustic properties. The more that is learned about how the ocean changes as a sound medium or a weather source, the more information the biologist and fishermen will have about the moving pastures of the sea and the flocks that feed on them. When all this is wrapped up into a package as neat as Newton's explanation of the tides, oceanography will be a unified science . . . and the sort of people we have met throughout these pages will be doing something else.

Until then, the unsolved problems are as appealing as those that confronted Aristotle. The one that keeps coming to the forefront is air-sea interaction, the transfer of energy along a two-way street between the ocean and the atmosphere. It preoccupies all those who are seeking the great synthesis. The newest of tools are being honed to attack it: those automatic buoys recording from the bottom up, and artificial satellites photographing current systems in color or measuring surface temperature by remote-sensing devices.

The world's leading long-range weather forecaster, Dr. Jerome Namias, does not think tools alone are enough. Namias heads the Extended Forecast Division of what used to be the U.S. Weather Bureau and is now part of the Environmental Science Services Administration. His office at Silver Spring, Maryland, makes three-day and five-day forecasts for the United States with an accuracy that he considers quite good. He is less satisfied with his 30-day outlooks. "Here, our skill is fairly low, although the outlooks appear to be of economic value. Sometimes, the character of the atmospheric circulation is so chaotic that we cannot explain it after the event, let alone predict it.

"I do not believe that acquisition of tremendous amounts of data will solve the problem. If we had temperature-depth readings for every square mile of the ocean and satellite observations of the atmosphere the world over, we still would not be able to make a perfect forecast. The difficulty lies in our lack of information as to how the ocean and the atmosphere are coupled, how they drive each other. As yet, the process will not yield to attacks by simple physics. There is a group of people — there are not too many left — that I call the 'naturalists.' I am among them. We study what happens, then we make speculations. We must go on doing this until we can get up to a dignified level of theory."

Namias speculates particularly about the role of the ocean in producing what the public insists on calling "abnormal" weather (the meteorologist has never yet found, over a large area, a given month or season that could be called "normal"). He regards the ocean as a reservoir of heat and moisture, tapped by the atmosphere's wind and weather. The most forceful example of the process is the hurricane: it thrives on the heat liberated when moisture is condensed. Since warm water supplies more moisture than cold water, the hurricane is kept alive over the sea at tropical temperatures. Air and sea interact so violently that the boundary between the two is blurred. Several scientists have suggested spreading a thin plastic film over the ocean to inhibit evaporation and nip hurricanes in the bud.

Sometimes the sea can prevent storms from reaching the shore. Namias investigated the great five-year drought that affected the northeastern United States from 1962 through 1966. During this period, an extensive pool of abnormally cold water lay along the Atlantic seaboard, with warm water on its flanks. He has ventured that the temperature contrast diverted spring and summer storms out to sea, leaving the land baking under dry northwest winds from the continent. The sea was acting on the air; then the air acted on the sea. These dry winds may have gone on robbing heat from the ocean's surface, keeping the pool cold and creating a "vicious circle which helped stabilize the drought pattern." What cooled the sea in the first place? Namias is not sure, but he suspects an influx of cold Labrador water in 1961, the year before the drought began.

The mechanism can work in reverse. In November and early December of 1967, Southern California suffered dismal rains. Namias traced them to intense September and October storms in the Gulf of Alaska. They transported warm water towards the shores of California, where it fed heat and moisture to the unruly atmosphere.

He also thinks that the sea contributed to the disastrous floods of the winter of 1966 in northern Italy. In the autumn of that year, a series of low-pressure areas in the Atlantic moved east through the Mediterranean all the way from Spain to the Black Sea. "Why did that trough remain alive and anomalously deep? The answer may be that it reached the western Mediterranean at a time when the sea was still warm. In other words, it was the Mediterranean that supplied the heat and moisture needed to keep the trough alive and migrating. I know this is way-out speculation, but if you ask anyone else what caused those floods, they'll concentrate on the immediate daily conditions. They frequently do not see the bigger picture, the ocean as well as the atmosphere. Too many people take too narrow a view of events in time and space."

Dr. Julian Adem, a Mexican geophysicist on Namias's staff, is now developing computerized models of the atmosphere and the ocean's upper layers. His immediate goal is to predict temperature changes a month in advance. Namias encourages his research but regards its ultimate consequences warily: "These models may also throw light on the feasibility of man-made manipulation of atmospheric or oceanic conditions for short or for long periods — possibilities which, if realized, will give international legalistic experts many sleepless nights."

What he had in mind has been expressed more specifically by Dr. Athelstan Spilhaus, one of the participants in the law of the sea conference held at Ohio State in 1967. The discussion had turned to the "seeding" of hurricanes with silver iodide to break them up before they reached American soil. Spilhaus puts things as clearly as he does in his science course in the Sunday comics: "I think that hurricane control will come within ten years. And the difficulty here, curiously enough, is an international legal problem. They [the U.S. Navy and the Weather Bureau] have Project Stormfury in Puerto Rico. One of the difficulties of doing the experiments which Stormfury would like to do is that there is no control. Supposing that the United States was to 'seed' a hurricane out in Antigua and the thing happened to go across and kick the hell out of Trinidad. The United States would be blamed, *whether or not* the 'seeding' had any effect . . . If we could, we would certainly like to break up a hurricane in the Gulf of Mexico which was approaching New Orleans. On the other hand, the only time that our neighbor Mexico gets rain is on the tail end of one of these hurricane situations. So, if we bust up that hurricane we might get into international problems with Mexico for cutting off their rainfall." But such legal problems amount to no more than a parking ticket compared to the implications of the much-bruited proposals to modify the climate of northern latitudes by melting the Arctic Ocean's ice cap with nuclear explosions or by darkening the ice so that it will absorb summer heat. A change in world sea level could result.

Less dramatic than Project Stormfury but of equal basic importance, a study of air-sea interaction in the Gulf of Mexico and the Caribbean is being carried out by the Environmental Science Services Administration, which has married meteorology and oceanography under its unwieldy title (and produced the greatest acronym of all: ESSA's ocean data program is called ODESSA). The study is now using ships, buoys, aircraft, land stations and satellites to examine the "total fluid environment" of sea and atmosphere in an area off Barbados. Its next step will be a large-scale investigation in the early 1970's of the tropical ocean, the area astride the equator and running 1200 miles from north to south where "the global furnace is fired and the world's reservoir of heat continuously replenished." This is to be followed by a global air-sea interaction experiment that will fit into the World Weather Watch organized by the World Meteorological Organization.

Everywhere, the sea dissolves the land's frontiers. This is as true for air-sea interaction research as it was for the exploration of the Indian Ocean, as true for rational fishing as it is for the use of the deep seabed or the stemming of pollution. The frontiers of marine science, too, are being broken down. The little worlds in the institutions that I was able to visit (and which exist in the others that I regretfully had to omit) are vanishing as oceanography descends to the forum and the market place. It was my good fortune to meet the oceanographers at a moment in time when the transition had not been completed. With their help, I have tried to tell their story as informatively and entertainingly as they told it to me.

References

An asterisk marks a book mentioned in "Some Further Reading," page 421.

PAGE   *2. The Fairest Corner of Heaven-on-Earth*

19   Source material for this historical sketch came from *Scripps Institution of Oceanography, First Fifty Years,* by Helen Raitt and Beatrice Moulton, the Ward Ritchie Press, Los Angeles, 1967.

3. A Wild, Uncontrolled Curiosity

26   Quotes on flying fish: Scholander article in *Scientific American,* December, 1963.

26   "Evolution pushes on blindly": paper presented by Scholander to the XXI Congreso Internacional de Ciencias Fisológicas, Buenos Aires, August 9–15, 1959.

28   "Moreover, as this mode of propulsion": *Science,* April 24, 1959, pp. 1085–1087.

28   Scholander's reply to critics: *Science,* December 11, 1959, p. 1658.

PAGE

33   *Scientific Results of Marine Biological Research,* published by Hvalradets Skrifter, Oslo, honored Scholander on his sixtieth birthday.

4. Any Boy's Mind Works the Same Way

49   "I have always been a bit resentful": "The Sea and Man," by John D. Isaacs, *Portal,* first edition, 1966, P.O. Box 15068, San Diego, California.

50   Isaacs's comments on harbors: *Proceedings of the Third Plowshare Symposium,* Davis campus of University of California, April 21–23, 1964.

53   Tonnage of Antarctic icebergs: *The Encyclopedia of Oceanography,* edited by Rhodes W. Fairbridge, p. 367.

53   Remarks on transporting of icebergs and on price of water: "The Planetary Water Problem," by John D. Isaacs, *Proceedings of the First International Conference of Women Engineers and Scientists,* New York, June 15–21, 1964.

54   "Our great religious progenitors": *Portal* article cited above.

55   "The human race": *ibid.*

57   "The elements that are the most worrisome": "General Features of the Ocean," by John D. Isaacs, lecture given as part of a series, March 8–11, 1966, p. 22 of preliminary draft.

62   Isaacs and Bradner quotes: *Journal of Geophysical Research,* September 15, 1964.

62   Quotes on skyhook: *Science,* February 11, 1966, pp. 682–683.

65   "Local changes of conditions": "Unusual Conditions in the Pacific," by John D. Isaacs and Oscar E. Sette, *Science,* March 20, 1959 (vol. 129, no. 3351), pp. 787–788.

67   "Man's hope for guidance": *Portal* article cited above.

5. The Fish Business

73   "The whales need only swim": *Whale Primer,* by Theodore J. Walker, published by the Cabrillo Historical Association, 1962.

78   Information on *El Niño* comes from articles by Rhodes Fairbridge and Warren Wooster in *The Encyclopedia of Oceanography.*

7. Sound Sees the Invisible

111–112   Figures and formula on speed of sound under water come from "Underwater Acoustics," by William T. McGuiness in *The Encyclopedia of Oceanography.*

112   Experiments with porpoises are reported in *Porpoises and Sonar,* by Winthrop N. Kellogg, University of Chicago Press, Chicago, 1961.

PAGE   *8. The Music of the Tides*

124 Estimates on English Channel tides come from "The Restless Tides," by K. F. Bowden, in *Seas, Maps, and Men,* edited by G. E. R. Deacon.
126 Quotes are from *The Gallic War and Other Writings by Julius Caesar,* translated by Moses Hadas, The Modern Library, p. 89 and p. 94.
134 "A party of sixty": *The Voyage of the Challenger,* by C. Wyville Thomson, Macmillan, London, 1877, p. 59.
136 "If we could view": *Tides of the Planet Earth,* by Walter Munk, Tenth Anniversary AFOSR Scientific Seminar, p. 137.

9. In Sight of Land

149 *Artificial Reefs — A Review,* by Iris Unger, American Littoral Society, Highlands, New Jersey, 1966.

10. Ocean Capital of the World

183–184 Rebikoff quotes: "The Evolution and History of Underwater Photography," by Dimitri Rebikoff, paper presented at the ASP/MTS Panel on Underwater Photography in Washington, March 1967.

11. The Birth and Death of Project Mohole

191 Hess's account comes from *Nature,* July 23, 1966, referring to the proceedings of a symposium on "Drilling for Scientific Purposes" held in Ottawa in 1965 under the auspices of the International Upper Mantle Committee.
193 "Project Rathole" and "Taxpayer's money down the Mohole": *Congressional Record,* August 18, 1966, p. 19058 and p. 19063.
195 Bascom quote: "The Mohole," by Willard Bascom, *Scientific American,* April 1959, pp. 41–49.
197 All quotes from the 1961 hearings come from *Oceanography 1961 — Phase 2:* Hearing before the Subcommittee on Oceanography of the Committee on Merchant Marine and Fisheries, 87th Congress, first session on Project Mohole, May 22, 1961, U.S. Government Printing Office, Washington, D.C., 1961.

12. The Drifters and the Spreaders

204 "Frankly, the ocean is": *Marine Geology of the Pacific,* by Henry W. Menard, McGraw-Hill, New York, 1964, preface.

PAGE

204   "Speculations about the history": "The Rocks of the Ocean," by Sir
       Edward Bullard, lecture delivered at the Second International Oceano-
       graphic Congress, Moscow, June, 1966.
205   The account of Dietz's ideas comes from an article he wrote in *Sea
       Frontiers*, March–April, 1967.
208–209 Hess's "essay in geopoetry," from which his quotes have been
       taken, is: "History of the Ocean Basins," by H. H. Hess, in *Petrologic
       Studies — A Volume to Honor A. F. Buddington*, Geological Society
       of America, 1962.
209   Dietz reported his conclusions in *Nature*, June 3, 1961.
210   "Magnetic Anomalies over Oceanic Ridges," by F. J. Vine and D. H.
       Matthews, *Nature*, September 7, 1963.
210–211 Vine quote and account of his later work come from his article in
       Science, December 16, 1966, pp. 1405–1415.
214   Laughton quote: *New Scientist*, January 27, 1966.

14. On Torrey Cliff

236   "I was so desperate": Ewing quoted in *Scientific American*, December,
       1956.
240   "Is there a pattern?": Ewing quoted in *Business Week*, June 22, 1965.
247   "The distribution of relative": "Marine Magnetic Anomalies, Geomag-
       netic Field Reversals and Motions of the Ocean Floor and Continents,"
       by J. R. Heirtzler, G. O. Dickson, E. M. Herron, W. C. Pitman III, and
       X. Le Pichon; preprint of an article submitted to the *Journal of Geo-
       physical Research*.

15. Chronicle of the Ice Ages

252   "The Pleistocene Epoch in Deep-Sea Sediments," by David B. Ericson,
       Maurice Ewing, and Goesta Wollin, *Science*, November 6, 1964, pp.
       723–732.
254   "We now had before us": *The Deep and the Past*, p. 191. Hays re-
       ported his work in "Radiolaria and Later Tertiary and Quaternary His-
       tory of Antarctic Seas," by James D. Hays, *Biology of the Antarctic
       Seas II*, Antarctic Research Series 5, published by the American Geo-
       physical Union, 1965.
255   Information on work of Conolly and Ewing from "Ice-Rafted Detritus
       as a Climatic Indicator in Antarctic Deep-Sea Cores," by John R.
       Conolly and Maurice Ewing, *Science*, December 31, 1965, pp. 1822–
       1824.
256   Donn and Ewing explanations of glaciation described in "Causes of the
       Ice Ages," by William L. Donn, *Sky and Telescope*, April, 1967; Colum-
       bia University press release 11572, June 20, 1966.
257   Figures on rise in sea level in Atlantic from "Marine Geology," by

PAGE

Maurice Ewing, in *Ocean Sciences,* p. 162, published by the U.S. Naval Institute, Annapolis, Maryland.

258 Article by Opdyke and Foster is in *Science Journal,* September, 1967, pp. 56–61.

16. This Is the Way the World Ends

262 "Death as the Compass Swings," *New Scientist,* June, 8, 1967.
264 "Tektites and Geomagnetic Reversals," by Billy Glass and Bruce C. Heezen, *Nature,* April 22, 1967; *Scientific American,* July, 1967.
265 *Saturday Review* quotes are from the issue of May 6, 1967.
266–270 "Santorini Tephra," by Dragoslav Ninkovich and Bruce Heezen, Vol. XVII of the Colston Papers, *Proceedings of the Seventeenth Symposium of the Colston Research Society,* held in the University of Bristol, April 5–9, 1965, Butterworth Scientific Publications, London.
274 "An offshore atomic blast": *Scientific American,* August, 1956.
275 Information on bottom currents from "Ocean Bottom Currents," by Charles D. Hollister and Bruce C. Heezen, *The Encyclopedia of Oceanography,* pp. 576–583.

17. The Oceanographic

280 Quote by Governor Bradford from *Cape Cod Pilot,* by Jeremiah Digges, Modern Pilgrim Press and the Viking Press, Provincetown and New York, 1937.
283–284 Quote from old whaler's log, *ibid.,* p. 356.

18. The Ocean Is Like the Stock Market . . .

301–303 All quotes are from *The Gulf Stream,* by Henry Stommel.
315–316 "Many catastrophes": *ibid.,* p. 136.

19. In Search of Absolutes

320 Von Arx quote from *Science,* December 30, 1966, pp. 1651–1654.
322 Von Arx quote from *Technology Review,* December, 1964, published by the Massachusetts Institute of Technology.

20. Brains in the Sea

336–337 Information on Soviet and Japanese submersibles from *The Deep Submersible,* by Richard Terry.
340 Quotes are from "Telechiric Devices and Systems," by H. A. Ballinger,

PAGE

paper delivered at the British National Conference on the Technology of the Sea and Seabed, A.E.R.E., Harwell, April 5–7, 1967.

350 Quotes are from *Archaeology Under Water, by George F. Bass.

21. Money in the Sea

353 Figure on British ocean business from Science Journal, December, 1967.

356 Drillers reacted to "dreary battle": The Sunday Times, London, March 3, 1968.

356 "DeBeers is obtaining several times": Sea Frontiers, May–June, 1967.

356 "Marine Diamond Corporation . . . lost $6 million": Geo-Marine Technology, April, 1967.

358 "Assuming that only 10 percent": *The Mineral Resources of the Sea, by John L. Mero, p. 277.

359 "Trying to suck up milk": from "A Policy for Ocean Industry," by Nicholas Valery, Science Journal, December, 1967.

359 Sea Frontiers, December, 1967.

360 New Scientist, January 11, 1968, pp. 90–91.

360 "Hot, Salty Water," by John Swallow, Oceanus, April, 1965.

361–362 Degens and Ross quotes are from "Hot Brines and Heavy Metals in the Red Sea," by E. T. Degens and D. A. Ross, Oceanus, June, 1967.

22. Blight in the Sea

369–370 Summary of responses to UN questionnaire from an unpublished paper, "Pollution of the Sea," UN Administrative Committee on Coordination (ACC), Subcommittee on Oceanography: ACC/SCO/1967/W.P. 3.

372 "A drop in the amount of oxygen": Science Journal, January, 1968.

375 Quotes are from Pollutional Effects of Pulp and Paper Mill Wastes in Puget Sound, March, 1967; U.S. Department of the Interior, Federal Water Pollution Control Administration, Northwest Regional Office, Portland, Oregon; Washington State Pollution Control Commission, Olympia, Washington.

376 Report on Baja California cove: "Tampico, A Study of Destructions and Restoration," by Wheeler J. North, Sea Frontiers, July–August, 1967.

379 "On this sunny July day": *"Torrey Canyon" Pollution and Marine Life, edited by J. E. Smith, pp. 56–57.

380 "If we ask why they are thought": ibid., p. 184.

23. The United Oceans

383 Emery quote from *The Law of the Sea, edited by Lewis M. Alexander.

383 Craven quotes are from "Technology and the Law of the Sea," a paper

PAGE

    he presented at the Conference on Law, Organization and Security in
    the Use of the Ocean, Ohio State University, March 17–18, 1967.

384 Senator Pell quotes are from *Congressional Record,* September 29,
    1967, pp. S13875–S13877.

384 Christy's proposal from *Resources,* No. 26, Resources for the Future,
    Inc., Washington, D.C.

385 Rep. Rogers quoted in *International Herald Tribune,* Paris, September
    20, 1967.

385 Governor Kirk quoted in *ibid.,* October 26, 1967.

386 Rebeyrol quote from *Le Monde,* Paris, October 31, 1967.

386 Maxwell quotes are from a paper published in *Conference on Oceanol-
    ogy,* edited by Peter Sammartino, Fairleigh Dickinson University Press,
    Rutherford, New Jersey, 1968.

391 Dietrich quoted in "Revival of Oceanography in Germany," by Victor
    K. McElheny, *Science,* October 2, 1964.

393 "Will man be able to see": "La Coopération internationale en océanog-
    raphie," by H. Lacombe, *Revue de Géographie Physique et de Géologie
    Dynamique,* Vol. IX, Fasc. 3, Paris, 1967, pp. 191–198.

24. The Past and the Future

400 "I just don't think our people": interview in *Science and Technology,*
    June, 1967.

405 Historical quotes from "Founders of Marine Science in Britain: The
    Work of the Early Fellows of the Royal Society," by Margaret Deacon,
    reprint from *Notes and Records of the Royal Society of London,* Vol.
    20, No. 1, June, 1965.

410 Dr. Spilhaus's remarks were made at the Conference on Law, Organiza-
    tion and Security in the Use of the Ocean, Ohio State University, March
    17–18, 1967.

Some Further Reading

The purpose of this rather arbitrary reading list, based on personal experience, is to offer some signposts to the reader who would like to explore the field further along the line I have chosen — by going to the scientist who expresses himself well, rather than to the professional writer.

If the reader insists on a true bibliography, there are several. I would recommend *Oceanography in Print*, published by the Oceanographic Education Center in Falmouth, Massachusetts. It was compiled by Lynn Forbes, with Dr. Mary Sears of the Woods Hole Oceanographic Institution as consultant.

Here are a few suggestions:

Popularizations

Carson, Rachel, 1961. *The Sea Around Us.* New York: The New American Library, Inc. 220 pp. The classic. Thorough, and a work of literature. Becoming dated, but still the best.

Cousteau, J. Y., and F. Dumas, 1953. *The Silent World.* New York: Harper and Brothers. 266 pp. (Also in paperback.) Cousteau's first and, in my opinion, his most moving book.

Deacon, G. E. R. (editor), 1962. *Seas, Maps and Men: An Atlas-History of Man's Exploration of the Oceans.* Garden City, New York: Doubleday and Company, Inc. 297 pp. Unusual combination of beautiful illustrations and good writing — the coffee-table book that deserves to be read.

By British scientists, each a top man in his field. A meaty appendix for the science-minded.

Dugan, James, 1956. *Man Under the Sea.* New York: Harper and Brothers. 332 pp. (Also in paperback.) The author was an excellent professional writer hopelessly smitten with the diving bug. His history of diving and submarining is unrivaled as a story of human ingenuity and courage . . . starting in 415 B.C.

Engel, Leonard, and the editors of *Life*, 1961. *The Sea.* New York: Time, Inc. (Life Nature Library). 190 pp. Copiously and well illustrated, as one would expect. The late author was also a serious science writer who went to sea with the Lamont Geological Observatory for his material.

Gaskell, T. F., 1964. *World Beneath the Oceans.* Garden City, New York: The Natural History Press. 154 pp. Supposedly for "boys and girls in junior high school," or so says the jacket blurb, but definitely adult fare for the non-science-minded. Extremely good on marine geology, the British author's profession.

Stewart, Harris B., Jr., 1966. *Deep Challenge.* Princeton: D. Van Nostrand Company, Inc. 202 pp. Head of ESSA's Atlantic Oceanographic Laboratories, the author is another of those missionary marine scientists carrying the gospel to the landsmen. He does it very well.

Popular, but More Specialized

Bascom, Willard, 1961. *A Hole in the Bottom of the Sea.* Garden City, New York: Doubleday and Company, Inc. 352 pp. As I noted on page 187, this is an excellent popularization of oceanography's many facets, even though it focuses on the Mohole that was never drilled.

Ericson, David B., and Goesta Wollin, 1964. *The Deep and the Past.* New York: Alfred A. Knopf. 292 pp. Two scientists relate how they pieced together the story of the Ice Ages from deep-sea cores. It's not always easy reading, but the job was not easy, either. The two men have also written *The Ever-Changing Sea* for the same publisher.

Raitt, Helen, 1964. *Exploring the Deep Pacific.* Denver: Alan Swallow. (A Sage Book). 272 pp. The story of Scripps's Capricorn Expedition of 1952–53 in the Pacific. Mrs. Raitt, wife of one of Capricorn's scientists, was the only woman aboard and she caught the atmosphere of an oceanographic expedition. A good introduction by Roger Revelle.

Economics and Politics

Prospective returns from oceanography are analyzed in a study published by the Investment Research Department of Hayden, Stone (their New York address is 25 Broad Street). Hayden, Stone, which must be the wettest of Wall Street firms, has published another booklet on its oceanography forum. Realistic reading for those who think about a plunge into the ocean.

The Bank of America National Trust & Savings Association has brought out a 20-page booklet: *Oceanography — The Challenge and the Opportunity.* A good survey in compact form of ocean resources.

The U.S. Government Printing Office is a source for background on the ocean and American public policy. The National Council on Marine Resources and Engineering Development has issued two reports: *Marine Science Affairs — A Year of Plans and Progress* (March 1968); and *Marine Science Affairs — A Year of Transition* (February 1967). *Effective Use of the Sea*, a report by the Panel on Oceanography of the President's Science Advisory Committee (The White House, June 1966), is a landmark document.

Draft of a General Scientific Framework for World Ocean Study, 1964. Paris: *UNESCO*. 76 pp. A concise review of the economic and intellectual benefits to be derived from international cooperation in oceanography. Not available anymore except in libraries, but a second edition is appearing as *Perspective in Oceanography*.

Alexander, Lewis M., 1967. *The Law of the Sea*. Columbus, Ohio: The Ohio State University Press. 321 pp. Professor Alexander has edited the proceedings of the first annual conference held by the Law of the Sea Institute at Kingston, Rhode Island, in 1966. A glimpse of what awaits us as man reaches out to grasp — and grab — the ocean floor. For the legal-minded, if not the legal minds.

Mero, John L., 1965. *The Mineral Resources of the Sea*. Amsterdam: Elsevier Publishing Company. 312 pp. The most-quoted work on the prospects of mining the sea, particularly for those manganese nodules. Semitechnical.

In Greater Depth

Bascom, Willard, 1964. *Waves and Beaches*. Garden City, New York: Doubleday and Company, Inc. 267 pp. The author is a scientist with a soul. Both aspects come through in this book, a fine technical piece on "the dynamics of the ocean surface" and an expression of a man's love for the sea.

Bass, George F., *Archaeology Under Water*. New York: Frederick A. Praeger, Inc. 224 pp. First an archaeologist, Bass typifies the new breed of diver who takes specialized knowledge under the sea and uses it there. A book, therefore, that talks as much about archaeology as it does about diving.

Fairbridge, Rhodes W. (editor), 1966. *The Encyclopedia of Oceanography*. New York: The Reinhold Publishing Corporation. 1,021 pp. The first attempt at an *encyclopedia oceanica*, so to speak. For the science-trained, working or with an interest in the subject. Contains 245 articles from authors, as editor Fairbridge says, "from Albania to Ethiopia, from the U.S.S.R. to Sierra Leone" (one lost his manuscript when a crocodile bite sank his rubber boat on Lake Tanganyika . . .). All are leading experts, not all are delightful writers.

Hunt, Lee M., and Donald G. Groves, 1965. *A Glossary of Ocean Science and Undersea Technology Terms*. Arlington, Virginia: Compass Publications, Inc. 173 pp. Really a dictionary of the language of oceanography in its broadest sense and a necessity for anyone either working in the subject or, as a preface says, "the many who are merely fascinated by the ocean . . ."

Shepard, Francis P., 1959. *The Earth Beneath the Sea.* Baltimore: The Johns Hopkins Press. 275 pp. (Also in paperback.) A survey of marine geology by one of the grand old men in the field (he explores undersea canyons in submersibles though he's over three-score-and-ten). Seriously written with no playing to the gallery.

Smith, J. E., 1968. *"Torrey Canyon" Pollution and Marine Life.* Cambridge: Cambridge University Press. 196 pp. Dr. Smith has edited this report by his Plymouth Laboratory of the Marine Biological Association of the United Kingdom, which made an intensive survey of the results of the *Torrey Canyon* disaster. It is also a good account of how marine biologists go about their tasks. Color plates showing the effects of oil and detergent on the sea and its life are beautiful in their horror.

Stommel, Henry, 1966. *The Gulf Stream: A Physical and Dynamical Description.* 2nd ed. Berkeley and Los Angeles: University of California Press, 248 pp. The historical introduction is very readable; the rest is very authoritative. Stommel is among the world's leading practitioners in his field.

Terry, Richard D., 1966. *The Deep Submersible.* North Hollywood, California: Western Periodicals Co. 456 pp. For the reader who shares Terry's intense enthusiasm for underwater travel. Well illustrated, with a plethora of historical material. Hard to get (doesn't seem to be sold by the usual bookstores).

Von Arx, William S., 1962. *An Introduction to Physical Oceanography.* Reading, Massachusetts: Addison-Wesley Publishing Company, Inc. 422 pp. Written for students, not for laymen. But the dry-land scientist will enjoy seeing how physics is applied to the ocean and Von Arx explains all terms clearly.

Wegener, Alfred, 1966. *The Origin of Continents and Oceans.* New York: Dover Publications, Inc. 246 pp. A new translation of Wegener's book first published in 1915 in which he stated his case for continental drift. Heavy going, certainly, yet a worthwhile glimpse of the onset of a scientific controversy that is only now being settled.

Periodicals

New Scientist. 128 Long Acre, London, W.C. 2. Weekly. A bright news magazine of science. Scours the scientific journals for developments — a good way to keep afloat in oceanography. Intelligently and intelligibly written.

Ocean Industry. The Gulf Publishing Company, 3301 Allen Parkway, Houston, Texas. Monthly. Slanted at the offshore oil industry, but covers all economic applications of oceanography and some basic science, too. Very valuable to those who look at the business side of the ocean.

Oceanus. Woods Hole Oceanographic Institution, Woods Hole, Massachusetts 02543. Quarterly. Distributed free to Woods Hole Associates. See page 284.

Science Journal. Dorset House, Stamford Street, London S.E. 1. Monthly. Another British general science magazine, but with longer articles. Has treated much of oceanography in articles available as reprints. Well illustrated.

Scientific American. Scientific American, Inc., 415 Madison Avenue, New York, New York 10017. Monthly. Not for beginners. Important articles on marine topics appear at irregular intervals. Its list of reprints in the field is worth mining.

Sea Frontiers. International Oceanographic Foundation, Institute of Marine Science, University of Miami, 1 Rickenbacker Causeway, Miami, Florida 33149. Bimonthly. General oceanography written for the general public, with an accent on marine biology. Readers' questions are answered in *Sea Secrets*, an accompanying pamphlet.

Undersea Technology. Compass Publications, 617 Lynn Building, 111 North 19th Street, Arlington, Virginia 22209. Monthly. A trade publication that briefs its readers not only on technical developments, but on the political side of oceanography, both national and international.

Picture Credits

Index